Canadian Shield

New England Highlands

Adirondack Mtns.

Appalachian Plateau

Valley and Ridge

Interior Lowlands

Blue Ridge

Ozark Dome

Interior Plateau

Piedmont

Ouachita Mtns.

Coastal Plain

BASIC CONCEPTS OF PHYSICAL GEOLOGY

Basic Concepts of Geology

Basic Concepts of Physical Geology

Basic Concepts of Historical Geology

Basic Concepts of

EDGAR WINSTON SPENCER

Chairman, Department of Geology

Washington and Lee University

Physical Geology

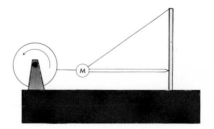

with drawings by

Elizabeth Humphris Spencer

THOMAS Y. CROWELL COMPANY, NEW YORK, ESTABLISHED 1834

Designed by Laurel Wagner

Library of Congress Catalog Card Number: 62-7082

Manufactured in the United States of America
by Rand McNally & Company, Book Mfg. Division, Chicago, Ill.

To the memory of my mother ALLIE BELLE SHELTON SPENCER

Preface

Basic Concepts of Physical Geology and Basic Concepts of Historical Geology were written as a single integrated book for a one year course in Physical and Historical Geology. The text is designed for students who are taking geology as a liberal arts subject as well as for students who plan to major in geology. It has been published in two volumes, each presenting the material traditionally covered in one semester courses in Physical and Historical Geology. The two volumes complement one another, but they may be used separately without difficulty. Because the concepts of geologic time and the place of the earth in the universe are so important, a brief treatment of these topics has been included in the volume on Physical Geology for those students who will not take a full year course. A more comprehensive treatment is given in the volume on Historical Geology.

This text has been written in the full recognition that there are a number of fine textbooks available which cover the principles and processes of geology. However, this book is written from a different point of view and with a some-

what different purpose in mind. It is assumed that the student comes to this first course in geology without a background in natural science, but with a curiosity about the earth on which he lives, an open mind, and a willingness to learn. It is hoped that he will carry away from the course a grasp of the fundamental ideas of geology, a knowledge of the scientific methods used by geologists, their limitations, and an awareness of the broad scope of the field and its major contributions to human knowledge. The material selected, its organization, and the manner of presentation are designed to accomplish these purposes rather than to stress terminology, processes, or detailed factual data. However, it is recognized that many of the basic and most important ideas can not be grasped without a working knowledge of certain scientific terms and processes. These are defined as they are introduced.

Treatment has been highly selective. Some topics are developed fully in order to give the student an appreciation for the thoroughness characteristic of scientific investigations. Other advanced, even controversial, ideas are discussed briefly to give the student a glimpse of the research problems faced in the earth sciences, and the scientist's need for imagination as well as factual information in seeking the solutions. The interdependence of the natural sciences is emphasized throughout.

Outlines are employed where they will be most useful to the student as a means of quick summary. Data which are often presented in appendices are incorporated in the chapters to which they are most pertinent. Each volume has a set of eight pages of color maps at the end of the book. These are intended to illustrate various types of geologic and topographic maps, and to provide the teacher with a valuable tool for map study.

Both volumes have a number of new features. The Physical Geology text presents:

1. An introductory section about the profession of geology, what geologists do, how the field is applied, the means of communication, and the methods used by geologists.
2. A chapter on the sources of energy for processes acting in and on the earth.
3. A chapter dealing with the major divisions of the crust of the earth.
4. A chapter on the concept of sequential development of land forms by various geomorphic agents. The limitations of this idea are also clearly explained.

The text on Historical Geology presents:

1. An expanded discussion of the methods used to unravel the history of the earth.
2. Discussions of the origin of the atmosphere and hydrosphere.

3. A chapter on the origin of life on earth.
4. A short chapter dealing with the controversy over the nature of the continental borders of North America during the Paleozoic. Both the borderland hypothesis and the island arc hypothesis are explained.
5. A chapter devoted to the description of the most important groups of invertebrates is presented before the history of North America. Thus the student is supplied with information about the morphology and ecology of each group before he is confronted with data about the time of its first appearance or its evolution.
6. The physical history of North America is taken up starting with the Precambrian and continuing to the present. These chapters are brief; each contains a summary of the life of the period, a summary of the physical history of the United States for the period, and a discussion of several of the most important aspects of the physical history. These are selected to illustrate particular concepts or methods.
7. The theory of evolution of life is treated separately from the physical history of the continent.
8. A chapter explaining the main trends of the evolutionary processes with examples from the invertebrates precedes the story of the development of fishes, amphibian, reptiles, and mammals.

This text is designed and written for the elementary college level student.

EDGAR WINSTON SPENCER

Washington and Lee University
Lexington, Virginia

Acknowledgments

It should be recognized by all who read this text that our knowledge of the world is based on the work of many individuals. The findings of some of these individuals are so often used and widely recognized that they become a part of our general knowledge. After a time the source may be forgotten. The efforts of others may never become widely recognized even though they provide the basis for important discoveries of later workers. Scientific methods lead to a pyramiding of knowledge. We owe a debt of gratitude to all who have contributed. In a text the findings of only a few individuals can be selected for discussion. Direct acknowledgment to these persons has been made in the text where it seems most appropriate. Likewise, acknowledgments for illustrations and photographs have been made in the headings for these.

I am especially indebted to the late Professor Marcellus Stow of Washington and Lee University whose teachings and personal friendship led me into the field of geology. To my teachers at Columbia University, Professors Arie Poldervaart, Walter Bucher, Maurice Ewing, Marshall Kay, Charles Behre, Sidney Paige, John Imbrie, and Arthur Strahler, I am most grateful for the inspiration of their teaching and their dedication to the study of the earth. The research and teachings of these men have greatly influenced my thinking and approach to earth science; however, I alone am responsible for any errors which may appear in this book.

My sincere thanks go to those friends, colleagues, and students who have given me the benefit of their ideas about teaching elementary geology, and to those who have helped directly in the preparation of the manuscript and illustrations in this book. For his patience and thoroughness throughout the work in editing this text I wish to thank my friend, Philip Winsor.

I appreciate the many helpful suggestions of Miss Agnes Creagh who assisted in editing the manuscript.

I am most grateful to my wife not only for her encouragement, but for drawing many of the illustrations and for reading and making suggestions about the preparation of the manuscript.

E. W. S.

Contents

V OUR DYNAMIC EARTH

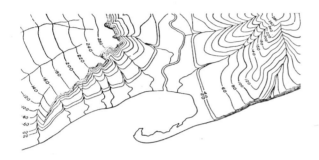

THE SCIENCE OF THE EARTH—GEOLOGY

1   Geology — The Profession

WHAT IS GEOLOGY?

Geology is the study of the earth—of rocks and fossils, of mountains, oceans, and the interior of our planet. Richard de Bury was the first to use the word "geology." In the year 1473 he applied it to the "law" or earthly science as opposed to "theology" or heavenly science. Such a definition suggests that geology includes all other natural sciences, and in a way this is true. You will learn in the study of geology that all the natural sciences overlap and are complexly interrelated. The division of natural science into the fields of biology,

Fig. 1-1. Recording the velocity of shock waves through the crust of the earth. (Photo by courtesy of Seismic Service Corp.)

chemistry, geology, and physics is superficial. As a result, many fields such as geophysics, geochemistry, paleontology, biophysics, and physical chemistry have sprung up to fill the gaps among the four. To the extent that other sciences contribute to our knowledge of the earth, the materials of which it is made, its shape and size, and the nature of the processes that take place on and within it, they are a part of geology. We may say that geology is the application of all scientific methods to the study of the earth and its mineral products.

Because of its great size and the many changes which have taken place during its long history, the earth is a complex body. It provides an unlimited number of challenging difficult problems, the solution of which requires a great variety of techniques and methods of approach. For this reason the work

of geologists is highly varied. Some geologists are concerned primarily with exploration for and recovery of the earth's natural resources such as oil, ores of metals, water, building materials, and fuels. Others are employed as consultants to help locate and construct dams, highways, tunnels, airports, docks, and other engineering projects. In addition many are devoted to the study of scientific problems which may appear to have no direct commercial applications. The field of geology includes a much greater breadth of interest than most beginning students realize. In order to help you grasp at the onset a broad picture of what geology is, brief outlines of the more important fields of geology are given below. These are largely based on the definitions given in the American Geological Institute's *Glossary of Geology*.

Mineralogy is the study of minerals, their composition, the ways in which they occur, their crystal structure, and their behavior. Minerals are the constituents of all soils, rocks, and ores.

Petrology is the study of the origin of rocks, their structures and textures, and their alteration. *Petrography* is the systematic description and classification of rocks. *Sedimentation* is a specialized branch of petrology that deals with the way in which sedimentary rocks are deposited in water, air, and ice.

Stratigraphy is the description and study of stratified rocks. It is concerned with the distribution, composition, thickness, age, variations, and correlation of rock strata.

Paleontology is the study of fossils, the remains and traces of the life of the past. Fossil assemblages are used to correlate rock units of the same age over large areas, and some assemblages are excellent indicators of the types of environments in which they lived. They give us an idea of the climates and distribution of seas that ceased to exist millions of years ago.

Structural Geology is concerned with the shape and configuration of the rocks in the crust of the earth. In places the strata are broken, displaced, and thrown up into folded belts of mountains. Study of their structures is used to decipher the history of these deformations, as well as to help in the location of mineral deposits that may be related to certain structural conditions in the earth.

Glacial Geology is the study of the cause, distribution, erosion, transportation, deposition, and other effects of the formation of large masses of ice on the continents. Both the continental ice sheets, such as those that cover the Antarctic and Greenland, and the alpine valley glaciers are within the province of this field.

Geomorphology means the study of the shape of the earth. It is specifically devoted to the description and origin of land forms. It is the systematic examination of land forms and the interpretation of them as records of past history.

Oceanography, the study of the oceans, includes investigation of the physiography and structure of the ocean basins, and the mechanism and nature of waves, tides, and oceanic circulations. It is concerned with the composition and variations in density of sea water, and with the past history of the oceans.

Meteorology is one branch of geology that has grown so fast it is often considered as a separate field. It is the study of the atmosphere, weather, and climates. The climatic belts of the past are also of importance in the reconstruction of the history of the earth. The investigation of these ancient climates is called *Paleoclimatology*.

Geophysics is a branch of experimental physics that deals with the structure, composition, and development of the earth, its atmosphere, and its hydrosphere. It includes geodesy, seismology, meteorology, oceanography, and earth magnetism.

Terrestrial Magnetism is the study of the earth's magnetic field—its causes, variations, and the history of changes that have taken place in the position of the field and the poles.

Seismology is devoted to the detection and interpretation of earthquake waves. These have

Fig. 1-2. A geologist measuring the force of the earth's gravitational field. (Photo by courtesy of Humble Oil and Refining Co.)

proven to be our best means of investigating the structure and composition of the interior of the earth and the structure of that part of the crust that is not exposed to direct observation.

Geodesy is the investigation of any scientific questions connected with the shape and dimensions of the earth.

Geochemistry is defined broadly to include all parts of geology that involve chemical changes. A more narrow definition would restrict it to the distribution of the elements. It may also be defined as the study of the relative and absolute abundances of the elements and of the atomic species, isotopes, in the earth, and the distribution and migration of the individual elements in the various parts of the earth.

Petroleum Geology is an applied field of geology in which the study of various other branches is brought to focus on the occurrence and migration of oil.

Economic Geology treats the origin, occurrence, and distribution of ore minerals and other economically important mineral and rock resources.

Engineering Geology is the application of the geological sciences to engineering practice. The purpose is to assure that the geologic factors affecting the location, design, operation, and maintenance of engineering works are recognized and provided for.

Hydrology is the science of the distribution and phenomena related to the water on the surface of the earth. Ground-water geology is concerned specifically with the occurrence, distribution, movement, and action of underground water.

SCIENCE AND THE SCIENTIFIC METHOD

At a time when science is considered to be of such great importance, it is not surprising that we find many definitions of the word and many misconceptions about its meaning. The definition given in the Merriam-Webster dictionary states that science is accumulated

Fig. 1-3. Field geologist at work. (Photo by E. W. Spencer.)

knowledge systematized and formulated with reference to the discovery of general truths or the operation of general laws. While this definition may be adequate, it is somewhat misleading. A library is systematized knowledge which may be used for the same purposes, yet it is hardly scientific. The study of science would indeed be rather dull if it were concerned with nothing more than the accumulation and systematization of knowledge. Most scientists would also take issue with the above definition regarding the discovery of general truths or general laws. First, it is a difficult problem to say exactly what truth is, and the so-called "general laws" usually have exceptions or limitations. The application of scientific methods has tended to lead more often to the discovery of exceptions to general laws than to the formulation of general laws.

One of the most satisfactory definitions of science is that of Dr. James B. Conant (from his book *On Understanding Science*): "Science is the process of combining hypothesis, observations, and experiments to obtain a better understanding of natural phenomena."

As Conant points out, it does not matter which of these three—hypotheses, observations, and experiments—comes first in the scientific method, and it is not necessary that all three be used. An observation often leads to the formulation of an idea or hypothesis. The hypothesis must be tested to see if it actually does help clarify our understanding of some natural phenomena. Experiments or other observations are made to test the hypothesis. In the process of an experiment other observations may be made that lead to new hypotheses, which may be almost totally unrelated to the original idea. It is for this reason that pure scientific research is most successful when it is carried on with few restrictions. The scientist needs time and the freedom to explore any new possibilities that may arise in the course of an investigation. In this fashion we add to the basic understanding of the world in which we live.

For the scientific method to be effective it is absolutely necessary that the investigator be strictly objective. It is often more difficult than we realize to overcome our own preconceived notions. It is entirely possible for us to prej-

Fig. 1-4. A geologist examining well cuttings at the site of a wildcat well. (Photo by courtesy of Standard Oil Co., N.J.)

udice our thinking unconsciously. Experiments and observations must be checked and cross-checked until there can be little doubt about the conclusions to be drawn from them. This is particularly important because the work of each scientist is dependent upon the validity of the work of those who have preceded him.

SCIENTIFIC COMMUNICATION

Professional organizations

There is no single organization of which all geologists are members, nor is there any international or national governing group. There are, however, many interrelated organizations, most of which are formed primarily to facilitate the communication of new scientific findings to other geologists who may be concerned with the same problems. Most of these organizations hold meetings at which members may report significant results of current research programs. A brief resumé of progress is often published to provide the data for those who do not attend the meeting. When the project is completed the entire work may be

Fig. 1-5. Two earth scientists examine records obtained by setting off explosions and recording the reflections of the shock waves from buried strata. The depth and attitude of the strata which reflected the waves are being computed. (Photo by courtesy of Standard Oil Co., N.J.)

International co-operation

Although international co-operation and communication leave much to be desired, there is more co-operation among earth scientists of different nations than we find in most other fields. In 1960 the International Geological Congress met in Copenhagen, Denmark. This marked the twenty-first meeting of this group, which is the world's oldest scientific congress; the first meeting was held in Paris in 1878. The congress meets once every 4 years in a different part of the world. Six official languages are used (English, French, German, Italian, Russian, and Spanish). The congress is subdivided into a number of sections, which have meetings devoted to specialized fields such as geochemical cycles, geological results of applied geochemistry and geophysics, submarine geology, problems concerning the origin of ores, structure of the earth's crust, and deformation of rocks. In addition to these sections, in which papers are formally presented and discussed, symposia and excursions are held. These excursions may last for 2 weeks or more and in 1960 included field trips to Greenland, Iceland, Norway, Sweden, and Finland. These trips give visitors a chance to study the geology of regions they rarely see. The meetings are open to all geologists throughout the world, although the papers presented are screened to insure that only the most pertinent ones are used.

The International Geological Congress is by no means the only such meeting of the world's geologists. Others include:

International Symposium on Physical Chemistry of Extractive Metallurgy.
International Conference on Scientific Information.
International Petroleum Exposition.
International World Petroleum Congress.
International Union of Geodesy and Geophysics.
International Commission of Optics.
International Oceanographic Congress.
International Geographic Congress.
International Paleontological Union.
International Union of Crystallography.

published in detail in one of the scientific periodicals. At a time when so much research work is being carried on by so many different groups in every part of the world, it is difficult to communicate new ideas fast enough to be useful to others who need the information. A relatively satisfactory solution has been found on the national level through the various national societies and periodicals, but language barriers and lack of opportunities for frequent personal contact between scientists in different parts of the world have created serious problems of international communication.

American societies

More geologic work is carried on by Americans than by any other national group. Within the United States the major groups are scientists employed (figures are for 1959 as reported by the American Geological Institute):

1. By the mineral industries (60%).
2. By the United States government (16%).
3. By colleges and universities (11%).
4. As private consultants (9%).
5. State geological surveys (3.5%).

Within the mineral industries most geologists are employed by petroleum companies to explore for and develop natural resources. Many of the larger companies also have research laboratories where basic problems, which may not have immediate commercial application, are investigated. Most of the information obtained during exploration is restricted because of its value to the company that possesses it, but later these data may be released and published to make them available for the use of all who are interested. Geologists have been used to a much smaller extent in the mining industries, which have depended on prospectors to locate the deposits and engineers to develop them, but, as deposits become harder to locate, more and more research and exploration are being carried on by geologists. However, the information obtained is not generally made available to others for many years because of its economic value.

The second largest group of geologists in America are those employed by the federal government. Most of these are employed in various branches of the United States Geological Survey, or the Coast and Geodetic Survey. Through the years these surveys, which operate within the Department of the Interior, have proven themselves to be among the most efficient and useful branches of the Federal government. They conduct studies of all phases of geology within the United States, and publish many of the results in series such as the following publications of the U.S. Geological Survey:

1. Professional Papers.
2. Bulletins.
3. Water-supply Papers.
4. Circulars.
5. Annual Reports.
6. Monographs.
7. Mineral Resources.
8. Folios of the Geologic Atlas of the United States.
9. Miscellaneous Reports.

In addition to the above, the Department of the Interior has produced thousands of topographic and geologic maps, which are available at low cost.

Many of the 270 colleges and universities within the United States that offer degrees in geology help support the research of science teachers. This support comes largely in the form of providing the necessary equipment for research and releasing time for the teacher

Fig. 1-6. Oceanographers of the U.S. Coast and Geodetic Survey and Scripps Institution of Oceanography examine rock samples collected by chain dredge from ocean floor near the Aleutian Islands. (Photo by courtesy of Scripps Institution of Oceanography, University of California, La Jolla.)

to work. Teaching offers many unique opportunities for geologists. An adequate library, the necessary equipment, the stimulation of ideas from other teachers and students, and the freedom to select research of greatest interest to the individual are rewards rarely available in other fields. Almost all geology teachers spend part of their time in research or field work of some kind.

Some universities and research groups associated with them publish the results of their research, but most generally the results are carried in one of the publications of a national society such as the Geological Society of America, the American Association of Petroleum Geologists, or the American Geophysical Union. Where the universities are State-owned, the work may be published by the State Geological Survey.

Most of the research of geologists who work as consultants for industry is not published until the industry releases it, but many

Fig. 1-7. The instrument man of a geological survey party is seen recording data between observations. He may be preparing a geologic map or a topographic map. (Photo by courtesy of Standard Oil Co., N.J.)

of these geologists publish in the periodicals of the professional societies when the work is not of a commercial nature. Many teachers also do consulting work in their spare time.

Almost all states in the United States have geological surveys that publish periodicals or books or circulars of some sort.

The groups cited above are arranged according to the nature of their full-time employment. The following are professional organizations and societies of people who share an interest in particular phases of geology. An oil company, for example, will hire many specialists from different fields. These specialists need to be in contact with others who are working in the speciality. The societies provide that opportunity. Some of the larger groups as indicated in a report by the American Geological Institute in 1960 were:

	No. of Members
American Association of Petroleum Geologists	14,000
American Geophysical Union	5,000
American Institute of Mining, Metallurgical, and Petroleum Engineers	18,000
Association of American State Geologists	47
Geochemical Society	1,500
Geological Society of America	5,000
Mineralogical Society of America	1,400
National Association of Geology Teachers	443
Paleontological Society	780
Seismological Society of America	874
Society of Economic Geologists	950
Society of Economic Paleontologists and Mineralogists	1,400
Society of Exploration Geophysicists	5,500
Society of Vertebrate Paleontology	460

Many geologists belong to several of these organizations.

Many of these groups hold meetings and publish periodicals to facilitate communication within the profession. All of those in the above list are associated with the American Geological Institute, which serves as a representative of the profession "on matters relating to public education, public relations, government relations, and professional relations. Whereas the member societies are concerned primarily with the advancement of scientific research and with the increase and dissemination of scientific knowledge, the A.G.I. is dedicated to serving the needs of the scientist and society."

In addition to these national organizations, there are many regional societies composed of those who are interested in the geology of a particular area. These groups hold meetings, conduct field trips, and publish guidebooks and other information concerning the region.

To summarize: Communication is a major concern in a field such as geology because most of what we know must come ultimately from field studies that are conducted in all parts of the world by people from different nations. Much of the work is carried on because of its direct economic importance.

Exchange of ideas, data, and significant results of research is needed if we are to gain a better understanding of the earth and make better use of the knowledge we have of its nature. All the organizations of geologists, whether Federal, State, or private, are dedicated to two principal purposes:

1. To serve society through geology.
2. To contribute toward a better understanding of the nature of the world.

International Geophysical Year

During the International Geophysical Year, from July 1, 1957, to December 31, 1958, the nations of the world undertook a concentrated series of geophysical observations in accordance with a well-formulated international cooperative plan. This work was carried on under a program of the International Council of Scientific Unions. The president of the Council stated that the objective of the plan was

.... to describe in detail the world-wide pattern of each of many terrestrial phenomena such as weather disturbances, ionospheric and geomagnetic storms, aurora displays, etc., and the changes of pattern of the disturbances as they develop in time. . . . Because terrestrial phenomena recognize no national boundaries, their description requires common agreement among nations on the places where observation should be undertaken, the kinds of measurements to be made, the observing apparatus to be used, the standards and timing of measurements, and the form of presentation and publication of the results.

He described the need for the plan in the following words:

Since man cannot 'see' very far, or very much, by direct observation, he must use the tools of every natural science to acquire information from which the character of his surroundings can be deduced. Since he is largely insulated inside his viewer, he must follow assiduously every observable clue that nature provides, so that its real meaning and its relationship to other parts of the system can be developed. Gradually, step by step, man is constructing a mutually consistent description of his surroundings. And as man learns to understand, and to describe the nature of his surrounding environment, he can invent means of utilizing it for his benefit. . . .

The results of the data accumulated during the International Geophysical Year on meteorology, geomagnetism, ionospheric physics, geodesy, cosmic rays, glaciology, oceanography, gravity, and seismology are of tremendous value. Perhaps the most important result of the program is the demonstration that the scientists of more than 40 nations, including countries behind the "iron curtain," can co-operate efficiently and with good will in an effort to push back the frontiers of the unknown.

2   The Earth — Its Place in Time and Space

The solar system

In this space age, very few people believe that the earth is the center of the universe, although this belief prevailed until many years after Copernicus demonstrated that the sun is the center of our solar system. However, it is difficult to perceive the true insignificance of the planet Earth when one compares its size with that of other bodies in the solar system and the universe.

Our sun is a star. It is one of many millions of stars that belong to an island universe or galaxy, which we know as the Milky Way. The sun has very little to distinguish it. It is a rather ordinary star of medium size and brightness. It is not located near either the center or the edge of the Milky Way. The Milky Way is one of thousands and probably millions of galaxies. Taken in its entirety, the Milky Way is shaped something like a saucer and is between 100,000 and 200,000 light years in diameter and about 10,000 light years in thickness. A light year is the distance light travels in a year. Light travels at the rate of 186,000 miles per second. Thus the light you see coming from the stars left most of them long before the birth of Christ.

Our solar system consists of the sun, nine planets that revolve about the sun, and a number of moons that revolve around their respective planets. The sun contains almost all of the mass of the solar system, over 98 per cent, and is by far the largest body in the system. It is 860,000 miles in diameter, and so hot that the surface is nearly 6,000° Centigrade. At depth the temperatures may reach up to 20,000,000° Centigrade. The planets in order of increasing distance from the sun are Mercury, Venus, Earth, Mars, Jupiter, Saturn, Uranus, Neptune, and Pluto. The earth, which is fifth in size, is located about 93,000,000 miles from the

Fig. 2-1. An island universe, or galaxy. This photograph of a spiral nebula shows the spiral nebula in *Canes Venatici*. This is how our universe, the Milky Way, might appear from far out in space. Compare with the view in Fig. 2-2 which shows a similar galaxy seen from a different angle. (Photo by courtesy of the Mount Wilson and Palomar Observatories.)

Fig. 2-2. The Great Nebula in *Andromeda*, one of the galaxies closest to the Milky Way. It can be seen by the unaided eye and appears as a small luminous cloud. It is about 800,000 light years away from earth. *Andromeda* is the largest nebula outside the Milky Way whose dimensions have been determined. It is 60,000 light years in diameter. (Photo by courtesy of the Mount Wilson and Palomar Observatories.)

sun. Data on the other planets are given in Fig. 2-3.

The processes and ideas you will learn in physical geology are more meaningful when viewed in terms of the over-all picture of the history of the earth. The present is just a moment in geological time. We think of it as being particularly unique because it is the time of man, but otherwise the earth is undergoing changes in the same way it has in the past. The physical and chemical processes that bring about alteration of rocks, and the forces that erode, transport, and deposit the rock materials of the crust, are acting today in the same way they have for millions, even billions, of years to bring about change in the face of the earth.

Age of the earth

The creation of the earth has always been an intriguing question in the minds of thinking men. How was it created, and how old is it? Disagreements on this question have led to bitter arguments. At one time the Church decreed that the earth was 6,000 years old, and those who refused to accept the decree were ostracized, and even physically punished. At that time even the wildest guesses about the antiquity of the earth were far short of the ages we now obtain from quantitative methods such as the radioactive decay of uranium into lead, potassium to argon, or rubidium to strontium. By these methods rocks from Southern Rhodesia have been dated as being 3.3 billion years old. This age is a minimum age for the earth. The best up-to-date estimates of the age of the earth are in the range of 4.5 to 6 billion years.

The principle on which radioactive dating is based is that radioactive isotopes undergo a systematic breakdown by the emission of radiant energy, eventually forming a stable isotope or element. For example, the end product of the decay of uranium 238 is the formation of a stable lead. The rate of this decay is known to be constant. One gram of the radioactive uranium will annually yield 1/7,600,000,000 gram of stable lead. Thus, if we separate and measure the amounts of each, we can determine the age of the rock. The length of time the decay has proceeded is equal to the ratio of the weight of lead to uranium multiplied by 7,600,000,000. The technique of dating rocks by radioactive means was discovered in 1907, but only since the 1940's has it been used very extensively. It is still not possible to date every rock by this means. Only those rocks containing uranium-lead, potassium-argon, or rubidium-strontium can be dated by the above methods. Geologists had learned a great deal about the earth before these techniques of dating were first used, and the geologic time scale had already been devised.

Geologic time scale

Because the geologic time scale is related to the rock units of the crust of the earth, and because there was no accurate means of

Fig. 2-3. The solar system.

	Mass Earth = 1	Radius (Km.)	Density	Gases in Atmosphere	Distance from Sun
Sun	332000.0	695000	1.4	many	
Mercury	0.05	2500	5.1	none	36 million mi.
Venus	0.81	6200	5.0	carbon dioxide	67 million mi.
Earth	1.	6371	5.5	many	93 million mi.
Mars	0.11	3400	3.9	{ carbon dioxide { water vapor	141 million mi.
Jupiter	318.	71000	1.3	{ methane { ammonia	483 million mi.
Saturn	95.	57000	0.7	{ methane { ammonia	886 million mi.
Uranus	14.6	25800	1.3	methane	1783 million mi.
Neptune	17.3	22300	2.2	methane	2793 million mi.
Pluto	0.03	2900	2.?	unknown	3666 million mi.

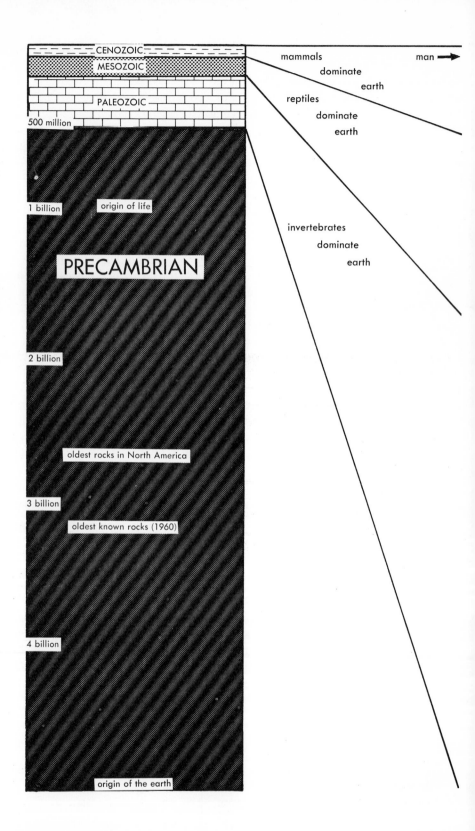

Fig. 2-4. Chart of the geologic time scale.

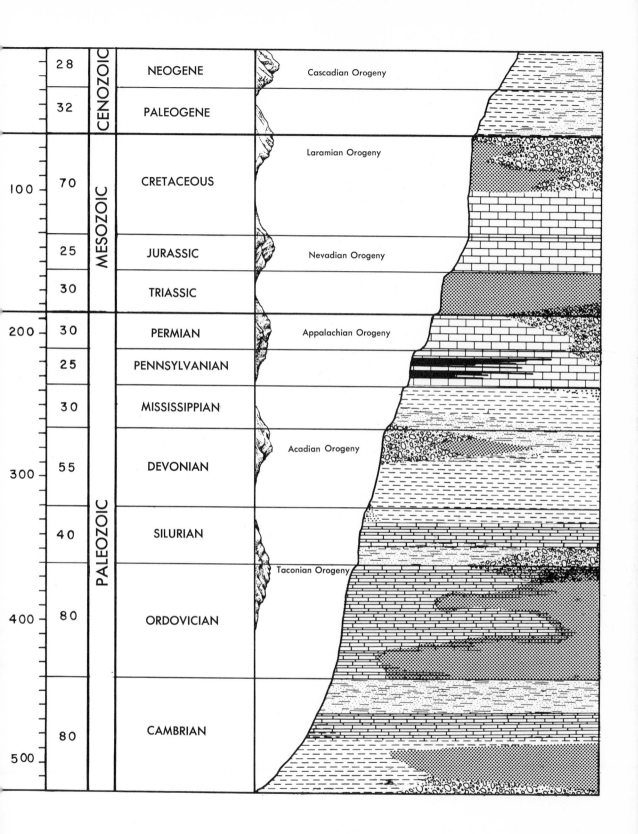

	28		NEOGENE	Cascadian Orogeny	
	32	CENOZOIC	PALEOGENE		
100	70	MESOZOIC	CRETACEOUS	Laramian Orogeny	
	25		JURASSIC	Nevadian Orogeny	
	30		TRIASSIC		
200	30	PALEOZOIC	PERMIAN	Appalachian Orogeny	
	25		PENNSYLVANIAN		
	30		MISSISSIPPIAN		
300	55		DEVONIAN	Acadian Orogeny	
	40		SILURIAN		
400	80		ORDOVICIAN	Taconian Orogeny	
500	80		CAMBRIAN		

measuring absolute time units when it was formulated, it is an arbitrary division of time. You will notice that the different intervals of geologic time have been given place names. Each of the divisions of time is based on exposures of rock units that were formed during a particular interval of time. These can be traced and correlated from one region to another. If the record is complete in a region, then the rocks formed in the following period of time are found above, and those of the next older period are below. Thus the age of any given unit is established in relation to the units above and below it.

The various periods of geologic time are often given geographic names. For example, the Permian Period is that interval of time during which a particular sequence of strata found in the province of Perm, Russia, was deposited. The Cambrian Period was that part of geologic time in which the Cambrian rock units were formed. The name of each such division of time is based on the outcrops in some particular region. Usually the period is named for the region or some unusual feature about it—i.e., the Pennsylvanian Period is named for certain outcrops in Pennsylvania, and the Jurassic Period is named for the Jura Mountains. Ideally these classic localities for which the period is named, are the best and most extensive sections of rocks of that age. A complete section is one that contains no lost intervals such as times of nondeposition or erosion. However, most of these localities are the places where units of a certain age were first recognized. The time scale underwent many changes at first because it was not

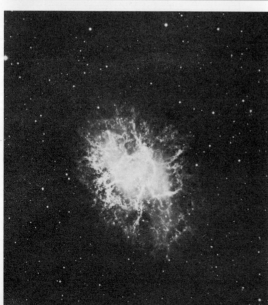

Fig. 2-5. A spiral nebula in *Cepheus*. This and Figs. 2-5 and 2-6 show some of the various forms taken by matter outside our own galaxy. (Photo by courtesy of the Mount Wilson and Palomar Observatories.)

Fig. 2-6. A globular star cluster in *Canes Venatici*. (Photo by courtesy of the Mount Wilson and Palomar Observatories.)

Fig. 2-7. The "Crab" Nebula in *Taurus*. This nebula is the remains of a supernova. (Photo by courtesy of the Mount Wilson and Palomar Observatories.)

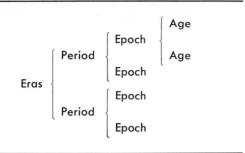

Fig. 2-8. Divisions of the geologic time scale.

complete, but rock units of all the major intervals of geologic time for the last half billion years have been found, and this part of the time scale has remained relatively unchanged for many years.

Once the classic locality for strata of a given age is established, other rocks of the same age in different localities are correlated with . them. Thus, correlation is one of the most important aspects of historical geology. Sometimes the units can be traced laterally by physical continuity. More often correlation is accomplished by identifying and relating fossils of the strata.

Natural boundaries were selected for each of the divisions in the time scale. These boundaries are breaks in the record, called unconformities. Several types of unconformities are known. Many parts of the crust of the earth have been highly deformed, folded, and faulted in the past history of the earth. After one of these periods of deformation the folded zones are usually high and mountainous. The mountains are subjected to erosion, and over long periods of time they are eroded away, and nothing more than a nearly flat plain is left. Once the mountains are gone the land may be warped downward and submerged below sea level, and new sediments may be deposited over the truncated edges of the folded and faulted strata. The new strata are nearly flat lying, so there is an angular discordance between the strata below and above; such a break is called an angular unconformity. Other breaks in the record may occur where the crust is warped upward, exposing older sediments. These are eroded, and part of the

record they represent is destroyed. If they are again lowered below sea level, new sediments are laid on them. In this instance there is no difference in the attitude of the strata above and below the unconformity, but there is a time gap between them; such a break is called a disconformity. The geologic time scale has been constructed on this basis.

Eras. The major divisions of geologic time—Precambrian, Paleozoic Era, Mesozoic Era, and Cenozoic Era—were originally thought to be separated by periods of world-wide mountain building and major changes in the forms of life on earth. The Precambrian rock units are almost completely unfossiliferous. They contain scattered remains of algae and a few questionable fossils of such animals as jelly fishes and worms. The Paleozoic was a period of nearly 300 million years during which the marine invertebrates were the most abundant forms of life on earth. The first fish appeared about the middle of the Paleozoic Era, and the first amphibians and reptiles were present before its end. The Mesozoic was a time of development for the land animals. The reptiles, particularly the dinosaurs, dominated the earth, and birds, mammals, and modern plants evolved. At the end of the Mesozoic the dinosaurs became extinct, and more modern forms of life appeared. We live in the Cenozoic. So it is easy to see why the terms "Paleozoic," meaning "old life," "Mesozoic," meaning "middle life," and "Cenozoic," meaning "modern life," were selected for these eras.

The story of the evolution of life and the means used to correlate rock units and establish the history of the earth will be taken up in your study of Historical Geology.

REFERENCES

ADAMS, F. D., 1954, *The Birth and Development of the Geological Sciences*, New York, Dover Publications, 506 p.

KUIPER, G. P., Editor, 1953–, *The Solar System:* 6 vols., Chicago, University of Chicago Press (vol. 1, 1953, vol. 2, 1954, vols. 3-6 in press)

KULP, J. L., TRYON, L. E., ECKELMANN, W. R., and SNELL, W. A., 1952, Lamont Natural Radiocarbon Measurements, II: Science, v. 116, p. 409-414

LIBBY, W. F., 1956, Radiocarbon Dating: Am. Scientist, v. 44, no. 1, p. 98-112

UREY, H. C., 1952, *The Planets, Their Origin and Development:* New Haven, Yale University Press, 245 p.

ZEUNER, F. E., 1952, *Dating the Past,* 3rd ed.: London, Methuen and Co., 495 p.

3   The Applications of Geology

Knowledge obtained in studying geology has many applications. The diversity of these applications far exceeds most people's initial impression. A thorough knowledge of geology can provide the basis for a better understanding of world affairs, history, economics, engineering, and industry.

    Most professional geologists are employed for the purpose of applying their knowledge

of geology. We have seen that almost 60 per cent work in the petroleum and mineral industry, directing exploration for oil and gas, and most of the remaining 40 per cent spend all or part of their time in applied work. The nature of this work ranges from evaluation of mineral properties for banks to studying methods of disposing of radioactive waste. The applied fields in which most geologists are directly employed are engineering geology and exploration for and conservation of natural resources.

MINERAL RESOURCES

The most important applications of geology are in the fields of exploration, development, and conservation of natural mineral resources. The occurrence and distribution of mineral resources have been one of the most important factors determining the course of human history since the industrial revolution, and undoubtedly will continue to act as a controlling influence in the future. One of the most succinct statements of the relation between man and minerals is given by T. S. Lovering in his Book *Minerals in World Affairs.*

The concentrated value of gold, silver, and other minerals has stimulated exploration; their exploitation has led to commerce and power, their exhaustion to national decline and poverty. Mineral production has been instrumental in determining the course of history many times in the past and promises to be of increasing importance in the future. The aggregate area underlain by mineral deposits of economic importance is only an insignificant fraction of 1 per cent of the earth's surface, and the geographic position of the individual deposits is fixed by some accidents of geology. Since no second crop may be expected, rich diverse mineral deposits are a nation's most valuable but ephemeral possession—its quick assets. Much of history has been made by men who have successively gained wealth and power in different countries through the liquidation of these assets. Because of their evanescent character, restricted occurrence, and indispensability to industry everywhere, the exploitation of mineral deposits engen-

Fig. 3-1. Open pit mine. Open pit operations are used when large quantities of rock must be removed in the mining operation, and when the ore body is not too deep. A low grade deposit of copper which occurs disseminated through an igneous rock is being mined here. You may get an idea of the size of this pit by noting the trains at the far right and at various levels in the pit. (Photo by courtesy of Kennecott Copper Corporation.)

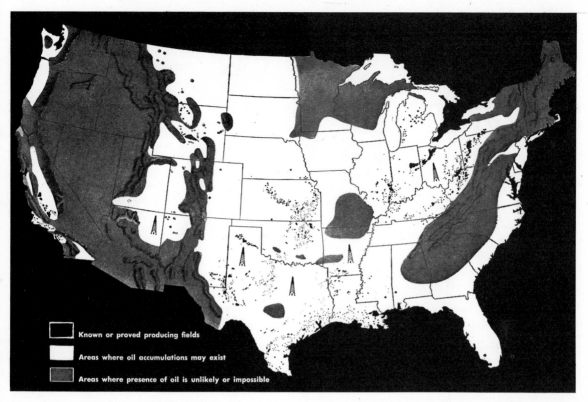

Fig. 3-2. Oil regions of the United States. The United States has been the world's largest producer and consumer of oil and gas. This important fuel resource is obtained from oil fields located in the light colored areas. The darker areas have not been important producing areas. In recent years new large reserves of petroleum have been discovered in the Near East and in North Africa. (From the American Petroleum Institute.)

ders many unique problems in national and industrial economy. An understanding of the geology and economics of minerals and the geographic distribution of past and future sources of production will enable us better to interpret history and will prepare us for the political changes to come.

History and current events afford a rich supply of examples of the importance of mineral resources and their influence on national policies and economic development. It is not a coincidence that the steel centers of the United States are located in Pennsylvania, around the Great Lakes, and in Alabama. The first major deposit of iron ore in this country was found at Cornwall, Pennsylvania, and the state has great reserves of coal needed for fuel and for making coke, and limestone which is used as a flux in the production of steel. Thus Pennsylvania became the logical center of our steel industry. As the Cornwall ores became ex-

hausted, new ores were shipped in across the Great Lakes from the iron mines around Lake Superior. If we had not been so fortunate in having these natural resources, the United States might today be one of the "have-not" nations instead of one of the leading industrial nations of the world.

Obviously certain mineral resources are necessary for war. Germany lacks large supplies of petroleum; therefore it is not surprising that one of the first moves of the German army during World War II was to occupy the oil-producing regions of Europe. We may assume that, if Rommel had been able to tap the oil resources discovered in the Sahara desert in 1959, he would undoubtedly have been more successful in the battle for North Africa. When Germany lost the European oil fields it was doomed to defeat. Tanks and other heavy machinery had to be abandoned for lack of fuel,

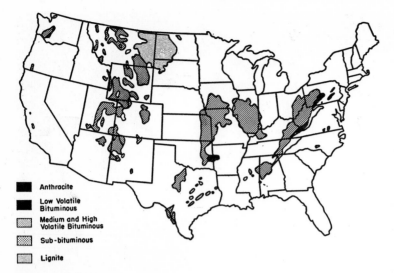

Fig. 3-3. Coal reserves in the United States. Coal, like oil, is an extremely important fuel resource. The United States has been extremely fortunate in possessing vast quantities of coal and oil. Coal is not only important as a fuel. It is a necessary ingredient in the manufacture of steel, and it is used as a raw material for the production of many synthetics. This map shows the distribution of important coal-bearing rock units in the United States. (From the United States Geological Survey.)

Anthracite

Low Volatile Bituminous

Medium and High Volatile Bituminous

Sub-bituminous

Lignite

and the country lost its ability to wage war. For several years before 1941 the Japanese government purchased American scrap iron. Japan has meager resources of iron ore and needed the scrap iron to manufacture armaments.

The discovery of valuable mineral resources in the Middle East, notably petroleum, has influenced our foreign policy toward the Middle Eastern countries.

Certainly it would be illogical to argue that the possession of mineral resources is the only important factor in determining a country's future, but it does afford a good means of estimating the potential development of a given area.

EXPLORATION FOR MINERAL RESOURCES

One of the most important functions and responsibilities of applied geology is to discover the raw mineral materials that provide the basis of an industrial society. It is the burden of the society as a whole to determine how these materials will be used—whether they will be used to improve the standard of living of the people or to destroy them.

Exploration for these raw materials is directed on the basis of our understanding of the nature of the origin and occurrence of the

mineral resources. Through geological studies we learn to associate certain mineral deposits with particular rock types, structural features in the earth's crust, and with mineral assemblages or with rock units of a certain age. This knowledge limits the areas in which exploration of a more detailed nature is conducted.

OIL AND GAS

The petroleum industry celebrated its first 100 years in 1959. However, oil seeps had been known for many years prior to 1859, and petroleum was used as far back as biblical times for medicine, waterproofing, and occasionally for fuel. American Indians used it for war paint. The first real pressure for more petroleum came from its use as a light source. Col. A. C. Ferris of New York discovered that petroleum made an excellent illuminant when run through his process for making coal oil. The first well drilled to recover oil for this purpose was put down by Col. Edwin Drake in Pennsylvania in 1859. The new industry expanded rapidly as new uses for oil were found. One of the most important changes in the industry occurred when the automobile became widely used. Since that time more and more uses have been found, and production has expanded until now more than 2 million barrels of oil are produced each year to meet the steadily growing demands of the world. In recent years as many as 5,000 wells have been drilled each year. About one-fifth of these are drilled in efforts to discover new accumulations. The remainder are drilled in and around areas where petroleum is already being produced.

Composition

Petroleum in the broad meaning of the word includes natural gas, crude oil, and solid bitumins. It is a complex mixture of compounds of carbon and hydrogen called hydrocarbons. The mixture is generally made up of one or more of the following groups of hydrocarbons:

1. Paraffin.
2. Napthene.
3. Acetylene.
4. Turpene.
5. Benzene.

The solid hydrocarbons, called bitumins, include asphalts and waxes.

Origin of oil

At one time a number of theories were held regarding the origin of oil and gas, but today there is relatively little disagreement over the nature of its source. Inorganic theories of its origin have been discarded in favor of an organic derivation, but there is still no direct evidence of how decaying matter is transformed into petroleum. Generally accepted ideas related to the origin of oil are:

1. Solid organic matter found in sedimentary rocks is composed mainly of carbon and hydrogen.
2. Oil initially forms in sedimentary rocks formed in the ocean. Where it is found in igneous or metamorphic rocks, those that were originally molten, or that have been highly altered, it is believed to have migrated there from sediments.
3. Petroleums almost always differ in composition.
4. Most oil is found in younger rocks.
5. Oil has not been subjected to temperatures above 39°F. It would be highly altered at that temperature.

Fig. 3-4. A cross section showing the nature of the occurrence of oil. Oil is stored in pore spaces between sand grains as shown in the enlarged sections at right. The oil probably gets into the sandstone from black muds or shales. Because oil tends to rise through water it moves up in sandstone units which contain water. This migration continues until the oil becomes trapped as shown in this anticlinal structure.

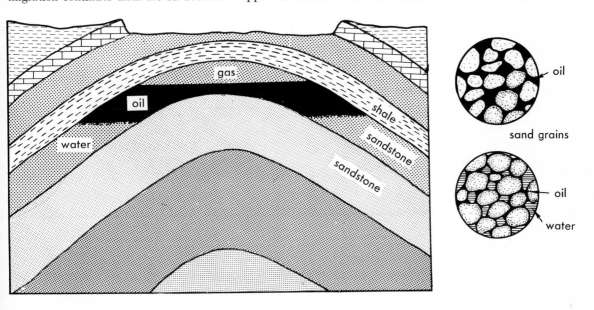

6. Oil forms under anaerobic conditions, in absence of oxygen, because carbon in it would be oxidized and go into carbon dioxide in a reducing environment.

7. Crude oil contains porphyrin pigments, formed from the red coloring matter of blood, hemin, or from the green coloring matter of plants, chlorophyll.

The most probable source materials for petroleum are diatoms, marine fungi, bacteria, and algae, among the forms of marine plant life, and marine invertebrates. The most important marine invertebrate sources would be the protozoans, extremely abundant single-celled animals. Other potential sources among the marine invertebrates are sponges, corals, worms, bryozoans, brachiopods, crustaceans, mollusks, and echinoderms. Vertebrates may also provide lesser amounts of the organic material.

The principal questions regarding the origin of petroleum deal with what happens to the organic matter to convert it into oil and gas. A number of processes may be responsible for the conversion, including distillation, cracking, hydrogenation, polymerization, bacterial action, and radioactivity. Of these the one generally thought to be likely is bacterial action and one or more of the other processes acting in conjunction with it. Bacteria are found universally with petroleum, and it has been definitely established that they can produce hydrocarbons from organic matter.

Environment of formation of oil

Within the bounds set by the facts stated above regarding the origin of petroleum, it is not difficult to visualize the general types of environments in which oil might begin to form. Areas similar to the shallow waters of parts of the continental shelves and the Gulf of Mexico are probable localities. Droplets of oil have been found near the top of the sediments deposited in the Gulf. These droplets have not had time nor the necessary conditions to accumulate in quantity, but their presence indicates that relatively short periods of time are necessary for

oil to form. One particularly suitable area would be bodies of marine water that have shallow connections with the ocean but are otherwise cut off. Here the free-floating and swimming plants and animals would be abundant at the surface, but because of the enclosed nature of the greater depth there would be poor circulation of water and thus a deficiency of oxygen. This would hinder oxidation, and poisonous gases produced by the decaying organic matter would form toxic conditions so that scavengers could not roam the bottom, eating and destroying the dead animal and plant remains. Clay, mud, sand, and silt might be deposited along with the organic material. Depending on the location of the area and the distance to shore, along with other environmental factors, one of the sediments would probably predominate. Black shales, the consolidated equivalent of mud, are known to contain unusually great quantities of organic matter. Although oil is rarely found in black shale, accumulations of petroleum are often found in sandstones that are overlaid or underlaid by black shales. Some think that the black shales are the principal source of oil, and almost all geologists agree that they are probable sources of at least some oil and gas.

Migration

In order for oil to move through a consolidated or semiconsolidated rock, the rock must have porosity and permeability. Porosity is a measure of the void spaces in the rock (percentage of space in a certain volume of the rock), and permeability is a measure of how easily fluids can be transmitted through the rock. Pore space may be original spaces between grains of sand or gravel, spots that have been dissolved by water in soluble rocks, or fractures in the rocks. The first step in the migration of oil is out of the source rock, if the source rock is something like black shale, into a rock that is porous and permeable. The shales are usually impervious and not very porous. This movement occurs when the accumulation of sediments on top of the oil-bearing unit becomes thick enough to begin to compress the source bed. Muds contain a lot of water; therefore, if a mud containing oil and water were compressed, the oil and water would migrate out of the mud and into the adjacent beds of rock. If these beds are porous and permeable, as many sandstone units are, the second phase of migration begins. Since oil is lighter than water, the oil tends to float on top of the water. If the sandstone unit was formed under marine water it already contains salt water in its pore spaces. The oil slowly moves up around the sand grains until it reaches the top of the sandstone unit. If the unit is tilted, the oil continues up toward the surface until it is stopped or trapped. Where the upward movement is halted, oil accumulates. Gases that have been produced are lighter than the oil and tend to move to the top of the oil accumulation.

We may summarize the factors necessary for oil accumulation:

1. A source of oil.
2. Migration from the source into a porous and permeable bed.
3. Migration within the permeable unit.
4. A trap to stop the migration and cause the accumulation.

Oil traps

Two general types of traps are recognized: structural traps caused by folding or rupture and displacement of the rock units, and stratigraphic traps in which some type of variation in the stratigraphy or lithology (composition and texture of the units) causes the oil to be trapped. In addition, there are combinations of these two types and a few that defy a clearcut classification.

Fig. 3-5. Oil traps. These six cross sections illustrate conditions in the earth which may lead to the accumulation of oil and gas. Oil from the oil sands in the top section would seep out on the ground surface. When this happens the gases tend to escape and a tar seal forms over the top of the unit making it a trap. The second section illustrates an anticlinal trap in a folded structure as does section three. The last three show how oil may accumulate along faults, over salt domes, and as a result of an angular unconformity. (From the American Petroleum Institute.)

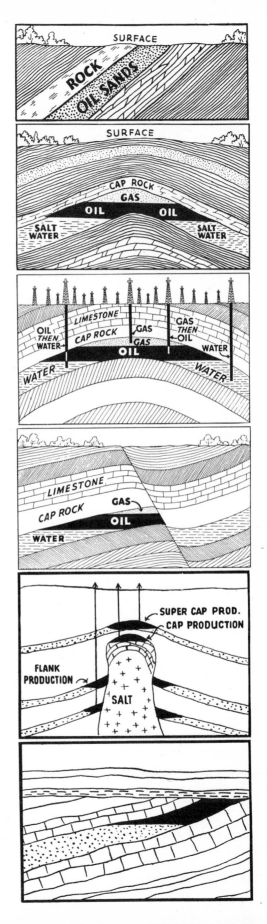

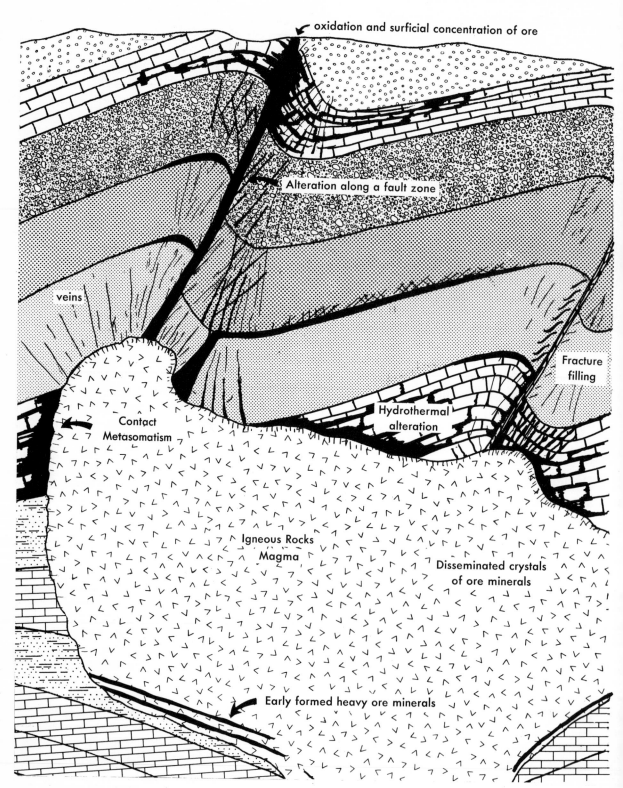

Fig. 3-6. Hypothetical section of an intrusion. This section shows some of the places where ores might become concentrated from the gases and liquids of the magma. The modes of origin are discussed in the text.

ORIGIN AND OCCURRENCE OF ORES

Miners frequently speak of whatever they are mining as an ore, but the term has a more specific meaning. An ore is a mineral deposit that is mined to produce a metal for a profit. The nature of most ore deposits is such that several metals are usually obtained from a single ore body. Other minerals of economic importance may also be obtained from the same ore body. A mineral deposit that yields a metal but cannot be mined at a profit is called protore.

Metals may occur in their native form, as do copper, gold, platinum, and silver, but more frequently the metal is contained in a compound, a mineral, and must be freed and concentrated by some chemical, mechanical, or electrical process. The origin and occurrence of each ore deposit is unique. Each one has its own characteristics, depending on the source of the ore, the alteration that took place when it was formed, the structure, and the history of the deposit. However, it is possible to classify many deposits in one of the following groups.

Modes of formation of ore deposits (metals)

I. *Magmatic concentration.* A magma is a body of molten rock that is generated within the earth. Many of the magmas are formed deep in the crust and cool and crystallize there. Other magmas break through to the surface and pour out as lava flows. A number of processes function within a magma to bring about localization or concentration of minerals. The diamonds of South Africa are found in a carrot-shaped intrusion of magma. The diamonds occur as small disseminated crystals. Chromite, the ore of chromium, is a heavy mineral, and it crystallizes while most of the magma is still liquid. It tends to sink to the bottom of the magma chamber and become concentrated there. The famous Bushveld chromite ores of South Africa are of this origin. Other deposits of ores are formed when the ore minerals are among the last to crystallize. These are formed from the residual liquids after the remainder of the magma is rock.

II. *Contact metasomatism.* Near the contact of a magma the heat and solutions from the magma alter the wall rock. The hot solutions carrying metals in solution may be highly reactive. When they come in contact with a limestone the chemical reactions are likely to bring about deposition of the ore minerals. This is the nature of the iron-ore deposit at Cornwall, Pennsylvania. The ore is concentrated at the contact of a limestone and a plate-like igneous intrusion called a dike.

III. *Hydrothermal processes.* Some deposits result from the deposition of ores by circulating hot waters. The hot solutions may come from a magma, or they may dissolve and concentrate ore minerals. Some are deposited from very hot water, others from moderately hot or even relatively cool waters. Most of the hydrothermal deposits are either cavity fillings or replacement deposits. Cavities occur naturally in the earth as fractures or fracture zones along which the crust has been broken, sheared and displaced. The native copper deposits of Michigan are found in the pore spaces in a gravel-like rock and in the pores in the top of a lava flow; the pore and pore spaces were produced by escaping gases. The lead and zinc deposits of the Tri-State District are found in the collapsed deposits in ancient caves and old stream channels. Other hydrothermal deposits are formed in volcanic pipes and where the rock layers of the crust have been crumpled by deformation associated with the formation of mountains.

The replacement deposits form when the hydrothermal solutions react with some mineral or substance in the crust, dissolving one substance and replacing it with the ore mineral. Many of the most important copper deposits in the United States are of this origin. These include the Bingham Canyon copper mine, the Bisbee, Arizona, deposits, and other deposits of the Southwest. The copper-bearing minerals have replaced other minerals along very small fractures. Another example is the petrified logs, which have been replaced by uranium ore minerals.

IV. Sedimentary ores. In the process of sedimentation, solids that are in suspension and elements that have been carried in solution out into the sea from the continents may be deposited. One of the most important of these deposits is iron ore. Iron ore used in Alabama comes from a sedimentary deposit. The iron mineral, hematite, has been deposited from sea water as a cement around grains of sand and replaces shell fragments of marine animals. It may be that the ancient iron deposits of the Lake Superior region were also formed in the sea. The mineral known as green sand, glauconite, is being deposited off the eastern coast of North America today. This mineral contains iron that has been freed from the rocks on the continents in which the element iron is a minor constituent. These green sands may some day be concentrated to form ore deposits.

V. Residual and mechanical concentration. Glauconite has a small amount of iron in it, but this may become concentrated through the weathering and leaching of the other constituents of the minerals, leaving the iron. Lake Superior iron ores contain up to 60 per cent iron, but at greater depth beneath the ground surface they contain only about 30 per cent iron. This might well represent the level in the ground below which residual enrichment did not occur.

Bauxite deposits such as those located in Arkansas, which yield about 96 per cent of the domestic production of aluminum ore in this country, were concentrated by weathering and leaching. These deposits have been formed by alteration of an igneous intrusion that was exposed at the surface of the ground many millions of years ago. At that time the climate in the south was tropical, and the minerals of the igneous rock were highly altered chemically. Some of the elements were removed, and aluminum was concentrated as a clay and altered to form bauxite.

Mechanical concentration occurs in streams, on beaches, and by wind separation. Most of these deposits are called placer deposits. The California gold placers are perhaps the most famous of this type. Native gold occurs in quartz veins in igneous rocks that have been intruded into the mountains of California. When these veins become exposed at the ground surface they are weathered and eroded. The gold is not easily weathered or altered by chemical action, nor is it soluble in water. Thus the gold is left unaltered in the streams. Gold is malleable; it does not shatter when it is hit. If it were brittle like quartz or glass it might become broken into such small pieces that they would be very difficult to find, but instead it remains intact. Its high density causes it to settle to the bottom of the stream and to become concentrated behind boulders or resistant ridges in the stream. Other minerals may become concentrated by the sorting action of the wind or water, which is capable of moving certain sizes and weights of particles and not others.

ENGINEERING GEOLOGY

It is interesting that the same man, William Smith, should be known as the Father of Civil Engineering and the Father of Historical Geology. To one who understands the scope of the two fields this is hardly a coincidence, for the fields overlap to a considerable extent. Geologists are concerned with understanding the nature of natural phenomena, while the civil engineer is mainly interested in directing natural forces for the use and convenience of man. Civil engineering includes the design and construction of all structures other than simple buildings, and the investigation, design, and construction of all systems of transportation, natural-power development, and water supply. It should be obvious that the engineer can best fulfill these aims when his knowledge of methods of construction is complemented by an understanding of the earth on which these structures are to be built. William Smith was a keen observer, and through his observations of the rocks and land forms in England he found many ways to accomplish engineering feats that others had deemed impossible. He used his understanding of the earth in constructing canals, in draining swamps, and in restoring springs. Unfortunately in this age of specialization few men take the time to become proficient in two or more fields. An engineering geologist needs to have a thorough understanding of the methods of design and construction as well as specialized training in all phases of physical geology. Yet the need for properly qualified men is great. Too many large-scale construction projects have been undertaken and completed with the finest engineering skill only to fail later because the geologic setting of the construction site was not considered. A most notable example of this was the failure of the St. Francis Dam near Los Angeles, California. The dam, which was built of concrete, was 205 feet high and 700 feet long. It created a reservoir that held 38,000 acre-feet of water. Soon after the reservoir filled, water seepage began through a consolidated gravel bed in which one end of the dam was anchored. A little later the dam failed. The side that was founded in the gravel gave way, opening the dam like a huge gate. The flood that ensued destroyed a small town, killed a number of people, and washed away valuable topsoil in the valley. Dr. F. L. Ransome in his report on the failure said this concerning the rock on the side that gave way. "When wet, the rock shows a considerable change, [a sample starting] to flake and crumble when placed in a beaker of water and in about 15 minutes slumps to the bottom of the vessel as a loose gritty sediment that can be stirred about with the finger. . . . So far as can be ascertained, no geological examination was made of the dam site before construction began."

Fig. 3-7. History of the Lake Superior iron ores. In the top section the iron-bearing formation and other sedimentary rocks are shown as they originally lay on the sea floor. Later these units were deformed, the mud changed to slate and the sands into a quartzite. As erosion laid the iron-bearing formation bare the unit became weathered, and iron became concentrated in the upper parts of the unit. Then the sea again advanced across the region and the older folded units were buried under new sedimentary rocks. In relatively recent times, during the past million years, the region was covered by a vast sheet of ice. When the ice receded the deposits of the ice were laid as a thin veneer over the region.

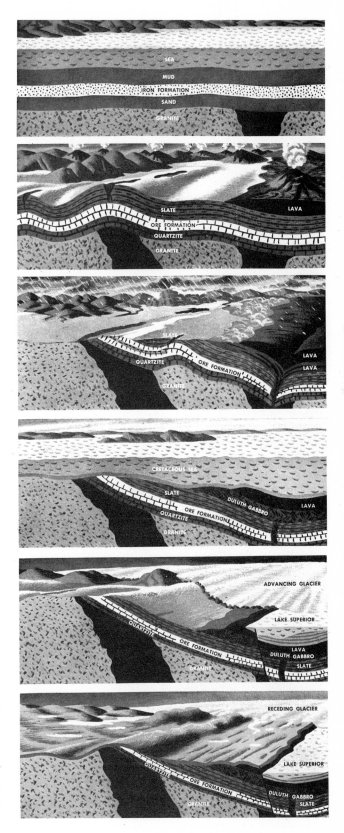

After a number of similar tragedies, many precautions are now taken. Some States require that geological consultants be used on all major earth-construction projects. Most civil-engineering schools now require their students to take at least one course in geology, and there is generally a greater awareness of the application of geology to engineering problems.

Knowledge of geology has been applied with considerable success on such engineering projects as:

1. Tunnel construction.
2. Excavation, fills, and retaining walls.
3. Prevention or protection from landslides.
4. Route location for highways, pipe lines, canals.
5. Foundation construction for dams, airports, bridges, and buildings.
6. River and flood control.
7. Prevention of silting of reservoirs and harbors.
8. Protection from beach erosion.
9. Location of building materials.
10. Water supply.

In the following paragraphs a brief explanation is given of a few of the more important geologic considerations in some of the above projects. Others are mentioned throughout the text.

Tunnel construction. This is an expensive type of construction. One of the main factors is the cost of removing rock materials. The cost of driving a tunnel in a hard rock like granite or diabase may be many times greater than for driving the tunnel the same distance in sedimentary rocks or unconsolidated sediments. Before construction is begun an intensive geological survey should be conducted to show what types of rocks will most likely be encountered along the proposed route. This is done by surface mapping and later by means of core drilling. Some cores, calyx cores, leave holes in the ground large enough to lower a man into. Once this work is completed, the engineer should know how much of each type of rock he will have to penetrate, how consolidated the rock is, if there are strata that are likely to swell in the area, where any faults are located, and what

the ground-water conditions are. Tunnels and mine faces driven through a dry rock unit have hit lenses or layers containing large quantities of water such as is found in old buried stream channels. This usually has resulted in loss of life and considerable property damage, and always in great expense, which might have been prevented by a careful preliminary study.

Route location. The engineer's problem is to lay a certain quality road designated to pass given towns. In choosing between two possible routes he must consider such factors as the distance, types of terrain over which the roads would pass, how much rock and dirt must be moved, the cost of moving it, and the availability of road-building materials. A geological survey may help answer many of these questions and may point out such dangers as potential landslides, stability of slopes on which the road may be built, flood dangers, and possible location of road materials.

Every region has its own particular problems because of variations in geology and climate. Consider the differences in laying a road across a swamp, where the main problem may be getting enough road metal to build a stable fill that won't sink, and putting a highway across the Alps, where long tunnels may have to be constructed. In building roads across the great salt deserts, engineers soon discovered that the salt deforms plastically under the weight of a road bed. The result is the necessity of adding more and more rock to the bed until it becomes stable. The main problem is the cost of transporting rock over long distances across the desert.

One of the most famous of all engineering projects was the construction of the Panama Canal, which was completed only after a long series of costly landslides and other difficulties. Much of the trouble lay in failure to recognize the character of the rock unit that underlies part of the area crossed by the canal. When excavated materials were dumped to the side of the cut its weight caused plastic clays under the canal to be squeezed. This weakened the slope and caused slides into the canal.

Foundations. Geological conditions are perhaps of more crucial importance in the construction of dams and foundations for bridge piers than in most other types of construction. The St. Francis Dam has already been mentioned. Some of the more important problems that have to be investigated in dam construction are:

1. Determination of the soundness of the underlying foundation beds, and their ability to carry the designed loadings.
2. Determination of how water tight the foundation beds at the dam location are and what measures, if any, are needed to make the underlying strata water tight.
3. The effect on the foundation bedrock of prolonged exposure to water.
4. The probability of earth movements occurring at the site of the dam, and the measures to be taken to safeguard against them.

Some of the costly errors that have been made in dam construction illustrate the need for careful geologic study of the proposed locations. At the Hales Bar Dam, part of the Tennessee Valley Authority, a project estimated to cost 3 million eventually cost over 11.5 million and required 8 instead of 2 years for completion because the reservoir was located in a limestone valley containing many solution cavities. The water drained out of the reservoir through caves. The Fort Peck Dam is one of the largest dams in the world (more than 3000 feet wide and storing 19 million cubic feet of water). It has been rebuilt after repeated failures because the foundation rock contained a layer of bentonite shale, which swelled on wetting, and because water pressure acting under artesian conditions exerted an upward pressure on the foundation. A third case is the Silent Valley Dam in Ireland. A test drill hit a granite boulder at a fairly shallow depth. This was interpreted as the depth to solid bedrock. Only after the contract was signed and construction started was it learned that the solid rock was much deeper and that a great deal more excavation was necessary.

REFERENCES

BATEMAN, A. M., 1942, *Economic Mineral Deposits:* New York, John Wiley & Sons, 898 p.

LEGGET, R. F., 1939, *Geology and Engineering:* New York, McGraw-Hill Book Co., 650 p.

LEVORSEN, A. I., 1954, *Geology of Petroleum:* San Francisco, W. H. Freeman Company, 703 p.

LOVERING, T. S., 1943, *Minerals in World Affairs:* New York, Prentice-Hall, 394 p.

MC KINSTRY, H. E., 1948, *Mining Geology:* New York, Prentice-Hall, 680 p.

MEINZER, O. E., 1923, The Occurrence of Ground Water in the United States: U.S. Geological Survey Water-supply Paper 489, 321 p.

RILEY, C. M., 1959, *Our Mineral Resources:* New York, John Wiley & Sons, 338 p.

VAN ROYEN, WILLIAM, and BOWLES, OLIVER, 1952, *Atlas of the World's Resources:* vol. II of *The Mineral Resources of the World:* New York, Prentice-Hall, 181 p.

4   Methods of Geologic Research

In its broadest sense, geology is the study of the earth's lithosphere, hydrosphere, and atmosphere. A myriad of problems and unanswered questions are found in each of these areas of investigation, and almost as numerous are the techniques, tools, and methods that may be used in attempts to answer these questions. We cannot begin to study the details of all the techniques that professional geologists use, but it is worth while to consider the general frame-work of the geologic approach to studying the earth. We will also find it helpful to understand a few of the tools and methods that have been used to gain the knowledge and understanding of natural phenomena we now have. Some methods or techniques are widely used; others are restricted to investigations in certain limited parts of the field; sometimes new methods must be found before new frontiers may be opened.

Adapting the method to the problem

What problems do we encounter in geologic work? Or, we might say, what questions do we ask the earth? It is easy to think of geologic investigations as being either academic or economic. Academic investigations involve any problem concerning the earth regardless of whether or not it is of direct practical value. Studies of such basic questions as the origin of the earth, the cause of mountain building, the crystal structure of some rare mineral, or the outlining of continents vanished from the earth millions of years ago may have little direct practical application, but they are problems that challenge the mind of man and kindle his imagination. The economic investigations are directed toward studying particular aspects of the earth; an understanding of them is of direct economic or practical value. These include exploration for mineral fuels and raw materials, which form the backbone of our industrial economy; selection of best and most economical routes for highways; selection of dam sites; and many other problems in engineering and other fields.

More and more we are coming to realize that a separation of problems into these two areas, academic and practical, is totally artificial and meaningless. In the 1920's only a few geologists expressed any interest in a group of rare minerals that exhibited certain peculiar properties, among them radioactivity. Twenty years later this problem changed from one of an almost purely academic nature into one of the most urgent and practical problems in geology — to find out everything we could about the uranium minerals, especially where and how they occurred.

Almost all mineral industries either sponsor pure research directly or support organizations that are carrying on research even though much of it has no apparent connection with the industries' current problems. One of the key strengths of the policies of the Soviet Union government of recent years is to sponsor pure research in almost all areas of science, secure in the knowledge that some of it will eventually pay for itself with dividends.

Many geologic investigations are carried on through field studies. Others may be almost exclusively laboratory experimental work, al-

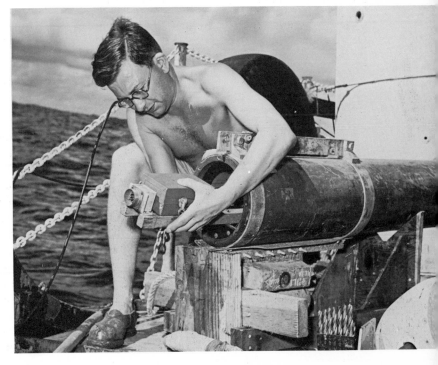

Fig. 4-1. The magnetometer. This instrument measures variations in the earth's magnetic field. These variations offer clues to the structure of the earth. This magnetometer is being used at sea where it is towed behind the ship. Magnetometers are also used from airplanes. Measurement by magnetometer is one of the many indirect methods of investigating the crust of the earth. (Photo by courtesy of the University of California, La Jolla, Scripps Institution of Oceanography.)

though this is usually combined with a certain amount of field work. There is no substitute for a thorough understanding of field geology even for those who carry on laboratory work. The laboratory experiments must be set up in such a way as to reproduce faithfully conditions in nature, and the results must be interpreted in terms of geologic processes.

A sample of the methods of investigation currently in use in various fields of geology are listed below. This list is far from complete but should give you some idea of the diversity of the techniques.

FIELD METHODS (WHAT A GEOLOGIST DOES IN THE FIELD)
1. Mapping and measuring land forms.
2. Mapping the distribution of rock types, the distribution of rock units of different ages, and tracing of particular units.

Fig. 4-2. Temperature probe being lowered into ocean. The amount of heat flowing through the crust of the earth into the ocean waters varies considerably in different regions. The cause is unknown. It may be that vast convection cells underlie the crust. Probes such as the one shown here are used to measure the heat flow. (Photo by courtesy of the University of California, La Jolla, Scripps Institution of Oceanography.)

3. Mapping of the variations in mineral composition, rock type, fossil content, or thickness of particular units of rock.
4. Collecting rocks, minerals, water, gases, and fossils for laboratory analysis or study.
5. Measuring the earth's magnetic field, the force of gravity, and the vibrations of the earth after earthquakes or explosions.

LABORATORY STUDIES
1. Scale-model experiments. The effects of many natural processes are tested in scale models, using such equipment as wind tunnels, sedimentation tanks, and presses.
2. X-ray and spectrographic studies are made of crystal structure and to identify minerals.
3. Radioactive decay rates are used to obtain the age of certain rocks.
4. The effects of passing polarized light through thin sections of rock are studied to determine the exact composition of the rock.
5. Sediments are analyzed by separation of sizes, and into types based on physical and chemical properties.
6. Chemical analyses, both quantitative and qualitative, are made in the study of the composition and origin of many rocks.

Selection of a method

The first step in starting an investigation is to formulate the questions to which answers must be found. Usually many others will arise in the process of the study, but once the initial question is raised a method may be selected or devised that is satisfactory to accomplish the intended purpose. Frequently what might be the most desirable method of approach must be given up for practical or economic considerations. Very little research is carried on under optimum conditions. There is almost always a limit to the amount of time, money, personnel, or equipment available. Sometimes results obtained with a rapid, inexpensive method may be almost identical with those of a much more time-consuming and expensive procedure.

One of the most important factors determining field procedures in mapping is the nature of the terrain. In the swampy thick underbrush of parts of Canada, mapping is done by cutting surveyed lines out in a grid pattern and digging into the mat of moss to find outcrops. These findings are then made into a geologic map. In the mountains above timber line there may be almost 100 per cent exposure of rock outcrop, but much of it may prove inaccessible without dangerous and time-consuming rope work. The use of ordinary surveying instruments is often too slow, but aerial photographs or topographic maps prepared from them may prove ideal as base maps on which the surface geology can be drawn. In large areas of the Gulf Coast and the Mid-continent the land surface is flat, and often the surface of the ground is covered by so much soil that few outcrops can be found. Thus it is difficult to obtain very much information about the geology beneath the ground from mapping on the surface. In such areas the distribution of soils and particular plants may give a clue to the rocks below, but drill holes are the best and most reliable, although certainly not the least expensive, way to find out what is under the ground.

Time is often an important factor, especially in investigations carried on for economic purposes. The outlay of money required for some equipment and for keeping certain types of field parties in operation is great. The amount of time and the purpose of the job may well determine the feasibility of a detailed study or a reconnaissance report. If a mining company is looking for a new deposit of ore in a large region, a reconnaissance is the logical requirement; but if it is necessary to locate exactly a certain vein of ore, the position of which is determined by local geologic conditions, then a very detailed mapping job is required.

Many investigations are started as field studies. The first job is ordinarily to prepare a geologic map of the area. As mapping is carried on, samples of the rocks are collected, and notes are made on all aspects of the geology of the area. Later these samples are studied in the laboratory, and the map and notes are analyzed to help formulate the best understanding possible of the geology of the area. Naturally,

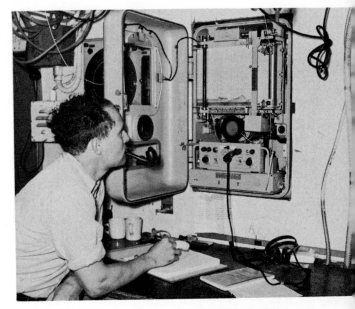

Fig. 4-3. Depth profile. Here a geologist from the U.S. Navy Electronic Laboratory examines a depth profile as it is being traced aboard a research vessel during an expedition into the Pacific. Such profiles of the sea floor are used to study the land forms of the ocean and the processes which might be responsible for their formation. (Photo by courtesy of the University of California, La Jolla.)

special attention must be given to various parts of the study, depending on the purposes for which the work is done. This pattern of work is usually the most practical one, since it is much easier to grasp the significance of the results of laboratory studies when they can be directly related to the other aspects of the geology.

To summarize: The factors most often affecting the selection of a particular method of approach and the actual techniques to be used in any investigation are:

1. Suitability of the method and techniques for satisfying the purposes of the investigation.
2. Capability of the methods to yield satisfactory results in the time available for the study.
3. Suitability of the methods for use in the particular terrain, region, or under the conditions to be found where the investigation must be made.

Fig. 4-4. Field mapping. Here a geologist examines the rocks high up in the Rocky Mountains. Field mapping is the basis for most geologic research. (Photo by E. W. Spencer.)

4. Feasibility of the method in consideration of the budget, the personnel available, and the particular equipment that is on hand.
5. Capability of the method to yield all the data necessary to answer the questions that are likely to arise in the course of the investigation.

General approach

Most investigations in geology fall into four general categories: (1) areal studies in which a regional study of the geology is made; (2) special-problem studies in which the answers to a particular question are sought; (3) group-research projects in which both special problems and areal studies may be made by a large group of investigators in efforts to gain as nearly complete knowledge as possible on problems too comprehensive for single individ-

uals to solve; and finally (4) the work of those who synthesize the work of others, bringing work from many fields and areas together to formulate general principles.

THE AREAL APPROACH

The geology of an area may be worked out either for the purpose of extending our understanding of the region in general or as a first step in more intensive studies of certain particular aspects of the regional geology. Special studies are always more significant if they can be related to the general geology of the area in which they are conducted. Because of its importance the technique of making a regional study should be mastered.

First, a search should be made of the geologic literature on the area to find out as much as possible about previous work. This may consist of such things as logs of physical and chemical properties of the rock penetrated in water or oil wells, as well as scientific studies. In some areas no such information is to be found; in others a large amount of data may already exist.

Second, the area should be examined in reconnaissance to help decide what type of base map to use. Three types of base maps may be available: topographic maps, aerial photographs, or outline maps. Once your work is started you will be primarily concerned with locating outcrops, studying them, recording notes, and representing the data on the map. It is absolutely necessary to be able to locate yourself accurately on the map. Which of the three

will you select? Generally the topographic map is the best choice. (See the section on topographic maps immediately following.) For most areal studies the scale of the topographic map is satisfactory (that is, the map is about the right size to contain all the detail desired in the study), or it may be enlarged. If the topography is such that you can readily locate yourself anywhere on the map then it is possible to make your geologic observations directly on the map without use of surveying instruments. However, if there are few distinctive features on the map, as in the plains or in the Gulf Coast, then it will be necessary to make an accurate survey as the study proceeds.

Outline maps are the least desirable of the

Fig. 4-5. Aerial photograph. Vertical aerial photographs such as this are used as a basis for many geologic maps. Note how the different rocks show as different colors. It would take months of tedious field work to discover what is obvious about the distribution of the different rocks in this photograph. (Photo by Royal Canadian Air Force.)

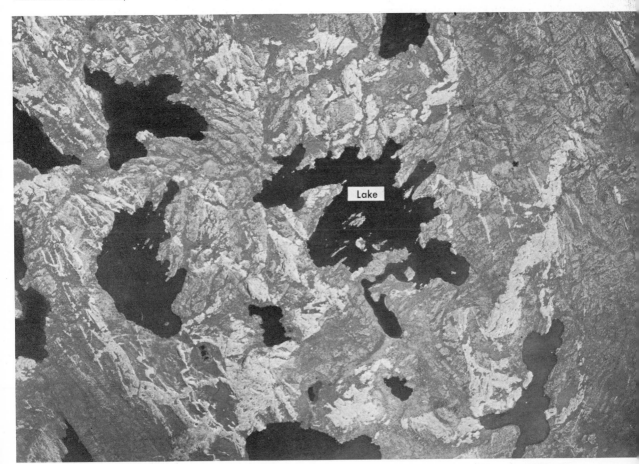

three types of base maps, but sometimes there is no other type of base available. Most outline maps contain only political boundaries and perhaps an outline of streams. When these are used, accurate surveying must accompany the geologic mapping.

Topographic maps are so useful that you may wonder why aerial photographs are ever used. They supplement the data available on the topographic map. The photographs used as base maps are taken straight down from high altitudes. Some of the reasons they are widely used are:

1. Photographs may be available in areas that have not been mapped topographically.
2. The photographs may have many easily recognizable features on them that are missing on topographic maps. For example, on a good aerial photograph you can pick out isolated trees and shrubs, small drainage lines, and changes in vegetation and soil colors.

3. You can often see the rock outcrops on a photograph and usually you can see indications of the rock structure of the of the area. Different rock types may appear as slightly different shades of color in the grass, trees, or soil. In recent years many geologists have specialized in photogeology, the study of the geology of an area from aerial photographs. It is often possible to learn a great deal from the photographs alone but they are usually used in conjunction with topographic maps if the latter is being used as a base.

The most serious disadvantage of aerial photographs is that, in spite of technological advances in their production, there is still optical distortion in the photographs. This is not ordinarily great near the center of the photograph, but toward the margins the distortion increases. For this reason they make poor base maps for any observations that involve directions, and almost all do. Distortion of another

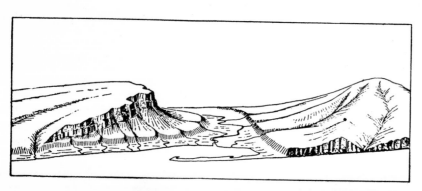

Fig. 4-6. A simple topographic map.

(Courtesy of U. S. Geological Survey.)

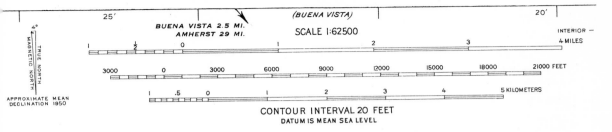

FOR SALE BY U. S. GEOLOGICAL SURVEY, WASHINGTON 25, D. C.
A FOLDER DESCRIBING TOPOGRAPHIC MAPS AND SYMBOLS IS AVAILABLE ON REQUEST

Fig. 4-7. The scale and other information given on all of the topographic maps published by the U.S. Geological Survey.

kind becomes great when differences in elevation, called relief, represented in the photo are large. The top of a mountain is closer to the lens of the camera than the bottom of the valley. Thus the relative sizes of the two are out of proportion. Also mountain tops appear shifted in position if the camera is to one side of them when the photos are taken. The consequence of these distortions is that the data plotted on a photograph must be transferred to a topographic map. The amount of work necessary to accomplish this is so great that it is usually much simpler to plot the data on the topographic map in the first place, and to use the photographs to help locate outcrops and indications of the geology that may not be as apparent on the ground as from the air. Since topographic maps play such an important role in field mapping, both for areal studies and in special problems, it is necessary to understand what one is, what it shows, and how it is made. Geologists are not primarily concerned with making topographic maps, but they sometimes have to make them to facilitate their work.

TOPOGRAPHIC MAPS

A topographic map is a means of accurately representing the configuration of the land on a piece of paper. Generalized impressions of the land form may be achieved by use of shading or hachure lines, but a topographic map is constructed so that a very close approximation of the elevation of any point on the map is possible from the map. This is made possible by a number of lines on the map each of which

represents a certain elevation. These are called contour lines. They are drawn at a given interval so that one contour may connect points at an elevation of 100 feet, the contour above connects points at a 110-foot elevation, and the one below a 90-foot elevation. Thus in this case the interval between the contours is 10 feet, vertically. From the definition of contour lines we can predict their behavior:

1. Any point on a contour line is at the same elevation as other points on the same line.
2. A single map may have contour lines that are closed, as around a hill top, or the lines may run off the edge of the map.
3. A single map may have more than one contour that represents the same elevation. If there are two hill tops each may be ringed by a contour at the same elevation.
4. Contours never cross one another unless there is a vertical cliff, over which they are superimposed, or an overhanging ledge.
5. The elevation of at least some of the contours is printed along the contour lines to serve as reference for the contours above and below that line. To make reading the contours easier every fifth one is a heavier line.

Topographic maps are made by the United States Geological Survey or the Coast and Geodetic Survey. Most of these maps are printed at a scale on which 1 inch of map distance is

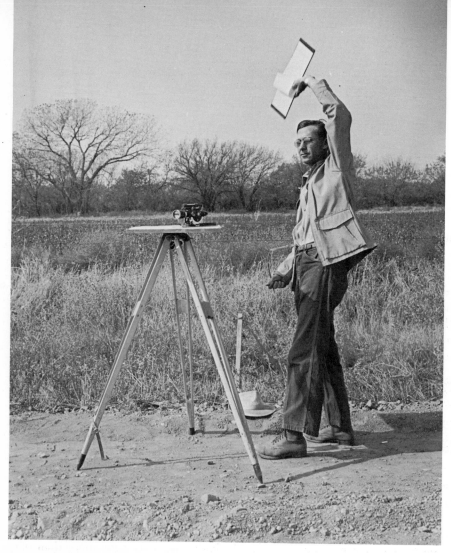

Fig. 4-8. Geologist with plane table and alidade set up for mapping. From a known position of the ground he can determine the distance to, and difference in elevation of, the ground at other points occupied by the rodman who carries a graduated rod marked in feet and tenths of feet. (Photo by courtesy of Seismic Service Co.)

equivalent to 1 mile of ground distance, and they cover areas 15 minutes latitude by 15 minutes longitude (12 by 17 miles approximately in the middle latitudes). These maps, called quadrangle maps, provide the following information:

1. Contour lines (each map has the contour interval printed at the bottom).
2. The scale in miles, feet, and kilometers. The scale is also written as a fraction, such as 1: 62,500, meaning that, regardless of the units of measure used, one of those units measured on the map is equivalent to 62,500 of the same units measured horizontally across the ground.
3. Cultural features such as roads, highways, towns, houses, churches, cemeteries, ranches, camps, irrigation ditches, trails, township lines, county lines, and park boundaries.
4. Physical features including rivers, lakes, marshes, levees, beaches, and mountain peaks.
5. The name of the map area (quadrangle) and the names of those that adjoin at corners and along sides, printed at map margins.

6. The exact elevations of points that have been determined by ground surveying. These include bench marks (BM with elevation) and triangulation stations, (triangle with elevation). The exact elevations of some peaks and other points are also given.

Topographic mapping

Two techniques are used in making topographic maps. The first is to survey details on the ground; the second is to use aerial photographs and a reconnaissance survey.

Essentially, topographic surveying consists of the following processes:

1. Surveying is started from a point of known latitude, longitude, and of known elevation if possible. Mapping may be done without such a reference point, but the exact location and elevations will be uncertain.
2. Geologists ordinarily use an alidade, a surveying instrument equipped with a straight edge parallel to the telescope, one vertical and three horizontal cross hairs in the telescope, and an arc so that the telescope may be raised or lowered and the angle of inclination measured. The horizontal cross hairs are spaced so that they will intersect a rod 100 feet away at two points 1 foot apart. At 1000 feet the intercept would be 10 feet. Thus it is possible to determine distances from the alidade to a point by setting up a rod which has feet and tenths of feet marked off on it at the point. The distance between the rod and the alidade in feet is then 10 times the intercept between the two cross hairs measured in tenths of a foot. If the point is not at the same level as the alidade then the angle of inclination of the tube and the distance to the point can be used to calculate the horizontal distance. The alidade rests on a flat table, called a plane table, to which a compass and a piece of paper are attached.

3. The plane table is set up so it is level, and it is rotated until the north-south line on the base map is oriented north-south.
4. A pin is stuck in the paper at a point that represents the position of the bench mark—the point of known elevation from which the survey is starting.
5. The alidade is set on the table, and the straight edge is placed against the pin.
6. A rodman carries the rod from one point to another, setting the rod up, while the person operating the plane table moves the alidade, using the pin as a focus until the rod is sighted. He notes the distance and the angle of inclination of the tube. From this he is able to calculate both the horizontal or map distance to the point and the difference in elevation between the alidade and the rod. He then uses a ruler and locates that point on the paper and indicates the elevation of the point. The rodman is waved on, and he sets up at the next point.

Fig. 4-9. Telescopic alidade. This instrument is used to measure angles, both vertical and horizontal, and distances. (Photo by courtesy of Standard Oil Co., N.J.)

7. In this fashion hundreds of points are located, and their elevations are determined. When all the points that can be seen from one alidade position are recorded, the alidade is moved and set up again, and more points are taken. Obviously it is desirable to set up the alidade and plane table in spots from which good views of the countryside can be obtained. Shots up to several thousand feet are possible.

8. Points for elevation determination are located on prominent features if possible—for example, on houses, roads, streams, mountain and hill tops, in valleys, in fact, anywhere the slope of the ground surface is noticeably changed.

9. After all the points have been determined, the surveyor draws in the cultural features, the roads, etc., and the contours. The method of contouring consists of connecting points of the same elevation, except that many points do not happen to fall exactly on a contour line. Nevertheless, these serve to indicate the position of a given contour either up or down the slope from them.

10. The contours are either drawn in the field where the general configuration of the land can be seen, or they are checked and corrected after being drawn in the office.

Fig. 4-10. Construction of a topographic map from points of known elevation. The points of known elevation serve as guides for the construction of contours. The lines rarely fall directly on the points, but they conform to them. Contours cut back upstream whenever they cross a stream. This knowledge helps in the construction of contours as does a familiarity with the shape of various types of land forms.

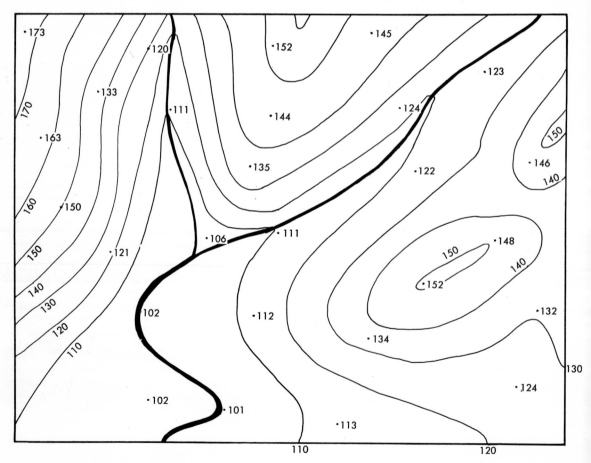

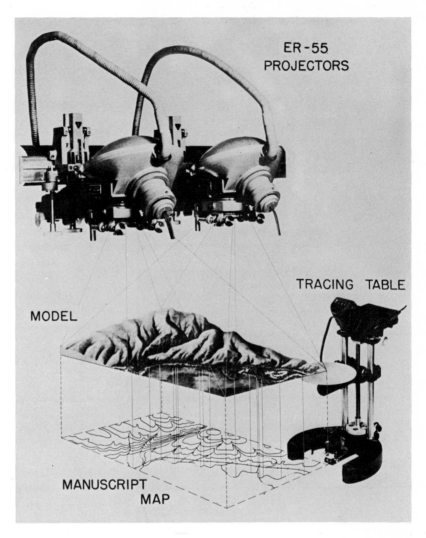

ER-55 PROJECTORS

TRACING TABLE

MODEL

MANUSCRIPT MAP

Fig. 4-11. Stereoscopic plotting of a map from aerial photographs. The optical model formed by a pair of projected photographs is converted to a topographic map by means of the tracing table, a device for measuring and drawing details of the terrain. The photographs used in the projectors are printed on glass slides, called diapositives. A red filter is used in one projector, a blue-green one in the other; the observer wears corresponding spectacles to obtain the 3-D effect. (By courtesy of U.S. Geological Survey.)

A new technique of making topographic maps is rapidly replacing the older plane-table mapping methods. The new method makes it possible to draw contours stereoscopically from aerial photographs with a machine known as a multiplex. This procedure is much faster, more economical, and usually results in much more accurate maps than the older methods. Aerial-photograph coverage of the area must first be obtained. The photographs must be taken under the best conditions so there will be a minimum of cloud shadows, shadows from cliffs, snow cover, or anything else that might detract from the clarity. The photographs are corrected for distortion caused by tilt of the camera. The photos must be taken so that there is about a two-thirds overlap of the area covered in one photograph by the next one to it. This makes it possible to obtain stereoscopic images of the landscape by the use of a stereoscope or a multiplex. The multiplex makes it possible for a person viewing the photos stereoscopically to trace out a contour line. Of course he cannot tell at what elevation he is tracing the contour, unless there is a known point of elevation on the ground. For this reason and as a check on the accuracy of the multiplex some plane-table surveying is done in the area. The bench marks are set by ordinary surveying methods, and the elevations of a number of points are determined. These usually include the tops of many of the mountains and hills.

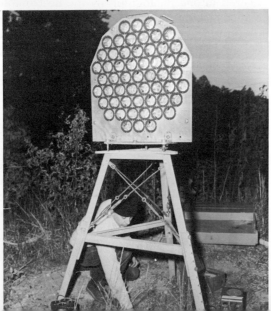

GEOLOGIC MAPPING

Not all geologic maps show exactly the same type of information. They are constructed for many different purposes and often differ in many respects. Usually a geologic map shows the areal distribution of one or more of the following:

1. Rock types such as granite, basalt, schists, sandstone.
2. The rocks of a certain age, those that were formed during a certain interval of geologic time.
3. Certain units of rock that can be easily recognized in the field. This differs from (1) in that there might be several units of rock of different types grouped together, none of which is the same age throughout.

In addition, there are many specialized maps that would in a general sense qualify as geologic maps. These are distinguished by special names such as structure-contour maps, maps showing thickness of strata, paleogeographic maps, paleogeology maps, and others. Like topographic maps, geologic maps may be of any scale. Some are done in detail at scales of a few feet ground measure to an inch on the map. More frequently the scale is between 500 feet to an inch and 1 mile to an inch, but others cover entire states or countries. Some are generalized maps of the world. When making a map, you must select a scale that allows enough room to show the amount of detail required by the purpose for which the map is being made.

Various kinds of information are provided on most geologic maps:

1. Many geologic maps are printed over topographic maps to make correlation of land forms and geology possible.

Figs. 4-12, 4-13, and 4-14. The Geodimeter. Instruments such as these are used by the U.S. Coast and Geodetic Survey to make very precise measurements of distance. (Photos by courtesy of the U.S. Coast and Geodetic Survey.)

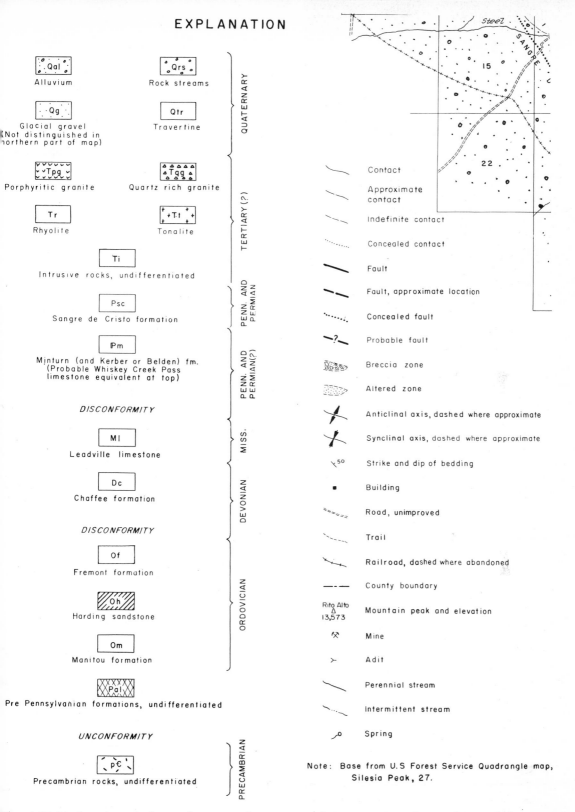

Fig. 4-15. Explanations similar to this are used on most geologic maps to indicate what symbols are used on the map. The column at left is known as a stratigraphic column. It gives in order of age the rock units mapped. (From a map of the Northern Sangre De Cristo Mountains by Litsey, *Bull. Geol. Soc. America*, v. 69.)

Fig. 4-16. Exposed dipping rock unit of sandstone. The trees are growing along fractures in the dip slope of this unit. (Photo by E. W. Spencer.)

2. The same types of cultural features found on topographic maps are put on geologic maps, but in general fewer such features are shown.
3. At least some of the physiographic features such as streams, lakes, coasts, and mountain peaks are indicated.
4. Lines of latitude and longitude are drawn.
5. The contacts between the units being mapped are drawn whether these are contacts between rocks of different ages or of different rock types. An exposed contact is that line on the ground surface separating one rock unit from another. The contacts are drawn as solid lines where they are exposed at the surface, and they are dotted or dashed if there is a soil, ice, or sediment cover.
6. Faults are drawn on the map. These are breaks in the solid crust along which displacement has occurred. The lines are solid if exposed, dotted or dashed if unexposed. Symbols are used as a means of indicating the direction of relative motion of the two sides of the fault.
7. Strike and dip are observations that provide the information necessary to describe exactly the position in space of

a plane. Both are made with a pocket transit called the Brunton compass. Strike is the compass direction of any imaginary horizontal line on a plane. Since all horizontal lines on a plane are parallel it doesn't make any difference which line is measured. The compass direction referred to here is the bearing of the line (i.e., N.-S., N. 36° E., or N. 89° W.) Dip is the maximum angle between a horizontal plane and the plane in question. The maximum angle is always in a vertical plane at right angles to the strike.

Strike and dip are used to indicate the local attitude of any features of geologic significance that can be approximated by a plane. Features of this nature include the plane of contact between two rock units, faults, fractures, and the orientation of platy minerals. Symbols indicating the strike and dip of these features are printed on some maps. It is highly desirable to have this information when making interpretations of the map.

8. A legend is provided. Along one margin of the geologic map a column or vertical series of boxes will be found. Each box contains the color pattern or symbols used to represent each of the rock units on the map. Standard procedure is to separate the three types of rocks (igneous, metamorphic, and sedimentary). Within each of the types the youngest rock unit is placed at the top of the series with successively older

Fig. 4-17. Strike of a rock unit is the compass direction of horizontal lines of the unit. The dip is the angle between the horizon and the surface of the unit measured at right angles to the strike.

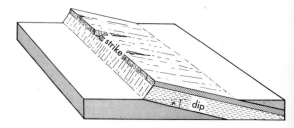

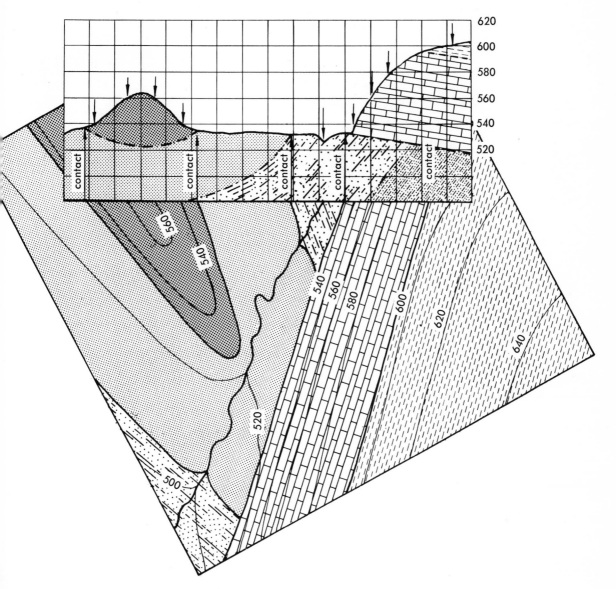

Fig. 4-18. Preparation of a cross section. See text for discussion.

units farther down in the column. The basic rock units used for the purposes of mapping are called formations. A formation is a body of rock, usually sedimentary rock, that has certain characteristics which make it recognizable and a mappable unit in the field. Most formations are approximately of the same age throughout their extent. The ages of the rock units are also indicated in the legend.

Interpretation of geologic maps

The greatest problem encountered by most students in their first experience with geologic maps is the problem of making interpretations of a three-dimensional structure from a two-dimensional map. But this is one of the most important aspects of map interpretation, and it must be mastered. By learning to make cross sections of a map you will find it much easier to interpret the entire map. Many geologic

Fig. 4-19. Sketch of the Waterpocket fold in the Colorado Plateau. Note that successively younger units are exposed from right to left. (After G. K. Gilbert.)

maps are accompanied by cross sections. A cross section is a view in two dimensions of what you would see if the land surface could be cut and parted. You see cross sections when you look into a cliff face (i.e., quarry walls, road cuts, tunnels).

How to prepare a cross section

First the line along which the section is to be made must be selected. Once this has been determined a piece of paper is placed along that line on the geologic map. Preferably, a piece of graph paper is used. Then a scale for the vertical dimension must be selected. If you want to draw the sections so it is a true picture then the vertical scale selected is the same as the horizontal scale of the map. Frequently this does not give enough exaggeration. A vertical exaggeration of two to three times often gives more satisfactory results. If the map has contours on it these should be used to draw a profile of the land surface along the line of the cross section. This is done simply by noting where each contour line intersects the line of the cross section, observing the elevation of the contour line, then making a point at the corresponding elevation on the graph paper. In this way a large number of points are determined. A smooth line connect-

ing these points gives a fair approximation of the land profile. Now, with a profile on the graph paper, go back and mark each contact between rock units, and the places where each fault intersects the line of the cross section. If the strike and dip of the rock units and the faults are given, it is possible to use a compass to measure these and draw the projection of these unit boundaries and faults as an initially straight line.

After the projections of the lines have been drawn it will be obvious that some of the lines should be connected to form folds, but a great deal of experience may be needed to make the correct decisions each time. Once these connections have been made the section is complete. Certain patterns of outcrops provide hints needed to make the correct subsurface connections.

Outcrop patterns on geologic maps

Some geologic maps are very simple, and the ordered nature of the distribution of rock units is quite apparent, but others may remind you more of some modernistic abstract paintings. Here careful study and a systematic scheme of approach are necessary for successful interpretation. A few simple observations will serve to demonstrate the significance of the outcrop patterns. Sedimentary rock units represented on maps are usually plate-like in shape. They are approximately uniform in thickness and they extend over large areas. This, like most generalizations, is not always a valid assumption, but it simplifies the problem of map interpretation to make this assumption at first. Outcrop patterns are determined by these five factors:

1. Thickness of the strata.
2. Slope of the ground surface.
3. Attitude of the sedimentary strata and the igneous and metamorphic rock units.
4. Structure of the rock units.
5. Sequence of events in the area.

If strata are flat lying in a plain the rock unit exposed at the surface may cover the entire map, but if the area has an irregular land surface the contacts between strata will be exposed. Their pattern will resemble that of contour lines. Many contacts are exposed if differences in elevation are great and the thickness of individual strata in the sequence is slight.

If a sequence of strata is uniformly tilted, the width of outcrop depends on the amount of the dip and the amount and direction of the ground slope. Note that the youngest strata are always in the direction of the dip, and that the outcrop pattern will be a sequence of bands.

If a sequence of strata is dipping vertically the outcrop of the contacts will form straight lines across the map regardless of the topography, and the thickness of the outcrop pattern will be equal to the thickness of the strata.

The law of V's. If the direction of the dip of a stratum is not given by a symbol on the map it is possible to determine this by noting the outcrop pattern where a stream valley cuts across the contact. A V-shaped pattern is usually produced. The V points upstream under these conditions:

a. In horizontal strata.
b. In gently dipping strata inclined upstream.
c. In strata inclined downstream if the slope of the stream is greater than the amount of the dip.

The V points downstream if the strata are dipping downstream at an angle greater than the slope of the stream valley.

No V is formed if the strata are vertical.

The metamorphic rocks of sedimentary origin can be mapped in much the same fashion as sedimentary strata. These metamorphic rocks are frequently stratified. However, the igneous rocks may have very irregular shapes. The outcrop patterns of these may be as regular as that of a stratum, as in the case of sills or dikes, but they may be very irregular and appear as patches on the map.

Structure on geologic maps

The term "structure" refers to the shape or relative positions in space of the sequences of rock. We have already considered the cases of horizontal, vertical, and uniformly inclined

Fig. 4-20. A simplified geologic map of the Black Hills. As a result of doming and erosion older units are exposed in the center of the dome and younger units are around the edges.

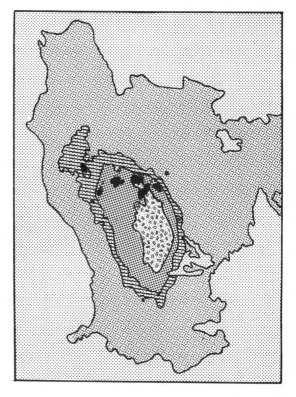

strata. Other structures with which we must become familiar are folds, faults, and unconformities.

Folds. The plate-like rock units, the strata, are sometimes folded by stresses in the earth's crust. These folds occur in systems and resemble the folds in a tablecloth in many ways. There are upfolds called anticlines and downfolds called synclines. These may be perfectly symmetrical, or they may appear to have been pushed over or inclined, in which case they are asymmetric. Some folds may have been pushed over so far that they are nearly flat lying; they are called recumbent folds. Like the folds in a tablecloth, some folds in the earth extend for long distances, and others die out at one or both ends. They are said to plunge. Very similar to folds are the symmetrical and nearly circular bulges or depressions called domes and basins. The identification of these structures is very simple because processes of erosion remove rock from the land surfaces. The removal is usually fastest on the top of high points. Thus, as a dome is raised, the top of the dome tends to be eroded more than the margins. This brings about removal of the topmost layer of sediment from the top of the uplift and exposes the older rock units in the middle. The result

is a series of circular contacts and exposure of successively older rock units toward the center. In a basin, the center of the basin is lowered, so the rims are subjected to erosion first, and a series of concentric contacts are exposed, but the youngest rock units are now found in the center. Likewise, anticlines and synclines may be identified by applying the same sort of reasoning. Erosion is fastest on the upfolded parts. Thus the axial zone of an anticline is truncated, cut off, first exposing older units, but the sides, called limbs, of a syncline are truncated before the axial zone, leaving younger units along the axis.

Faults. By studying the rocks exposed on either side of a fault you can usually determine which side moved up relative to the other. Remember that before the fault formed the strata continued unbroken across the fault. When the break occurred the displacement may have been vertical, it may have been parallel to the strike of the fault, or it might have been a combination of the two. Whichever side moved upward was subjected to more rapid erosion than the other side, and therefore the rocks exposed at the surface on the up side are likely to be older than those directly across the fault. Be careful in making interpretations of faults.

Fig. 4-21. Block diagram illustrating various types of folds.

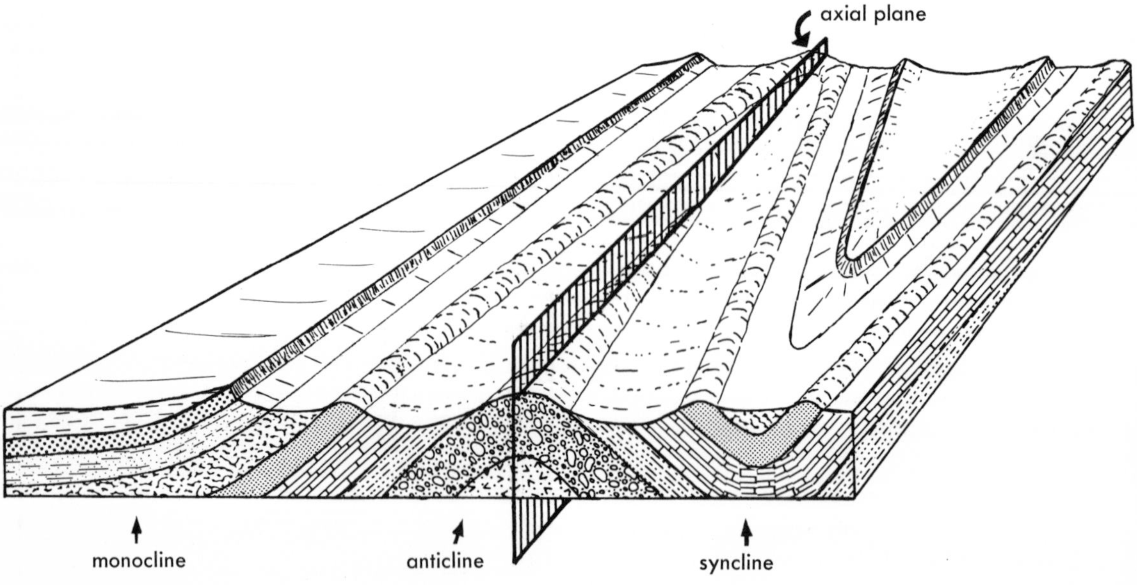

monocline   anticline   syncline

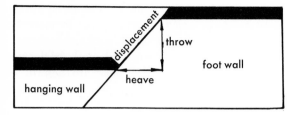

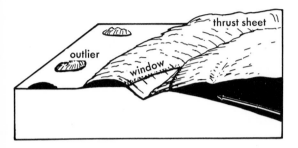

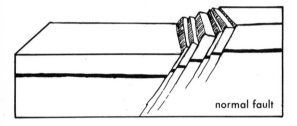

Fig. 4-22. Faults and fault nomenclature.

Faulting plus the effects of erosion and other structures such as folds may present a confusing problem. The low-angle faults called thrust faults, can create some particularly peculiar situations. A thrust fault may move a sheetlike mass of rocks from one area to another. In the process, older rocks in the thrust sheet may have been brought to lie on younger strata. In this event it is possible for the processes of erosion to erode through the sheet, exposing young rocks surrounded by older rocks. This particular form is called a window or fenster. Such a sheet may become isolated by erosion, leaving a patch of older rocks lying on younger rocks. This feature is known as an outlier. An outlier may also be formed through erosion when a portion of a rock unit becomes isolated from the main body of the unit.

Unconformities. Breaks in the history of sedimentary sequences bring unconformities into existence. They may be simply prolonged interruptions in the process of deposition of sedimentary rocks. They may be brought about by uplift of the sediments from the sea bottom to the surface where they are attacked by the agents of weathering and erosion and partially removed, or the unconformity may represent a major break in the sequence during which uplift, folding, faulting, and erosion all take place before sedimentation is resumed and more units of rock are deposited. The first two types of unconformities affect map-outcrop patterns only in that the expected sequence of units is not found. Some of them were either not deposited, or they were eroded away. The third type, angular unconformities, may greatly influence the outcrop pattern. For example, the break in the record may have been preceded by deposition, folding of the strata into synclines and anticlines, and erosion of these before new strata were formed, which are probably now horizontal or tilted.

4-23. Unconformities. The block diagram at top depicts an angular unconformity. That at the bottom is a disconformity. The topographic forms shown are only two of many possible land forms which might develop.

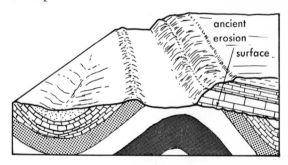

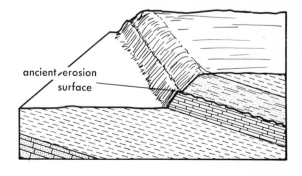

SPECIAL-PROBLEM APPROACH

The primary distinction between this approach and the investigation of an area is that the objectives of the study are much more precise. All aspects of the geology of a region may be treated in an areal study, including the structure, stratigraphy, physiography, and economic geology, but when a special problem is under study the natural tendency is to give attention only to those matters that are directly connected. The special problem may be one mainly of economic or academic interest. The special problem may be limited in scope to a small area, or it may encompass study of data collected from around the world. Areal studies are carried on for the purpose of systematically obtaining data on the geology of a region. Once this is accomplished it serves as a backlog of data, which may be needed in more specialized investigations. It is often necessary for the first to precede the second. Examples of a few of the special problems currently under investigation are:

a. How do ore deposits originate? Each deposit or type of deposit may be a complicated problem in itself.
b. What is the behavior of rocks under great confining pressures?
c. What is the exact composition and structure of the rocks beneath the crust of the earth?
d. How can radioactive waste be disposed of without contaminating our drinking water?
e. What causes glaciation?
f. What forces in the earth cause mountains to rise?
g. What is the origin of the craters on the moon?
h. How can we map the bottom of the oceans?

Obviously the methods used in special studies of this nature are much more varied than those we have already discussed, and, in fact, some problems require the development of new methods and techniques. Many of the methods employed in such studies are developed in other fields of science. Physics is the science of measurement. It is often necessary to make exact measurements in geology, and physical methods are the obvious answer. Because methods developed and ordinarily used in other fields of science are helpful in solving geologic problems, a premium is placed on those geologists who are well trained in two or more sciences.

You will judge from the nature of the special problems listed that some require field mapping and sampling, and others may be dealt with largely in the laboratory.

GROUP RESEARCH

Some problems in geology are of such great magnitude that the work of many men over a long period of time is necessary to a satisfactory solution. A problem such as the cause of mountain building is so complex and so difficult that only through the co-operation of many scientists over long periods of time can we hope to come up with satisfactory answers. Within a problem of this nature there are many smaller problems that must first be solved before any final answer can be obtained. One such question that bears on this problem is the behavior of rocks under high pressures in the earth's interior. We know the pressures are much higher than we can produce on the surface in our most modern engineering and physics laboratories. Our theories of behavior are based on observations at the earth's surface. To find a satisfactory answer to the problem we must wait until we can produce higher pressures in our laboratories. Often scientific advances must wait for technological advances.

One successful approach to problems of this magnitude is for a group of scientists to band together, pool their individual knowledge and energies, and through close co-operation attack the problem from all sides. Groups of this nature are becoming more common in universities and research organizations.

One such group is the Yellowstone-Bighorn Research Association. This association of university professors and mineral-industry geologists has as one of its objectives to study as completely as possible both areally and through special problems the region of northwestern Wyoming and south-central Montana. This region is a segment of the Middle Rocky Mountains and is a typical example of one type of mountain range. By studying every aspect of the geology and by co-ordinating these studies it may be possible to provide a complete history of a segment of one such mountain system and thereby provide a key to the basic causes of mountain building, and their histories. Several hundred geologists have participated in this program since 1930, and their publications of scientific articles dealing with this region number in the hundreds. Each is contributing toward the eventual goal through studies in his own special researches.

The most outstanding program of this nature in recent years is the program carried out in the International Geophysical Year. Earth scientists from all parts of the world co-operated for a period of about 16 months toward making observations and collecting data simultaneously all over the world. These data are being analyzed, and the results are being published for each area of specialized investigation. The particular emphasis during this research was on the earth's hydrosphere and atmosphere, but many other studies were undertaken as well.

For many years group research has proven to be the most effective way of approaching the tremendous problems and questions still unanswered about the oceans and their floors. The method as applied here is expedient economically, and it facilitates better co-ordination of findings. Since the cost of maintaining ships for research at sea is great, it is most practical to make as many different types of studies as possible at the same time. Consequently, groups of scientists work together on a single vessel. They have at least one common interest—the study of the oceans. Although their studies may appear to be unrelated at the onset, they may prove to be intimately connected. On a single ship there may be studies of the structure of the rock beneath the ocean bottom by analysis of artificial shock waves, water sampling to study the composition of sea water, sampling of the life forms in the water, recordings of the temperature variations with depth in the ocean, and recording of the depth of the water to obtain profiles of the bottom.

THE SYNTHESIZER

Synthesis means a combination or composition of parts, elements, etc., so as to form a whole. A synthesizer is one who performs this synthesis. Although we do not ordinarily think of any particular geologists as being synthesizers, that is one of the functions they serve. Most geologists who publish scientific papers perform part of this function. A thorough scientific paper will often give not only the work of the person writing the paper, but it will include the latest finding of other scientists working on related topics. Some geologists spend a large portion of their time in studying the writings of others and bringing these together to formulate general principles.

One of the greatest needs in modern science is for more and better synthesizers. So much work is going on and so many scientific papers are being written in this and other countries that it is often nearly impossible for any person to be fully informed in his own field of speciality, much less the whole field of geology. The same applies to other scientific fields as well. Books provide one form of synthesis, but too often the time lag between completion of a particular research project, publication of its findings in a scientific paper, and the time it takes for the author to read the paper, write his book, and finally publish the book is very great.

REFERENCES

BILLINGS, MARLAND P., 1954, *Structural Geology*, 2nd ed.: New York, Prentice-Hall, 514 p.

BISHOP, M. S., 1960, *Subsurface Mapping:* New York, John Wiley & Sons, 198 p.

LAHEE, F. H., 1952, *Field Methods*, 5th ed.: New York, McGraw-Hill Book Co., 883 p.

LOW, JULIAN, *Plane Table Mapping:* New York, Harper & Bros., 365 p.

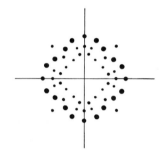

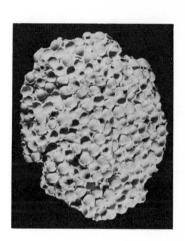

II   RAW MATERIALS IN GEOLOGY

5   Energy for Earth Processes

Undoubtedly you can name some natural processes acting on the earth day after day that require great quantities of energy to accomplish the work they do. Streams flowing from higher to lower parts of the continents of the world carry billions of tons of rock, soil, and debris with them. Moving glaciers gouge out the sides of mountains. Rocks exposed near the surface are almost constantly under attack by agents tending to decay and break them down. Volcanoes pour forth lavas and throw out huge blocks of rock. Whole sections of the crust of the earth are buckled and folded as mountain systems slowly rise. The top of Mount Everest was once at sea level; it has been raised 30,000 feet! It is hard to conceive of the energy needed to accomplish such a feat. To sustain these processes, great sources of energy must be available in and on the earth.

What is energy?

All of us have some idea of what energy is, but when we try to pin it down exactly we find it is almost as elusive as the definition of matter. One relatively satisfactory definition is:

"Energy is the ability to do work." Work is the overcoming of a resistance for some distance, as when a block is carried up a flight of steps. Work is done to overcome the resistance of the force of gravity on that block through the vertical distance between the top and bottom of the steps. This energy arises through a mechanically produced arrangement of matter. It is one of three forms of energy and differs somewhat from the energy possessed by a hot body, thermal energy, or chemical energy, which is involved when a chemical reaction takes place between two compounds.

Kinetic and potential energy

Energy possessed by bodies for mechanical reasons is of two sorts. The first is the energy possessed by a body in motion, called kinetic energy. Once a body is set in motion it has a tendency to stay in that state of motion until something happens to it—until some force acts upon it to change the state of motion. When a force does come to bear on the body in motion, some form of work is performed, or the energy is converted into thermal energy. Water in motion, such as that in streams or breaking waves,

has kinetic energy. This energy is expended in part by the transportation of rocks, soil, and other matter. When water flowing over a waterfall hits the bottom of the falls it has a large amount of kinetic energy and expends much of this in breaking up the rocks it hits and in undercutting the falls. It appears that the water suddenly obtained more energy at the bottom of the falls than it had at the top. Actually a transformation in the type of energy has taken place. At the higher elevation the water had potential energy because of its position. A block of rock has potential energy because of its position, regardless of whether it is suspended at the top of a hoist or buried in the top of a mountain. Both have the potential of accomplishing work if they are freed and move down under the force of gravity. In our example of the waterfall the potential energy of the water was partially converted into kinetic energy, which was in turn partially used in breaking the rocks.

Chemical energy

The other forms of energy are thermal and chemical. A body, when heated, possesses the ability to accomplish work with consequent loss

Fig. 5-1. Iguassu Falls, Brazil. The water at the top of the falls possesses the potential to do work. As it hits the bottom of the falls some of this energy is used to undercut the falls, break up rock, and move rock debris. Running water is one of the agents which effectively erode and shape the face of the earth. (Photo by courtesy of Real Airlines.)

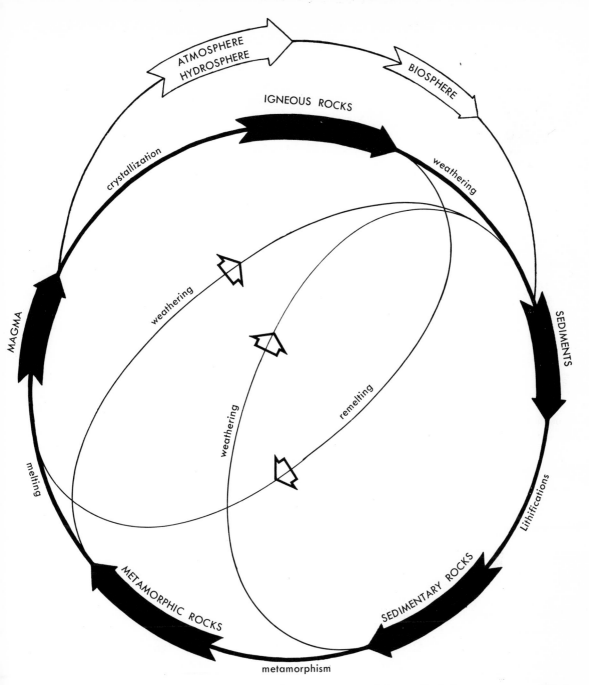

Fig. 5-2. The geochemical cycle. It is possible to depict in a general form all of the processes, and their products, acting in and on the crust of the earth. The crust is constantly undergoing change as a result of these processes. Most of them require the expenditure of great quantities of energy which are supplied from the sources discussed in the text. The crust is not a closed energy system. That is, energy is supplied to it and is lost. Heat energy may be introduced in the crust along with molten rock, magma, from the interior of the earth. This magma crystallizes to form igneous rocks. As the magma cools, gases are produced which go to make up the earth's atmosphere and oceans. Life sprang from the oceans. The remains of decaying plants and animals along with the decayed and decomposed rocks make up the unconsolidated sediments typical of the earth's surface. These sediments may be compressed, dried out, compacted, and thus transformed into sedimentary rocks. These may then be eroded and weathered to form more sediments or they may be altered by heat, pressure, and fluids to form metamorphic rocks, those which have undergone a change of form. If heating is excessive, the metamorphic rocks melt to form secondary magma and the cycle is completed.

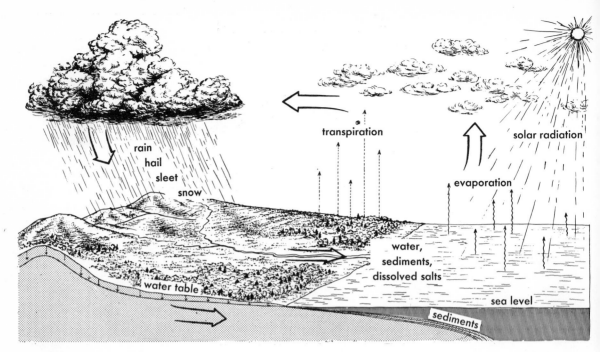

Fig. 5-3. The hydrologic cycle. Water is an important agent in bringing about change near the surface of the earth. This is possible because it is recycled through the oceans, atmosphere, and land. Solar radiation causes evaporation of water from the oceans. Plants release water vapor directly into the air by transpiration. This water vapor then moves through the atmosphere until conditions favorable for precipitation as rain, hail, sleet, or snow occur. Then the water falls to the earth. The runoff carries sediment in streams and erodes the land. That water which seeps into the earth moves much more slowly through the soil and bedrock promoting solution and decomposition of rock. The broken sediments and dissolved solids are carried by the runoff and ground water into the ocean where they are deposited as sediments on the sea floor. Then the cycle is complete.

of heat. Likewise certain chemical reactions may take place between substances with the evolution of heat energy, exothermic reactions. The heat energy is produced from within the atoms of the elements involved. In the exothermic reaction, part of the mass of the atoms is converted into heat energy. One of the greatest contributions of Albert Einstein was the demonstration of the equivalence of energy and matter. He showed that mass may be converted into energy as follows:

E equals mc^2 where E is the energy produced,
m is the mass, and
c is the speed of light.

First and second laws of thermodynamics

The most exceptional aspect of the concept of energy is that energy is neither created nor destroyed. It may be transformed from one type of energy to another, but it is not lost. If this theory is correct then it would appear that a certain quantity of energy was initially present in the universe. Since the origin of the universe or galaxy this energy has been exchanged from one body to another and transformed from one type to another. This particular feature of energy is expressed in the physical law of the conservation of energy. (Energy can be converted from one form to another, but it can never be created or destroyed, or, stated in another way, the total energy of an isolated system is always constant). A special aspect of this is the first law of thermodynamics: When a given quantity of work is completely converted into heat an equivalent amount of heat is produced, and conversely when heat is transformed into work a definite quantity of work is produced. Thus this first law is a statement of the principle of conservation of energy. The second law of thermodynamics as stated by Clausius is: "It is impossible for a self-acting machine, unaided by any external agency, to convey heat from one body to another at a higher temperature, or heat cannot of itself pass from a colder to a warmer body."

The conversion of thermal energy to mechanical energy is very important in earth processes. Consider our solar system, as a whole. Radiant energy from the sun comes to the earth, making possible many natural processes such as life, and it propels the hydrologic cycle (Fig. 5-3). Gradually this thermal energy is being lost, since according to the second law of thermodynamics each reaction takes place with a movement of heat from hot to cooler bodies. In a sense, then, the free energy available for the processes is slowly diminishing.

The law of the conservation of energy and the second law of thermodynamics are two of the most important laws of physical science. All the natural processes may be reduced to simple physical or chemical processes. These may be considered in terms of the energy transformations that characterize them. Thus these laws provide a basis for unifying the diverse natural processes in a single coherent picture.

ENERGY SOURCES

We must distinguish between ultimate and immediate sources of energy. The ultimate source of the energy content of the universe is unknown to us. But we can discern the immediate sources of energy responsible for certain processes. It is possible for us to see that there are certain primary sources from which most of this energy springs.

Solar radiation

Of the sources of energy on earth none is more important than the solar radiation received each day. Without solar radiation life as we know it would disappear. The oceans would freeze, and the continents would become covered by snow and ice as the temperature fell toward absolute zero ($-256°$ Centigrade). With the end of rainfall and with freezing temperatures, rivers would cease to flow. Erosion would be almost stopped as running water ceased to transport erosion products across the surface.

The amount of thermal energy coming to the earth each year amounts to about 6800×10^{20} calories. One calorie is the heat needed to raise the temperature of 1 gram of water $1°$ Centigrade. This heat is partially held to the earth by our atmosphere, which forms a blanket of insulation over the earth. Because the moon does not have an atmosphere, extremes of temperature exist on its surface. The solar radiation coming to the earth is used primarily in three ways:

1. Most of it is used to evaporate water.
2. Some is absorbed by the earth.
3. A small amount is needed in the process of photosynthesis of plants.

Fig. 5-4. Sources of the energy which drives earth processes.

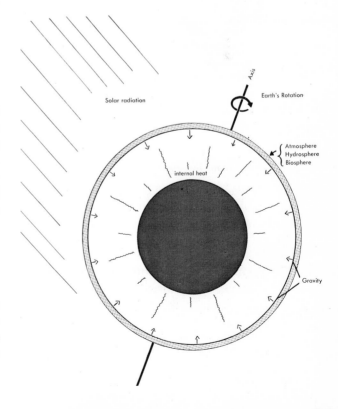

That part of the solar radiation used in evaporating water is transformed from thermal energy to mechanical energy. The evaporated water forms water vapor in the atmosphere. This water vapor possesses great potential energy by virtue of its high position above the earth. It condenses to form rain, and this falls back to earth. Some of the rains fall on the high continents, and the potential energy is converted to kinetic energy as the waters collect, erode the ground, transport matter, and bring about chemical reactions with the rocks.

Gravity

The force of attraction between all masses and in particular the force that pulls masses toward the center of the earth may be considered as the main source of potential energy. It is this force that causes the ocean water carried into the atmosphere as a water vapor to return to the earth. It makes possible the conversion of potential energy into kinetic energy by exerting a continuous force on the water and maintaining it in motion until it reaches the oceans. Gravity is responsible for the mass movement of rock debris and soils down slopes. It is the driving force behind glaciers. Without this force of attraction very little erosion would be accomplished. Rocks might decay to form soils, but even this is questionable since it is largely the interaction between the atmosphere and rocks that brings about this decay, and the atmosphere is held to the earth by gravitational attraction.

Heat from the earth's interior

In the deep mines at Butte, Montana, and in the diamond pits in South Africa temperatures of the ground are found to increase with depth. The rate of increase near the surface is about 1° Centigrade per 100 feet descent. The temperatures at the bottom of the mines at Butte reach 140° Fahrenheit, so hot that fresh cool air must be blown into the mine to protect the men working there. If the rate of increase in heat, known as the geothermal gradient, continued to rise it is obvious that exceedingly high temperatures would be found at depths in the earth's interior. They would in fact approach the temperature of the sun's surface. This seems unreasonable, and there is geologic evidence supporting the idea that the gradient is not a constant rate all the way down. Records from some deep wells support this conclusion, and it may be observed that rocks once buried to this depth have not been altered as they would have been if the temperatures had been as great as would be predicted by a constant geothermal gradient. Nevertheless, the temperatures in the earth's interior are high. Seismic evidence indicates that it is probably that the interior is hot enough to be a liquid at a depth of about 1800 miles.

There is still much uncertainty about how much of this internal heat energy makes its way to the surface. Studies of the heat flow through the earth's crust are in progress, and within a few years we may expect some answers. Probably solar radiation alone would be sufficient to maintain most processes now acting at the surface. The importance of the internal heat is found in the geologic processes taking place within the earth. The most important of these are the deformation of the earth's crust, which is most certainly connected with internal heat energy, and the generation of molten rock, called magma. Both of these are considered at length later in this book.

Earth's rotation

The earth's rotation provides a source of mechanical energy. The most important of the uses of this energy is the maintenance of the earth's form. As a rotating body the earth tends to maintain its somewhat pear-shaped form against the pull of external bodies such as the moon and the sun. It is true that the gravitational attraction of the moon not only causes tides in the oceans, but it pulls the solid crust of the earth out toward it also. This bulge is very slight. Because the earth rotates, a frictional drag is created between the solid earth and the fluid media, water and air, which are in contact with it. This sets wind and water currents in motion and imparts kinetic energy to them.

Energy from changes of state — chemical reactions

Most chemical reactions that take place under falling temperatures are exothermic. That is, as the reaction occurs, heat is given off. Such a reaction taking place in the earth is the crystallization of masses of molten rock. Thus heat energy is released that can accomplish more work—perhaps to contribute toward the melting of more rock. Other reactions take place between the constituents of the earth's lithosphere, the solid crust, hydrosphere, the watery envelope, atmosphere, and biosphere, the sum total of the organic life on earth. These reactions are known collectively as weathering phenomena.

REFERENCES

JACOBS, J. A., RUSSELL, R. D., WILSON, J. T., 1959, *Physics and Geology:* New York, McGraw-Hill Book Co., 424 p.

MASON, BRIAN, 1958, *Principles of Geochemistry,* 2nd ed.: New York, John Wiley & Sons, 310 p.

6   Elements, Compounds, and Minerals

We quickly learn that there are many different types of rocks, easily recognized by certain peculiar physical characteristics. The great variety and the unusual beauty in color and pattern of different rocks are always a source of amazement to those first beginning to study minerals and rocks. If we could place these rocks under a high-powered microscope it would be apparent that most of them are made up of a great many smaller units called grains or crystals. Most of these grains appear to have irregular shapes, but we would probably see a few bounded by smooth planes, giving them a nearly perfect geometric shape such as that of a cube, a tetrahedron, or a hexagonal prism. If a large number of such crystals of the same mineral could be obtained and studied it would become evident that they all had a similar shape in that each would have the same number of bounding planes or faces, and the angles between certain of these planes would always be the same. They would differ in that the size of the faces and the size of the crystals would vary. The most logical explanation of this is that the crystals are all built up of small units fitted together in a systematic symmetrical pattern.

What is matter?

This question has intrigued man for thousands of years. The Greek philosophers were much concerned with this problem. Some considered that all things were derived from fire; others, like Lucretius, held to a concept not totally unlike those of the modern scientists.

... There is an ultimate point in visible objects which represents the smallest thing that can be seen. So also there must be an ultimate point in objects that lie below the limit of perception by our senses. This point is without parts and is the smallest thing that can exist. It never has been and never will be able to exist by itself, but only as one primary part of something else. It is with a mass of such parts, solidly jammed together in order, that matter is filled up. (From Lucretius, *The Nature of the Universe.*)

What is your concept of matter? Most generally when we ask this question the answer given is not a definition of matter but a description of it.

1. Matter occupies space.
2. It exists in three states: liquid, solid, gaseous.
3. It has a certain quantity of mass.
4. It has certain physical properties such as color, density, melting point, hardness, crystal form, and mechanical strength.
5. It has certain chemical properties. It reacts when brought in contact with certain other substances.
6. It has inertia. It tends to resist a change in its state of motion.
7. It exerts a pull on other matter. This pull or force is called gravitational attraction. The amount of this force of attraction depends on the mass of the two objects and the distance between them. It is greater between larger objects and between those closer together. The relation is shown in the following equation.

Fig. 6-1. Beryl as it appears in natural crystals, at top, and cut in gems. Emeralds and aquamarines are varieties of beryl. (Photo by courtesy of the U.S. National Museum.)

$$F = k \frac{m_1 m_2}{d^2}$$

F = Force of gravitational attraction
k = a numerical constant
m_1 = mass of one object
m_2 = mass of the second object
d = distance separating the two objects

The force of attraction between an object on the earth and the earth is called the weight of the object. Because all planets do not have the same size and mass as the earth you would have a different weight on each.

THE ATOMIC THEORY OF MATTER

All the matter around us may be grouped into three very broad categories or states: gases, like air and steam; solids, such as stones and metals; and liquids, like water and oils. The solids are characterized by their rigidity and the tendency to retain their shapes and volumes. Liquids flow under their own weight, conforming to the shape of their container, but changes in volume are negligible. Gases, on the other hand, have neither rigidity nor a specific volume. They tend to expand to fill any container in which they are placed. Not all matter can be confined exclusively to a single category. For example, a wax may shatter like a very rigid material when dropped, yet it will flow under its own weight if sufficient time is allowed.

Matter may change from one state to another, as in the melting of a solid to form a liquid or evaporation of a liquid to form a gas. These transformations are induced by changes in temperature, and they are reversible. Boiling occurs when the temperature of the liquid is high enough for bubbles of vapor to form through the liquid. Crystallization is the slow solidification of a solid from a cooled liquid, while freezing is the result of a rapid cooling.

The early natural philosophers were well

Fig. 6-2. Cerussite, a lead carbonate. (Photo by courtesy of The U.S. National Museum.)

Fig. 6-3. Quartz crystal. (Photo by courtesy of the U.S. National Museum.)

aware of these phenomena. About 400 B.C. the Greek philosopher Democritus first suggested that matter was composed of certain very small, indivisible particles called atoms. These particles were visualized as being in motion, and, as you will recognize, this explanation of the nature of matter proved to be a most useful one in explaining the observed phenomena. As the atoms are heated their motions become more intense. When these motions reach a certain point in each solid they begin to move over one another or flow as the solid melts. Likewise, on further heating, they separate completely and go into a gaseous state. Although this theory comes very close to the modern concept of matter it was not followed through by the later Greeks.

Law of combining weights. The modern atomic concepts originated in 1811 with the English chemist, John Dalton. He experimented with the proportions by weight in which certain substances react. His law of combining weights states that elements and compounds combine to form other compounds only in certain definite proportions. This is most easily explained if the elements consist of some basic units, atoms, for example, which combine in various ways to form elements and compounds. Dalton's work is the first experimental evidence of the atomic nature of matter.

The electrical nature of atoms was first described by Michael Faraday, who discovered the laws of electrolysis. The experiments of Faraday and those of Maxwell, Clausius, and Boltzmann in the development of the kinetic theory of gases are beyond the scope of this book; however, it was from these experiments that the first direct measurements of the dimensions of atoms were made and the existence of atoms confirmed.

Electrons, protons, neutrons, and atoms

One of the greatest differences between the atom as visualized by Lucretius and Democritus and that of the modern atomic physi-

Fig. 6-4. Hematite. Hematite occurs in many forms. This type is called botry-oidal. (Photo by courtesy of the U.S. National Museum.)

cists is found in the internal structure of the atom. The Greek philosophers thought of atoms as indivisible particles, but we now know that they are composed of a number of smaller particles, specifically electrons, protons, and neutrons. An individual atom is so small that it virtually defies the imagination. If an atom could be enlarged 100 million times it would be about the size of a pea, and even at that magnification the electrons, protons, and neutrons that make it up would be too small to be seen through a high-powered microscope. We are compelled to marvel that man has successfully measured and described such small particles.

No scientist has yet been able to observe an atom, or the particles of which it is composed, yet, through ingeniously designed and carefully executed experiments and calculations, it has become possible for us to measure and describe these particles in some detail. Most commonly they are described in terms of their mass and their electrical charges.

Mass of atoms. The mass of an atom is so small that to attempt to refer it to any of the systems of weight with which we are familiar would lead to exceedingly small fractions, which would be difficult to handle. Instead, an arbitrary mass unit is used for atomic weights. This unit, one mass unit, is defined as being equal to one-sixteenth of the mass of an oxygen atom. There are two reasons for using this as the basis for the scale. First, oxygen is the most abundant element in the crust of the earth. Secondly, this scale gives the simplest known element, Hydrogen, a mass of 1 unit.

Electricity. The concept of electricity can be traced back to 600 B.C. One of the "seven wise men" of ancient Greece, Thales of Miletus, observed that amber will attract small fibrous materials when it has been rubbed with a piece of fur. Amber was called "electron" by the Greeks, and the name "electric" was applied to these effects by Sir William Gilbert 2000 years later. Gilbert discovered that many materials may be electrified by friction, and that both of the rubbed substances become electrified. If, for example, a rubber rod is rubbed by a piece of fur and then separated from it a

Fig. 6-5. Moss agate. (Photo by courtesy of the U.S. National Museum.)

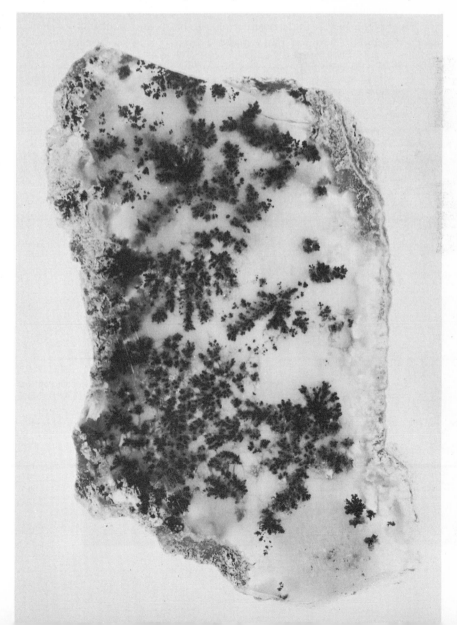

short distance, the fur will be attracted to the rod. An interesting effect is noted when two rods are rubbed by the fur and then brought close together. Instead of attracting one another they move away as though repelled by an invisible barrier. This observation led to the recognition of two types of electrical charges, which for simplicity are called positive and negative charges. When two bodies with like charges are brought close together they repel one another, but when unlike charges are close they attract one another.

The electron is the smallest of the three fundamental particles we will consider. It has a mass of 0.00055 mass unit and it possesses one negative charge of electricity. It is the flowage of electrons that sets up electrical currents.

The proton has a single positive charge of electricity, but it is much more massive than the electron. It has a mass of 1.00758 mass units, which makes it about 1800 times as massive as the electron.

The neutron represents a compounding of a single electron and a single proton. It has a net resultant electrical charge of zero; the positive charge of the proton exactly negates the negative charge of the electron. The mass is equivalent to the addition of one electron and one proton or 1.00896 mass units.

Protons, electrons, and neutrons combine in various ways to form complex structures called atoms. Some of the atoms formed in the various combinations are stable and cannot be broken down by ordinary chemical methods. We know of 102 of these atomic configurations. They differ in the number of protons, electrons, and neutrons in each. The number of protons and electrons present range from 1 of each to

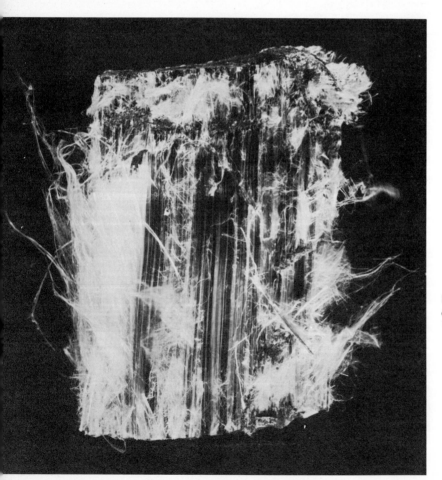

Fig. 6-6. Natural asbestos, variety chrysotile. (Photo by courtesy of the U.S. National Museum.)

Fig. 6-7. Radiating clusters of tourmaline in lepidolite. (Photo by courtesy of the U.S. National Museum.)

102 of each. Each of the resulting atoms possesses certain unique physical and chemical characteristics, and they are known as elements.

Atomic structure

One of the simplest models of the structure of an atom is that conceived by the Danish physicist, Bohr. His model suggests certain superficial similarities between the structure of the atom and that of the solar system. For example:

1. Mass is concentrated at the center. The great mass of the sun finds its parallel in the nucleus of the atom where the protons and neutrons are concentrated. Their combined mass accounts for practically all of the mass of any given atom (in excess of 99.9 per cent of the total).

2. Electrons occupy orbits around the nucleus, but unlike the planets it is impossible to isolate the electrons, to trace out their paths, or predict their exact positions.

3. Like the solar system, an atom consists mostly of space. The atomic structure occupies a very large volume relative to the size of its components. We say relatively because the actual dimensions are so small that we can hardly conceive their size. For example, it has been shown that the atoms of many of the more common elements have diameters on the order of 2×10^{-8} cm (or .00000002 centimeter), while the diameter of the nucleus of one of these may be in the range of 1/10,000 to 1/100,000 of the diameter.

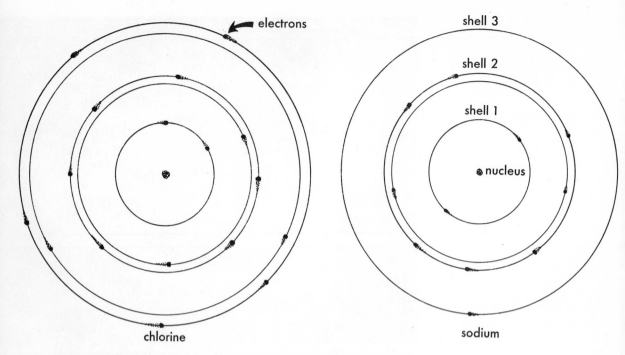

Fig. 6-8. Hypothetical model of the atomic structure of sodium and chlorine. This model shows the distribution of electrons in various shells.

As already stated, the atoms of each of the 102 elements are different. Each represents a unique combination of electrons, protons, and neutrons. Each is known both by a name and a number. The names have been derived from many sources. The name hydrogen, for example, comes from two Greek words meaning water and to be born; thus literally the word means "born from water."

Water is formed when hydrogen gas is burned in air.

The numbers are assigned on the basis of the number of protons in the nucleus; element No. 1 has one proton in its nucleus, No. 2 has two, No. 3 has three, No. 102 has 102. Most of the elements have the same number of neutrons as protons in the nucleus, and so long as the element is stable or electrically neutral it contains the same number of electrons in its orbits as it has protons in the nucleus. Remember that each proton has one positive electrical charge, and each electron one negative charge; therefore, the atom as a whole is neutral electrically as long as there are the same number of electrons and protons present.

Grouping of electrons in atoms

We may visualize the nucleus of the atom as a tightly packed mass of protons and neutrons, but according to Bohr's model the electrons are distributed in orbits at various distances from the nucleus. The distribution of electrons is such as to give an ordered rather than random configuration. The electrons tend to be grouped at certain distances from the nucleus. We may visualize each of these groups as being confined, their orbits located within a shell of a certain radius. It is found that the shell located closest to the nucleus of the atom will contain only 2 electrons. If more than 2 electrons are present they will be found in the second shell farther away from the nucleus. The second shell consists of two subshells. The inner one of these, like the first shell, will contain only 2 electrons, but the second subshell will hold up to 6, giving the second shell a total capacity of 8 electrons when it is filled. The third shell consists of three subshells. The inner one will hold only 2 electrons, the second one will hold 6 electrons, and the third subshell will hold up to 10, making a total of 18 in the third shell. The fourth shell is made up of four subshells which contain respectively 2, 6, 10, and 14 electrons each, or a total of 32. Thus the arrangement of electrons in orbits or shells surrounding the nucleus is systematic.

The order in which these various shells and subshells are filled in successive elements is shown in the following chart. The first group is located closest to the nucleus of the atom. Others are at successively greater distances.

element No.	1	2	3	4	5	6	7	8	9	10	11	12	13	14	15	16	17	18
1st shell	1	2	2	2	2	2	2	2	2	2	2	2	2	2	2	2	2	2
2nd shell			1	2	3	4	5	6	7	8	8	8	8	8	8	8	8	8
3rd shell											1	2	3	4	5	6	7	8

Certain of the elements that are built up in this fashion are remarkably stable—that is, they do not react with other elements, they are inert chemically. All of these are gases, and they are known as the noble or inert gases. They are helium, element No. 2, neon, No. 10, argon, No. 18, krypton, No. 36, xenon, No. 54 and radon, No. 86. Because these gases are inert, the grouping of the electrons in these elements must be very stable.

electrons in the outer shell or orbit of an atom makes it particularly stable, but we do not fully understand why this is so. It is also well known that atoms have a tendency to reach this stable form. The question then arises as to what happens when an atom gains or loses an electron to achieve stability. Can we predict which atoms will lose electrons, which will gain electrons, and how many electrons they will lose or gain?

First of all, let us consider what happens if an atom does lose an electron. It will no longer have the same number of electrons in orbits around the nucleus as it has protons in the nucleus; therefore, it will have a net positive charge because it has one more proton than electron. Likewise, if it should lose 2 electrons it will have an excess of 2 positive charges. Charged atoms of this sort are called ions. Ions may be either positive or negative, depending on whether they gained or lost electrons. Which

	Helium	Neon	Argon	Krypton	Xenon	Radon
Group No. 1	2	2	2	2	2	2
Group No. 2	..	8(2/6)	8(2/6)	8(2/6)	8(2/6)	8
Group No. 3	..	..	8(2/6)	18(2/6/10)	18(2/6/10)	18
Group No. 4	..	..	..	8(2/6)	18(2/6/10)	32
Group No. 5	..	..	..	..	8(2/6)	18
Group No. 6	..	..	..	..	..	8

The most important observation from this is that the most stable electron configurations all except helium, which has 2, contain 8 electrons in the outermost shell, or orbit. The elements that have these configurations do not lose electrons from their outer orbits, but the other elements tend either to lose or gain electrons, until there are 8 electrons in the outer orbit.

Ions

It is an observation soundly based on experimental evidence that the presence of 8

atoms are most likely to become positive ions and which negative ions is easily predicted. If a given atom has 8 electrons in the next to the last shell and 1 in the last, outermost shell, then it is reasonable to expect that it will lose that 1 electron more readily than it will gain additional ones to achieve the stability of having 8 in the outer shell. Likewise, an atom with 2 electrons in its outer shell is more likely to lose these than it is to gain 6. On the other hand an atom with 6 or 7 electrons in its outer orbit is more likely to gain 1 or 2 than it is to lose 6 or 7.

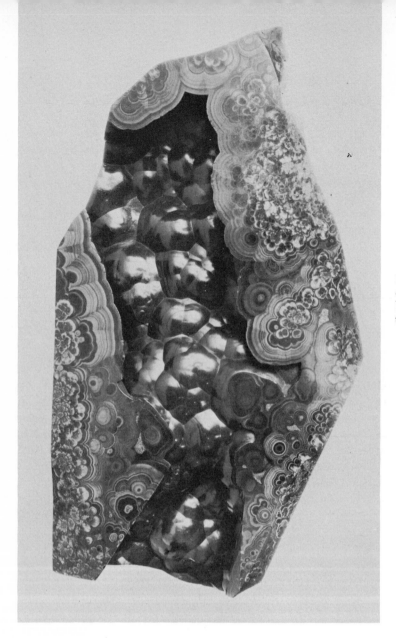

Isotopes

Normally we find that each element has a nucleus composed of equal numbers of neutrons and protons; however, each element has alternate forms in which there are different numbers of neutrons in the nucleus. These forms have chemical and physical properties that are almost identical with those of the element. Such forms are called isotopes of the element. Some of these isotopes are unstable and break down spontaneously by the emission of radiant energy. Such isotopes are said to be radioactive. The energy they radiate is composed of the protons and neutrons that make up the nucleus of the isotopes. Thus, through the emission of these particles, the isotope disintegrates. The rate of this disintegration is constant for each isotope. Disintegration rates are such that a certain constant amount of time is required for one half of the mass of the isotope to break down. This amount of time is called the half life of the isotope. As a result of the breakdown of an isotope new isotopes or elements may form. The new ones may also be radioactive and break down again, but eventually a stable isotope or element is formed. Because the half life of a radioactive isotope is constant, and because a stable element is formed as an end product, it is possible to use radioactive isotopes as geologic clocks. This is possible only if the half life is known, if the steps in the radioactive breakdown and the half lives of each intermediate isotope are known, if decay is not complete, and if the stable end product is present.

COMPOUNDS

Compounds are formed by the combination of elements through organic and inorganic processes. With the exception of some of the native metals such as pure gold, silver, platinum, and copper, and a few other substances such as sulfur and pure carbon, we do not find many elements in pure uncombined form. By far most of the minerals, rocks, and mineral products that surround us are compounds of two or more elements held together by electrical forces. Compounds have physical and chemical properties that are different from those of their component elements. The bonds holding elements together in the compounds are of three types: ionic bonds, covalent bonds, and metallic bonds.

Ionic bonds

Ions form when an atom gains or loses one or more electrons to become charged. The amount of the net charge is dependent on the difference between the number of protons in the nucleus and the number of electrons in the orbits of the ion. These ions obey the laws of static electricity and are therefore attracted to ions with an opposite charge and repelled by those of a like charge. If a large number of ions, some positive and some negative, are placed in solution in water or in some other medium through which they can move freely they will tend to form an ionic compound. The negative ion will attract positive ions toward it, and they in turn will attract more negative ions. In this manner a large solid crystal may be built up.

Shape of the crystal. The particular shape that this crystal will assume is dependent on the size of the ions that make it up. Atoms and ions are visualized as spherical or nearly spherical, but they differ greatly in diameter. Ions with more shells or electrons may have diameters many times greater than those of the lower-numbered elements. The forces acting on the ions tend to pull them as close together as possible. How many positive ions can fit around one negative ion is dependent on the relative size of the two. Therefore, the most important factor in determining the shape of the configuration is the size of the ions involved.

NaCl. One of the most common ionic compounds is common table salt, the mineral halite. It is a compound of sodium (Na) and chlorine (Cl). Sodium is element No. 11. We can predict that it will have 2 electrons in the first shell, 8 in the second, and 1 in the third. Therefore, it will have a tendency to lose the single electron in the outer shell and become a sodium ion with a positive charge (Na^+). Chlorine is element No. 17. It has 2 electrons in its first shell, 8 in its second, and 7 in its third shell. Therefore, it tends to gain one electron in the third shell to become a chlorine ion with a negative

Fig. 6-10. Hexagonal quartz with inclusions of tourmaline. (Photo by courtesy of the U.S. National Museum.)

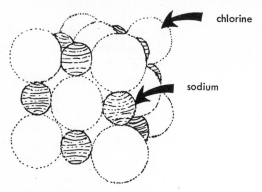

Fig. 6-11. Packing of sodium and chlorine ions in the ionic compound sodium chloride, NaCl, or common table salt. Salt is known as the mineral halite.

charge (Cl⁻). The Na^+ ion has a radius of $.98 \times 10^{-8}$ cm, and the Cl^- ion has a radius of 1.8×10^{-8} cm. The two, having different charges, are attracted toward one another and pack in as closely as possible. The sizes are such that each ion has 6 positive ions adjacent to it in the configuration shown (Fig. 6-11). The resulting crystal is cubic in shape.

Covalent bonding

A second type of bonding between the atoms of different elements is formed when, instead of exchanging electrons, the elements simply share electrons. Thus it is possible for each of the atoms to achieve the stability of having 8 electrons in its outer orbit by sharing those of one or more other atoms. An example of this type of bonding is methane, marsh gas, which is formed in swamps from the decay of

Fig. 6-12. Water molecule. Because the hydrogen atoms are close together the molecule acts somewhat like a small bar magnet. How this makes water a good solvent is explained in the text.

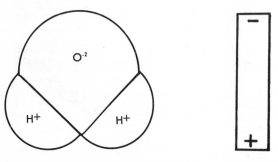

organic matter. Methane is a compound of carbon and hydrogen. Hydrogen (H), element No. 1, has 1 electron in its orbit. Carbon (C) is element No. 6. It has 2 electrons in its first orbit and 4 in its outer orbit. A stable configuration is formed when the carbon is able to share the electrons of four hydrogen atoms. Thus methane is expressed as CH_4.

Another common compound that is held together by covalent bonds is water, a compound of hydrogen and oxygen. Hydrogen again has 1 electron, and oxygen, element No. 8, needs 2 electrons in its outer orbit to have 8. Thus one oxygen atom combines with two hydrogen atoms to form the compound H_2O. Just as the atom is the smallest unit of an element, a molecule is the smallest unit of a compound that exhibits the properties of that compound.

Solution in water. Some covalent compounds are made up of molecules that behave somewhat like small magnets. Water is one such molecule. Its magnetic qualities are caused by the way the two hydrogen atoms are attracted to the oxygen atom (Fig. 6-12). By increasing the density of the electrons on one side of the molecule it acts as though one end is slightly positive and the other slightly negative. This polar nature of the water molecule is the reason why it is such an effective solvent.

Consider a grain of salt or other ionic compound that is placed in water. First of all we should remember that the arrangement of the ionic compounds is the result of electrical attractions between the ions of which it is made. When the compound is placed in water, the water molecules acting as small magnets become oriented with the positive ends of the molecules toward the negative ions in the solid, and the negative ends of the molecules toward positive ions. The effects of these attractions thus set up between water molecules and ions tend to pull the ions out of the solid structure as soon as enough molecules are oriented to counter-balance the forces within the crystal.

There is a limit to the amount of solution that will go on, however, for when a large number of ions have gone into the solution there will not be enough molecules left to break down the solid effectively.

Metallic bonding

Metallic bonding, which is characteristic of pure metals, is different from ionic and covalent bonding in that electrons are shared throughout the crystal lattice. The atoms, all of which are the same size, are packed tightly together so that each has 12 others around it. The electrons are free to move through the crystal lattice, making it possible for metals to conduct electricity.

MINERALS

What is a mineral?

So far our discussion has been concerned with the elementary particles of matter and their arrangement in atomic structures. Geologists must normally deal with large quantities of elements or compounds in the form of minerals and rocks. A mineral is defined as a naturally occurring element or compound formed by the processes of inorganic nature and having a definite chemical composition and a certain characteristic atomic structure which is expressed in an external crystalline form and in other physical properties. Minerals are in turn the components of rocks. A rock is an aggregate of minerals. These then are the raw materials with which we must become thoroughly acquainted if we desire to seek a basic understanding of this and other planets.

Most common elements

Of the 102 known elements, 94 occur naturally on the earth, and of these only a few make up most of the minerals and rocks. The most common appear in the following list:

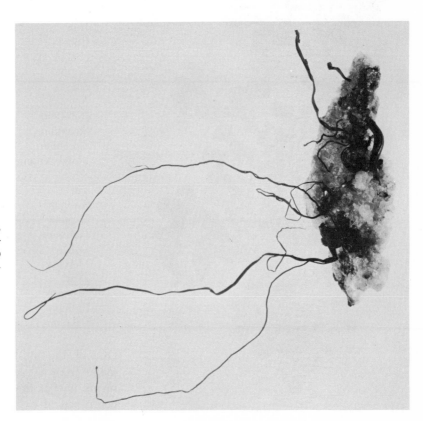

Fig. 6-13. Wire silver. Silver, like many other metals, occurs in a native state. (Photo by courtesy of the U.S. National Museum.)

Element	Symbol	Atomic No.	Percentage of volume of earth's crust	Percentage of weight of earth's crust
Oxygen	O	8	93.77	46.60
Silicon	Si	14	.86	27.72
Aluminum	Al	13	.47	8.13
Iron	Fe	26	.43	5.00
Magnesium	Mg	12	.29	2.09
Calcium	Ca	20	1.03	3.63
Sodium	Na	11	1.32	2.83
Potassium	K	19	1.83	2.59

In addition to the foregoing the following list will help if you are unfamiliar with the symbols of geologically important elements:

	Symbol	Atomic No.
Hydrogen	H	1
Helium	He	2
Lithium	Li	3
Beryllium	Be	4
Boron	B	5
Carbon	C	6
Nitrogen	N	7
Oxygen	O	8
Fluorine	F	9
Sodium	Na	11
Magnesium	Mg	12
Aluminum	Al	13
Silicon	Si	14
Phosphorus	P	15
Sulfur	S	16
Chlorine	Cl	17
Potassium	K	19
Calcium	Ca	20
Titanium	Ti	22
Vanadium	V	23
Chromium	Cr	24
Manganese	Mn	25
Iron	Fe	26
Cobalt	Co	27
Nickel	Ni	28
Copper	Cu	29
Zinc	Zn	30
Arsenic	As	33
Rubidium	Rb	37
Strontium	Sr	38
Zirconium	Zr	40
Molybdenum	Mo	42
Silver	Ag	47
Tin	Sn	50
Antimony	Sb	51
Barium	Ba	56
Platinum	Pt	78
Gold	Au	79
Mercury	Hg	80
Lead	Pb	82
Bismuth	Bi	83
Radium	Ra	88
Uranium	U	92

Fig. 6-14. Native copper from Bolivia. This is the natural form of this native copper. (Photo by courtesy of the U.S. National Museum.)

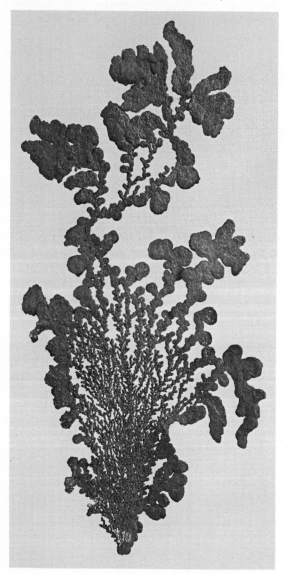

One of the most striking observations to be made from the list of the most common elements is that the crust of the earth is largely composed of oxygen atoms. The ions of these

atoms are held together primarily by silicon ions and by ions of some of the common metals such as iron and magnesium.

Crystals

A crystal is a homogeneous body bounded by smooth plane surfaces. The definition of a mineral points out that minerals are composed of atoms arranged in certain definite patterns, and that these patterns may find outward expression in the shapes that the crystals of that mineral assume. We have already seen that one important factor that determines the internal arrangement of the atoms in a compound is the diameter of the elements making up the compound. The orderly arrangement of the atoms resulting from this packing together of ele-

ments or ions may or may not give rise to a crystal. If, in the process of growth or formation, a mineral is restricted by the shape of the space in which it can grow, then it may not achieve the perfect shape of a crystal. Many minerals are formed from a molten mass of rock. As this melt cools, crystals begin to form, but before solidification is complete there is much competition for space, and many minerals are forced to crystallize in restricted spaces. Such a mineral still has an orderly internal atomic structure, and it is said to be crystalline although no crystal of that mineral may be seen. If the faces or surfaces of the crystal are perfectly formed we say it is a euhedral crystal. If the faces are imperfectly developed it is subhedral, and if no faces are present it is anhedral.

Fig. 6-16. Clusters of naturally occurring quartz crystals. (Photo by courtesy of the U.S. National Museum.)

Fig. 6-17. Pattern formed by X-rays which passed through a piece of halite. See text for discussion.

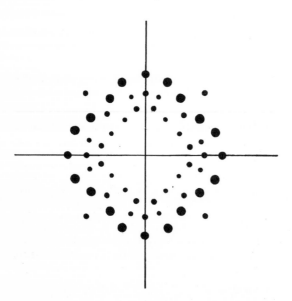

X-ray method

About 1912 Dr. Max von Laue, a theoretical physicist, devised a method to test the hypothesis that crystals possess orderly internal arrangements of atoms. His experiments consisted of placing a crystal in the path of a beam of X rays. The X rays passed through the crystal, and their paths were recorded on a photographic plate placed behind the crystal. When developed, the plate showed a dark spot in the center where the X rays had traveled directly through the crystal, and a large number of small dark spots arranged around the center in a regular geometrical pattern. These small spots represent reflections of the X rays from the systematically oriented planes of atoms within the crystal. Study the pattern in Fig. 6-17. Notice how the spots are arranged in symmetrical patterns. The symmetry of these patterns is an indication of the internal symmetry of the atomic arrangements.

Crystal symmetry

What exactly is meant by symmetry? Your first thought may be that of an object reflected in a mirror. This is one type of symmetry. An exact repetition in size, form, and arrangement of objects on opposite sides of the plane represented by the mirror is produced. Similarly, symmetry may be relative to a line or to a point, as well as to a plane.

A symmetry line or axis is an imaginary line through a crystal, around which the crystal may be revolved with the effect of showing two or more identical views of the crystal's shape in one revolution. Symmetry relative to a point is shown if it is possible to pass an imaginary line from any point on the surface of a mineral through the center of the mineral and to a similar point on an opposite face. If this is possible the crystal is said to have a center of symmetry.

Using these concepts of symmetry it is possible to classify the crystals of almost all of the thousands of minerals into six systems characterized by similarities of symmetry:

ISOMETRIC

Three mutually perpendicular axes of equal lengths.

HEXAGONAL

Four axes; three horizontal of equal length intersecting at 120-degree angles and one of different length perpendicular to the plane of the three.

TETRAGONAL

Three mutually perpendicular axes; two horizontal and of equal length, and one vertical of a different length.

ORTHORHOMBIC

Three mutually perpendicular axes of different lengths.

MONOCLINIC

Three axes of different length; two inclined to one another, and the third perpendicular to the plane of the first two.

TRICLINIC

Three axes of different length, all inclined at angles to the others.

PHYSICAL PROPERTIES OF MINERALS

I. SPECIFIC GRAVITY: The density or specific gravity of a mineral is the ratio of its weight to that of an equal volume of water. Graphite such as that used in your pencil is about twice as dense as water; that is, 2 cubic inches of water would weigh the same as 1 cubic inch of graphite. We say the specific gravity of graphite is therefore 2. Some idea of the range of values found for the specific gravity of various minerals is gained from comparing graphite, 2, with hematite, the most commonly used ore of iron, 5.2, and gold, which has a specific gravity of 19.

II. CLEAVAGE: This is the property that some minerals exhibit of breaking along definite smooth planes. The presence of these planes is a simple indication of the difference in strength of bonds between atoms in the crystal. If the bonds are very strong between the atoms in one plane and relatively weaker between those in other planes then it will be easier to break the mineral along the planes of weakness. In some minerals these differences are great; in others there is little difference in the strength of the bonds in different directions through the mineral. Cleavages are very useful in the identification of minerals. They differ in several ways in different minerals:

1. In number: there may be one or as many as six directions of cleavage.

Fig. 6-18. X-ray diffraction diagrams showing the oriented molecular structure of a coal. (After Tyler, Bull. Geol. Soc. Am., v. 69.)

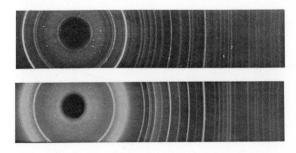

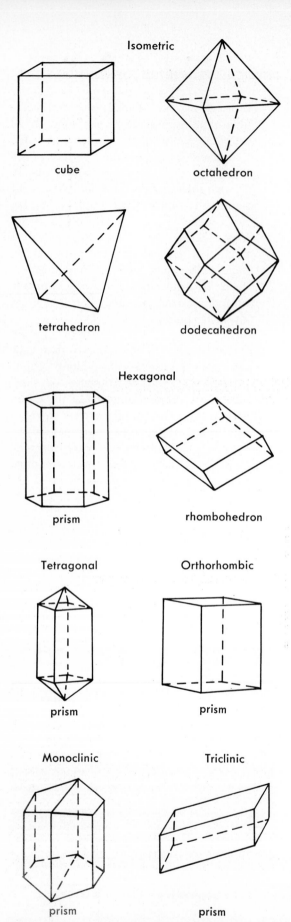

Isometric

cube

octahedron

tetrahedron

dodecahedron

Hexagonal

prism

rhombohedron

Tetragonal

Orthorhombic

prism

prism

Monoclinic

Triclinic

prism

prism

2. In angles between them: two may be at right angles, or oblique to one another; three may be mutually perpendicular; or they may all intersect at acute angles.

3. In degree of development: some minerals break, forming very smooth cleavage surfaces in which case the cleavage is said to be perfect; others are not so easily broken—they have imperfect cleavage. Still others may break along cleavage only with difficulty.

III. HARDNESS: Hardness in the sense used here does not mean breaking strength, but the ability of one mineral to scratch another. A scale of 10 relatively common minerals is used as a basis for hardness comparisons. The scale is nonlinear (that is, No. 5 is not five times harder than No. 1; actually it is many times harder.)

Hardness scale:
1. talc.
2. gypsum.
    (fingernails)
3. calcite.
    (a copper penny)
4. fluorite.
5. apatite.
    (a knife of steel)
    (plate glass)
6. feldspar.
    (a file)
7. quartz.
8. topaz.
9. corundum.
10. diamond.

A mineral with a hardness of 6.5 will scratch feldspar, but it will not scratch quartz. Also it can be scratched by quartz, but not by the feldspar. The hardness of an unknown mineral may be found by scratching it with minerals or objects of known hardness.

IV. FRACTURE: It is sometimes helpful to note the way in which a mineral has fractured.

Fig. 6-19. Some common crystal forms.

Some break into splinters; others have smooth, even fractures. Some are rough, irregular surfaces, and a few, such as quartz, break with a smooth, shell-shaped fracture known as a conchoidal fracture.

v. LUSTER: The luster of a mineral is the appearance of its surface in reflected light. Two large groups are recognized: metallic and nonmetallic lusters. You must be careful at first not to confuse color and luster. Luster depends on the structure of the surface of the mineral, its transparency, and the way light is reflected or refracted from it. There is great variation in the nonmetallic lusters, and there is no substitute for personal observation in learning to identify these. The most common are:

> adamantine: brilliant, as the luster of a diamond.
> vitreous: the luster of glass.
> resinous: luster of yellow resins.
> greasy: luster of oily glass.
> pearly: luster of pearl.
> silky: like silk, usually results from fibrous structures.

Fig. 6-20. Cleavage in halite. The arrows point to prominent cleavages on the surface and within the crystal. If this specimen were broken many more cleavages would become apparent. They would be parallel to one of the sides of this specimen. (Photo by courtesy of the U.S. National Museum.)

Fig. 6-21. Bladed crystals of gypsum. (Photo by courtesy of the U.S. National Museum.)

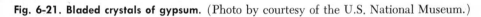

Fig. 6-22. Hornblende crystals in calcite. The calcite crystals show very prominent cleavages. (Photo by courtesy of the U.S. National Museum.)

VI. COLOR: Of all the physical properties of minerals the color is frequently the most impressive and the least definitive. The color of most nonmetallic minerals is due to impurities in the mineral. Very small quantities of some elements are sufficient to give large masses of other minerals bright colors. It is not uncommon for a single mineral to occur in as many as five or six very different colors. Do not depend on color in identification of nonmetallic minerals.

VII. STREAK: The color of the powder of a mineral is called its streak. Although the mineral may occur in several different colors, the color of the powder will always be the same. The streak is tested by rubbing a piece of the mineral on an unglazed porcelain plate.

VIII. MISCELLANEOUS TESTS (SPECIAL PROPERTIES):
1. A few minerals may be identified by their taste.
2. Radioactivity may be tested by use of geiger counters, scintillation meters, or similar instruments. All minerals containing uranium, vanadium, thorium, or other radioactive elements will register, and it is possible, by noting the amount of radiation, to estimate which of the uranium-bearing minerals you have.

3. A few minerals are magnetic. One variety of magnetite, lodestone, will pick up bits of metal. Others will be attracted to a magnet.

4. Some minerals show a play of colors, the appearance of several colors in rapid succession when the mineral is turned. If a milky reflection is seen from the interior of the specimen it is said to display opalescence.

5. A relatively large group of minerals have the property of fluorescence—that is, the emission of light from within when the mineral is subjected to ultraviolet light. The colors produced may sometimes be useful in their identification.

IX. TWINNING: Some of the common rock-forming minerals exhibit the property of having two or more crystals or parts of

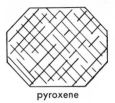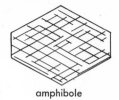

pyroxene · amphibole

Fig. 6-23. Pyroxene and amphibole. Cleavage is one of the best means of distinguishing pyroxenes from amphiboles. Both of these are important rock-forming mineral groups.

crystals grow together in such a way that the individual parts are related to their crystal structure. Some are simply two crystals growing side by side with a single plane between them; others appear to have grown so that one crystal penetrates the other. Twinning serves as a useful means of identifying certain minerals.

Fig. 6-24. Cleavage specimens of calcite at left and feldspar at right. (Photo by courtesy of the U.S. National Museum.)

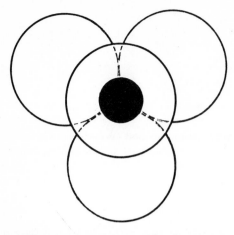

Fig. 6-25. Silica tetrahedron. The large atoms are oxygen atoms. Four of them fit around one silicon atom. The combined unit has a net charge of minus four. Thus it attracts positive ions such as the metals.

Building blocks of the earth's crust — the silicates

One group of minerals, the silicates, make up almost a third of all the minerals and more than 95 per cent by volume of the crust of the earth. Many of the complexities of the silicate structure were not unraveled until the development of the X-ray techniques of mineral study. Then it was learned that all the silicates have one basic unit in common. That structure is composed of four oxygen atoms and one silicon atom. The structure is a tetrahedron with an oxygen atom at each corner (Fig. 6-25). The bonds in this configuration are very strong between the oxygen and silicon. Remember that silicon, element No. 14, has 4 electrons in its outer orbit. Oxygen, element No. 8, needs 2

Fig. 6-26. Twinned crystal of microcline feldspar. (Photo by courtesy of the U.S. National Museum.)

electrons in its outer orbit. When the 4 oxygen atoms and the 1 silicon atom combine, they form a unit that has a net of 4 negative charges, (SiO_4^{-4}). These silica tetrahedra form the basic building blocks of most minerals. They are joined together in the following ways:

1. Independent tetrahedra groups: the SiO_4^{-4} may combine with positive ions with two positive charges each, such as magnesium (the result is the mineral forsterite, Mg_2SiO_4), or with 4 ions with 1 positive charge each.
2. Double tetrahedral structures: in these structures the silica tetrahedra share an oxygen atom with the adjacent tetrahedra. This gives rise to a structure Si_2O_7 which has a net of 6 negative charges.
3. Ring structures: three types of rings can form between tetrahedra, one in which each of three tetrahedra shares an oxygen atom, one in which each of four tetrahedra shares an oxygen atom, and one in which each of six tetrahedra shares an oxygen atom.

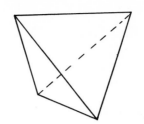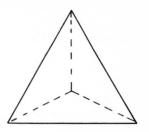

Fig. 6-27. A tetrahedron seen from two different angles. In the silica tetrahedron oxygen atoms occupy the corners of the tetrahedron.

4. Chain structures: chains of tetrahedra may form to any length. These may be single chains of tetrahedra joined one to another through the sharing of an oxygen atom, or double chains may form by cross-linking of two single chains.
5. Sheet structures: these are formed when each of three of the oxygen atoms of each tetrahedron is shared with other tetrahedra to form extended sheets of the tetrahedra.
6. Three-dimensional structures: these are formed when each of the four oxygen atoms of each tetrahedron is shared by another tetrahedron.

Fig. 6-28. Sheet structure formed through sharing of each of three oxygen atoms of each tetrahedron. Micas have such a structure.

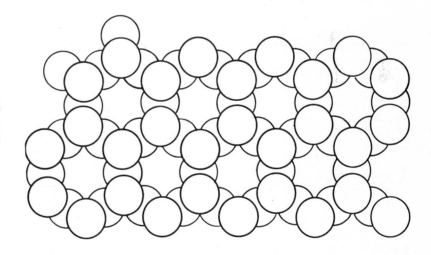

Fig. 6-29. A chain formed by sharing of one oxygen atom by two tetrahedra.

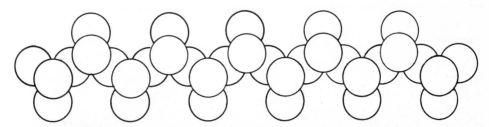

MINERAL IDENTIFICATION CHART

Name	Composition	H	Color
Amphibole Group			
Hornblende	$Ca_2 (Mg, Fe)_5 (OH)_2 (Al, Si)_8 O_{22}$	5½	black
Apatite	$CaPO_4$	5	variable
Azurite	$CuCO_3$	3½	dark blue
Bauxite	Al hydroxides	varies	variable
Bornite	$Cu_5 Fe S_4$	2½	bronze
Calcite	$Ca CO_3$	3	variable
Carnotite	(K, U, O, V, H_2O)	—	bright yellow
Cassiterite	$Sn O_2$	6½	black
Chalcopyrite	$Cu Fe S_2$	3	brass yellow
Chert	SiO_2	7	white
Chlorite	$Mg_5 Al (OH)_8 Al Si_3 O_{10}$	2½	greenish

Streak	Special Characteristics
greenish black	It occurs in long, prismatic crystals and in massive forms of small bladed, fibrous, granular, or compact grains. Cleavage is the most distinctive characteristic. There are two good cleavages at angles of 56° and 124°.
white	Crystals of apatite are hexagonal prisms. It also occurs in nodular or earthy massive form. The color is highly variable. There is only one cleavage and that is imperfect. It occurs in crystalline limestone, ore deposits, and in igneous rocks.
blue	The azure-blue color is characteristic. It will effervesce in hydrochloric acid. It is a minor ore of copper and is most commonly found with malachite.
variable	It is usually found in a massive, earthy or clay-like form. Rounded pea-shaped concretions are characteristic. It is the main ore of aluminum.
gray black	This important copper-bearing mineral occurs in massive forms that are usually granular or compact. Like all metals it is opaque. The peacock colored tarnish is most characteristic. It is found associated with chalcopyrite, chalcocite, malachite, and other copper bearing minerals.
white	Crystals of this mineral are found in many shapes. Crystals or granular aggregates are most common, but it is also found in stalactitic form in caves. Color is highly variable. In clear specimens the double refraction of light through calcite may be observed. Two images of objects below the calcite will be seen. Cleavage is one of the best means of identification. There are three perfect cleavages that are not at right angles. Calcite will effervesce in dilute hydrochloric acid.
yellow	It usually occurs as a powdery incrustation in sand or sandstone. The canary yellow color and radioactivity are the most distinctive characteristics.
pale brown	It occurs as short prismatic crystals or in granular forms. Radial fibrous structures can sometimes be seen. Cleavage is indistinct, and the color is highly variable.
greenish black	Crystals are usually in the shape of tetrahedra, but it also occurs in compact and granular forms. It may be distinguished from pyrite by its deeper color and it is softer. Common associates are pyrite, bornite, galena, sphalerite, and chalcocite.
grayish	It is found only in massive forms that may be nodular, banded, concretionary, stalactitic, or compact. It is a variety of quartz and exhibits many of the same physical properties. It has no cleavage. Fracture is conchoidal.
pale green	It is micaceous in appearance in most occurrences. Crystals are tabular, hexagonal, and are often bent. Colors are shades of green. One perfect cleavage is responsible for the micaceous appearance. It occurs in metamorphic rocks, and as a scaly coating on other minerals.

MINERAL IDENTIFICATION CHART—Con't

Name	Composition	H	Color
Chromite	Fe Cr$_2$ O$_4$	5½	black
Copper (native)	Cu	2½	copper red
Corundum	Al$_2$ O$_3$	9	variable
Diamond	C	10	colorless
Dolomite	(Ca, Mg) (CO$_3$)	3½	variable
Epidote	(Ca, Al, Fe, Al, Si, O)	6½	green, brown or yellow
Feldspar Group			
Microcline	K Al Si$_3$ O$_8$	6	green
Orthoclase	K Al Si$_3$ O$_8$	6	pink, yellow, or brown
Albite	Na Al Si$_3$ O$_8$	6	white or gray
Labradorite	(Na, Ca) (Al Si$_3$O$_8$)	6	gray or green gray
Anorthite	Ca Al Si$_3$O$_8$	6	colorless or white
Fluorite	Ca F$_2$	4	variable

Streak	Special Characteristics
brown or gray	It is usually found in granular masses. Grains are cubic. It is opaque, has a metallic luster, and is sometimes very slightly magnetic. It is an important ore mineral of chromium.
copper red	It occurs in irregularly-shaped masses in pore spaces in lavas and gravels. It is ductile, copper red in color, with the same hardness as a copper coin.
variable	It is frequently found in hexagonal and barrel-shaped prismatic crystals, but it also occurs in massive granular forms. Color is variable, but the most common colors are gray, green, and blue. Hardness is the most distinguishing feature, but care must be exercised in determining the hardness because chlorite is often associated with corundum and makes it appear softer than it is.
white	The hardness of diamond is its most distinguishing feature. Diamond crystals are most commonly octahedra, cubes, and slight modifications of these shapes, but they are often rounded and distorted. Diamond has octahedral cleavages which are perfect. In addition to the colorless varieties there are yellowish, red, green, blue, and black diamonds. The brilliance of diamond is due to its high dispersion of light.
white or gray	It is similar in appearance to calcite, but the crystals of rhombohedral shape have curved faces. It also occurs in massive forms. It is distinguished from calcite by its failure to effervesce in weak hydrochloric acid.
white	It occurs as elongated prismatic crystals, but is more commonly found in massive forms that may be columnar, fibrous, or granular. The greenish brown, greenish yellow, and yellow colors are characteristic. Common associates are feldspars, amphiboles, and pyroxenes.
white white white white white	Both orthoclase and microcline contain potassium. They occur as thick tabular crystals and in massive forms that may be granular or cleavage masses. Common colors are white, gray, pink, and for microcline, green. They may be distinguished from other feldspars by rectangular cleavage, and by the absence of fine striations on the cleavage surfaces that are the result of twinning. Albite, labradorite, and anorthite are members of a group known as the plagioclase feldspars. These contain various amounts of sodium and calcium. Albite is one end member of the group. It contains only sodium. Anorthite, the other end member, contains only calcium. Other members of the group contain varying amounts of sodium and calcium, and the physical properties vary with the relative amount of each of these constituents. The plagioclase feldspars are all twinned. Thus there are fine striations on the crystal and cleavage faces. Labradorite is the most easily identifiable member of the group because it is usually a gray color and has a play of colors as it is turned in light.
white	It occurs in cubic crystals and in cleavage masses or in granular form. The color is variable, but purples and greens are most common. The cleavage is octahedral and it is perfect. Fluorite is most often confused with calcite, but differs in that it has a hardness of 4.

MINERAL IDENTIFICATION CHART—Con't

Name	Composition	H	Color
Galena	Pb S	2½	gray
Garnet	(Ca, Mg, Fe, Al) (Si O$_4$)	6½	variable
Gold (native)	Au	2½	gold
Graphite	C	1	gray
Gypsum	CaSO$_4$ · H$_2$O	2	white
Halite	Na Cl	2½	colorless
Hematite	Fe$_2$ O$_3$	6	red or black
Kyanite	Al$_2$ SiO$_5$	4–7	blue
Limonite	Fe O (OH) · H$_2$O	5	rust
Magnetite	Fe$_3$ O$_4$	6	black

Streak	Special Characteristics
gray	Cubic crystals and lead gray color combined with its high specific gravity make galena easy to identify. But it also occurs in granular aggregates. It has perfectly developed cubic cleavage.
white	Crystals are common and they are cubes or dodecahedra, but it occurs in massive granular forms also. Color is highly variable, but deep red colors are characteristic of some varieties. Cleavage is not distinct. Hardness is one of the best ways of distinguishing it from similar minerals.
gold	It usually is found as rolled scales, grains, or nuggets. Its high specific gravity and color distinguish it from most other metals. It is malleable and ductile, has no cleavage.
gray	Massive forms are most common. These are scaly, foliated, granular, or earthy. The color, dark gray, hardness of 1, and one perfect cleavage make it easy to identify. It feels greasy.
white	Crystals are tabular or prismatic. Massive forms may be laminated, granular, fibrous, or earthy. It is usually colorless, white, or gray. The colorless transparent crystals or cleavage plates are called selenite. Fibrous forms that have silky luster are called satin spar. The granular forms are called alabaster.
white	Crystals are cubic in shape. Massive forms may be cleavable masses, granular, fibrous, stalactitic, or crusts. Colors are white, gray, or colorless. Because halite can absorb water it may feel damp and slick. The salty taste is characteristic as is its perfect cubic cleavage.
red	There are several important varieties of hematite. Specularite is characterized by its metallic luster, steel gray or iron black color, and reddish streak. It occurs as crystals, in a micaceous form and as granular masses. Oolitic or fossil hematite is characterized by the egg-shaped bodies that are very small. Hematite may occur as a cement in sandstone, as oolites, or as a replacement of fossils. Compact hematite occurs as kidney-shaped masses that have radial internal structures that are fibrous. The luster is submetallic, and the color is iron black or brownish red. All hematite has a red streak.
white	Long, bladed crystals that are curved and radially grouped are characteristic of kyanite as are the bluish streaks or spots in it. The hardness varies with direction, being 4 in one direction and as much as 7 in the other. It occurs in metamorphic rocks.
yellowish brown	It is usually in massive forms that are nodular, compact, earthy, or stalactitic. The structures are often porous. The rusty color is characteristic of the surface. The hard compact forms are fibrous, but soft earthy limonite is more common.
black	Crystals belong to the cubic system and are thus octahedra. Magnetite also is found in compact, granular, and lamellar forms. Cleavage is indistinct, but unlike most other minerals it is strongly magnetic.

Name	Composition	H	Color
Malachite	$Cu\ CO_3$	4	green
Mica Group			
Biotite	$K\,(Mg, Fe)_3\,(OH, F)_2\,Al\,Si_3\,O_{10}$	2½	black
Lepidolite	$K_2Li_3Al_3\,(F, OH)_4\,(AlSi_3O_{10})_2$	3	pink
Muscovite	$KAl_2\,(OH,F)_2\,Al\,Si_3\,O_{10}$	2½	white
Olivine	$(Mg, Fe)_2\,SiO_4$	6½	green
Pyrite	$Fe\ S_2$	6	brass yellow
Pyroxene Group			
Augite	$Ca\,(Mg, Fe, Al)\,(Al, Si)_2\,O_6$	5½	black
Pyrrhotite	$Fe\ S$	4	bronze yellow
Quartz	$Si\ O_2$	7	variable
Serpentine	$Mg_6\,(OH)_8\,Si_4\,O_{10}$	2–5	green or black
Sillimanite	$Al_2Si\,O_5$	6½	gray brown
Sphalerite	$Zn\ S$	3½	brown yellow

Streak	Special Characteristics
green	Crystals are needle-like and form in groups. More commonly it is found in massive fibrous, stalactitic, kidney-shaped masses with internal banding, as velvety crusts or as earthy masses. The silky luster and bright green color are characteristic.
dark white white	Members of this group are hexagonal in shape and scale-like sheets formed as a result of the one perfect cleavage are the most characteristic occurrence in rocks. Biotite is black, brownish, or blackish green. Muscovite is colorless, white, or yellowish. Lepidolite is pink or lavender. The colors are characteristic of these three.
white	It is usually found in granular masses. The green color is typical, and striations of the crystal faces may be apparent in larger crystals, but are difficult to see in granular aggregates.
greenish black	Cubic crystals are commonly found. These crystals usually are striated. It may also be found in massive granular forms. When weathered pyrite may turn into limonite.
gray green	Augite is the most common member of this group. It is most easily confused with hornblende, but the two can be distinguished by the angle between the cleavage faces. The acute angle between cleavages in augite is 87° compared with an angle of 56° in hornblende.
black	Compact or granular massive forms are most common. It may be distinguished from similar minerals, pyrite and chalcopyrite, by color. The surface tends to tarnish to a dark brown. It is also slightly magnetic.
white	Crystalline varieties are hexagonal prisms. The crystal faces are horizontally striated. This group includes rock crystal quartz and milky quartz. The conchoidal fracture, glassy luster, and hardness are characteristic. Cryptocrystalline varieties are also very common. In these the crystal structure is not apparent. They appear as massive forms which may be nodular, kidney-shaped, banded, concretionary, stalactitic, or compact masses. The luster of these forms is waxy or vitreous. Chalcedony has a waxy luster, hardness of 7, and conchoidal fracture. Agate is banded chalcedony. Onyx is agate in which the lines or bands are even and straight. Jasper is distinguished by its red color which is derived from specks of hematite in the quartz.
white	It is found only in massive forms which may be compact, columnar, fibrous, or granular. The luster is greasy or waxy. It is often spotted, clouded, or multicolored. Asbestos is a variety of serpentine or amphibole.
white	It occurs as long, thin needle-like forms or as radiating fibrous masses in metamorphic rocks. Silky luster is an important characteristic of most occurrences.
light brown	Luster is one of the important characteristics. It is resinous. The yellowish colors are also typical. When in crystals they are tetrahedral. Cleavage is prominent in six directions.

MINERAL IDENTIFICATION CHART—Con't

Name	Composition	H	Color
Staurolite	$Fe(OH)_2 \cdot 2 Al_2O SiO_4$	7	gray, brown, or black
Sulfur	S	2	yellow
Talc	$Mg_3 (OH)_2 Si_4 O_{10}$	1	variable
Tourmaline	$Na Fe_3 B_3 Al_3 (OH)_4 (Al_3Si_6O_{27})$	7½	black, pink, or brown

Streak	Special Characteristics
white	Prismatic crystals are common. These are usually in a cross-like shape. It is found in metamorphic rocks.
yellow	Granular, fibrous, crusts, or compact forms are most common. The straw yellow color is characteristic. There is no cleavage.
white	When in crystals it is thin and tabular. More common are the foliated massive forms or fibrous, granular, or compact masses. The luster is pearly, and it feels greasy.
white	Crystals are common. These are long or short hexagonal prisms. They are characterized by a triangular outline in cross section. Color is sometimes distributed zonally along the crystals which may vary from transparent to nearly opaque.

REFERENCES

HURLBUT, CORNELIUS, JR., 1952, *Dana's Manual of Mineralogy*, 16th ed.: New York, John Wiley & Sons, 530 p.

KRAUS, E. H., HUNT, W. F., and RAMSDELL, L. S., 1951, *Mineralogy:* 4th ed., New York, McGraw-Hill Book Co., 664 p.

PAULING, LINUS, 1953, *General Chemistry*, 2nd ed.: San Francisco, W. H. Freeman and Company, 710 p.

POUGH, FREDERICK H., 1953, *A Field Guide to Rocks and Minerals:* Boston, Houghton Mifflin Co., 333 p.

7   Volcanism

On February 20, 1943, a Mexican farmer was plowing his corn field when he noticed a thin cloud of smoke rising from the ground. Within a day frequent small explosions were taking place in that part of the field, and clouds of smoke and dust were boiling up from a small hole. Before the end of that week a volcano almost 400 feet high had been built from the ash, and a flow of basalt lava had issued from a fissure located near the cone. Within the first year the cone rose to a height of 1400 feet. Activity continued until 1952 when the volcano,

Paricutín, became one of many inactive volcanoes in the western part of Mexico.

Volcanism is one of the most dramatic evidences of the dynamic nature of the earth. Other natural processes may be so slow that the casual observer misses the long-range effects produced by them, but no one who has witnessed a volcanic eruption and watched the clouds of smoke, fire, and debris ejected can fail to sense that the earth is actively undergoing change. Our planet is not a dead mass of rock reeling through space, it is alive.

Igneous activity is the name applied to all the processes that are related to the generation, movement, or crystallization of molten rock, magma. Great quantities of molten rock are intruded into the crust of the earth. Other magma finds its way to the surface where it is extruded, building up volcanoes and extensive plateaus composed of layers of lava. About 450 volcanoes have been active within recorded history, and the cones of many thousands of others show such slight evidence of erosion that they cannot be very old. The present may well be one of the greatest periods of volcanic activity since the beginning of the Paleozoic Era almost half a billion years ago.

Volcanoes take many forms, and the activity that is associated with their eruption is highly varied. The activity of volcanoes differs in the amount and type of material ejected. The sizes, temperature, and composition of the material ejected determine the shape of the volcano or the form of the extrusion. Volcanoes also differ in the violence and the timing of successive eruptions. Examine the following case histories of some of the most outstanding eruptions on record and note the variety.

Tamboro. The most violent explosion of all recorded history occurred on a small island

Fig. 7-1. Kilauea flank eruption (eruption on rift zone) near the town of Kapoho in the Puna District, Hawaii, 1960. (Courtesy of Volcano Observatory, U.S. Geological Survey.)

a. (top). Rift of fountains which have already built a spatter rampart along them but before the nearby trees were destroyed. Subsequently the fountains built a pumice and spatter cone over 300 ft. high.

b. (second from top). Steam cloud formed by pahoehoe lava entering the ocean. In less than two days after the eruption started the half mile wide lava front had flowed two miles from a sixty-foot elevation to the ocean and had begun to extend the Hawaiian shoreline.

c. (third from top). Fountains about 200 feet high throwing new spatter onto the ramparts they are building around the erupting rift.

d. (bottom). Aa lava front creeping slowly into the ocean with its still hot fragments heating the near-shore water and killing the fish.

in the East Indies in 1815 when the volcano Tamboro exploded, blowing about 50 cubic miles of the crust of the earth into the air. The debris broken up by these tremendous explosions covered islands for hundreds of miles around. Explosions of this sort are relatively rare, and most of them occur in volcanoes that have been dormant for long periods of time. The explosion is a means of release of pressures built up beneath the volcano's vent in the pipe, the connection between the volcano and the magma, or within the magma itself. Magmas contain large quantities of gases. Gases are compressible and may continue to build up pressure until the pressure exceeds the strength of the plug of frozen lava in the pipe. If the gases may be released slowly, violent explosion is unlikely.

Krakatoa. One Sunday afternoon in August of 1883 a few mild explosions rocked the island of Krakatoa located in the Sunda Strait between Java and Sumatra. The next morning the cone of this volcano was ripped apart by an explosion that sent more than a cubic mile of rock into the air. The cloud of dust, gases, and debris rose from the explosion

e. (top). A moving aa lava flow burning the Kapoho School building and covering the spot a few minutes later. The galvanized sheets of roofing mark the position of another school building site just covered.

f. and g. (second and third from top). Fountain of molten lava reaching over 1000 feet above the previously flat sugar cane fields on which it has built an extended cone over 300 feet high. High fountains produce a dark cloud of light-weight pumice fragments which are scattered over distances of several miles by the winds. Lava flows extend toward the observer and the cane and cane roads are covered with over 6 inches of pumice.

h. (bottom). Pahoehoe apron at the ocean front. One method by which lava flows extend the island boundaries is shown here as countless little tongues of pahoehoe lava form the patchwork apron. At the ocean front are several newly formed black sands areas formed by the molten lava being blown into glassy, sand-sized fragments by jets of steam produced at the littoral zone. Steam is seen to be rising from many places over the still hot lava field.

nearly 17 miles into the atmosphere. The heavier debris fell back to earth, but the smaller particles of dust were caught in the upper air currents and were blown around the earth. For the next 2 years, before this great quantity of dust settled, it colored sunsets. Krakatoa and a neighboring island were literally blown to bits. A sounding was made over the original peak of the volcano, which had been 2600 feet above sea level; the sounding was −1000 feet. Few people lived on Krakatoa, but in the lowlands of the southwest Pacific islands thousands were killed by a great tidal wave created by the explosion.

The island of Krakatoa resembled numerous other volcanic islands in the Pacific. The majority of these have composite cones. The cones are built up in the course of many eruptions. During some of these eruptions pyroclastic (broken by fire) debris comes to the surface. This consists of such materials as dust, ash, blocks of lava, and volcanic bombs. Because such materials are generally heavy and angular they tend to pile up near the vent of the volcano, building the cone up until the slope of the ground near the vent is equal to the angle of repose for the debris. Interbedded with these pyroclastic materials are layers of lava. Usually the lava is very fluid, and the flows move rapidly down the steep sides of the cone and extend the margins of the volcano.

The site on which Krakatoa was built was one previously occupied by volcanoes. A fringe of islands marks the rim of a former volcano which collapsed or exploded before recorded history. Collapse features of this sort are common. They are formed when the top part of a cone subsides or collapses into the space vacated by the material extruded to form the cone. Such collapse features are called calderas.

Fig. 7-2. Distribution of modern volcanism on the continents. The volcanos indicated are discussed in the text. In addition to the shaded belts many volcanos are known in the ocean basins. In the Atlantic Ocean they are concentrated along the Mid-Atlantic Ridge. In the Pacific many volcanic islands are located in the southwestern part of the ocean, and many others are submerged in the waters of the central and northern Pacific. In the Indian Ocean activity is concentrated along the Mid-Indian Ocean Ridge.

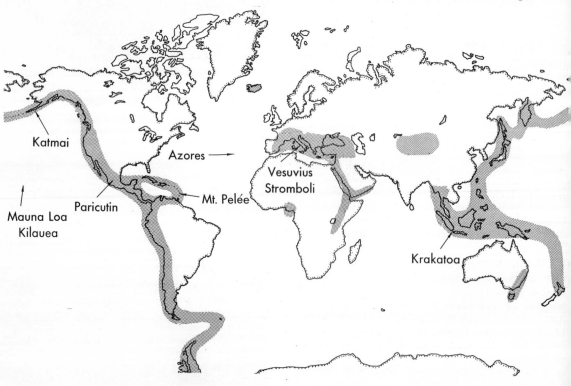

Fig. 7-3. An extinct cinder cone surrounded by its own erosion materials. This recently active volcano is located in Alaska. Note the steep slopes which are characteristic of cinder cones. (Photo by courtesy of the U.S. Air Force.)

A new volcano is being built on the site of Krakatoa today.

Mt. Pelée. This famous volcano is situated on the slopes above the city of St. Pierre on the island of Martinique in the West Indies. In the last months of 1903 a spine of frozen lava began to project from the vent of this composite cone. A spine is actually a solidified mass of glassy lava cooled in the vent following the previous activity of a volcano. It forms what is known as a plug and serves the same function. For several months before the eruption of Mt. Pelée the spine rose more than 100 feet, and steam and some dust and a glassy froth called pumice were blown out around the edges. The activity culminated in a series of violent explosions. Most of the material ejected was incandescent dust, ash, and gases. These formed a cloud which ascended from the peak and rose as a huge seething turbulent mass. Because it contained great quantities of heavy

particles the cloud was heavier than air and settled back to the slopes of the cone. The continued evolution of gases from the incandescent mass buoyed it up, and it moved down the slopes of the cone as a gigantic density current. The town of St. Pierre, which lay in its path, was totally destroyed, and all its population of 28,000 persons were killed with the exception of a single individual who was chained in a dungeon.

Vesuvius. The story of the city of Pompeii is one of the classics of ancient Roman history. The city of Pompeii was buried to a depth of as much as 50 feet by dust and ash mixed with steam to form a hot thick mud that flowed down the steep slopes.

Vesuvius, the present volcano, stands about 4000 feet high in the center of the collapsed crater of an older and larger volcano, Mt. Somma. All that is now left of Mount Somma is a ridge that makes a half circle

Fig. 7-4. Two composite volcanoes in Alaska. Volcanoes such as these are built up by the eruption of lavas and pyroclastic debris—ash, cinders, blocks, and bombs. (Photo by courtesy of U.S. Coast and Geodetic Survey.)

Fig. 7-5. A composite cone in Alaska. Compare this with Fig. 7-6. (Photo by courtesy of U.S. Coast and Geodetic Survey.)

around Vesuvius. Varied and periodic activity has been the course of Vesuvius' history in modern time. It has been active frequently since the explosion of the year 79 A. D. when Pompeii was destroyed. The activity seems to follow a pattern. After a period of violent eruption and explosion the remains of its composite cone begin to collapse where unstable or oversteepened. The crater catches much of this debris. Within a few years lava begins to flow into the crater and may eventually fill it. The weight of this material in the crater allows pressure to build up within the pipe. Lava may break through the sides of the cone, and some may flow over the rim of the crater. Small craters form within the larger crater; these are accompanied by minor explosions. Eventually the pressures within become too great to be contained, and a major eruption begins. This may take the form of a brilliant fireworks display with incandescent ash, bombs, and dust blown more than 1000 feet into the air before it comes pummelling back to earth, or the activity may be the relatively quiet extrusion of glowing rivers of red-hot lava. On the steep slopes these flow rapidly downhill, carrying partially cooled blocks and pyroclastic material along with them. At the foot of the volcano, where the slopes break, the motion is slowed, and the lava begins to consolidate. A crust forms over the top of the flow, but internal heat keeps the center fluid, and it flows, breaking and cracking the crust as it moves. The front margins of the flow look like a pile of smoldering broken blocks. The top blocks keep breaking off and falling in front as the margin gradually moves forward.

Katmai. Located on the Alaskan penin-

Fig. 7-6. A caldera located in Alaska. This is what remains of a large volcano which has either exploded or collapsed into the magma chamber from which it was built. The central part of the caldera is filled with snow. This volcano probably resembled that shown in Fig. 7-5 at one time. (Photo by courtesy of U.S. Coast and Geodetic Survey.)

sula, Katmai has been a source of much information about volcanoes since its eruption in 1912. There was no previous record of activity at this deeply eroded and dormant volcano until it exploded, sending great quantities of dust and bits of pumice (a natural frothy glass) into the air. The finer dust was carried around the world while the larger particles were dropped out within a few hundred miles. So much material was ejected that parts of Kodiak Island, 60 miles away, were covered with several feet of dust. Robert Griggs described the activity at Katmai as follows in his report of 1922:

Over an area of fifty square miles the ground is all broken open, and hot gases from the molten material below are even now everywhere pouring out, forming the several millions of fumaroles that constitute the Valley of Ten Thousand Smokes . . . .

If such an eruption should occur on Manhattan Island, the column of steam would be conspicuous as far as Albany. The sounds of the explosions would be plainly audible in Chicago. The fumes would sweep over all the states east of the Rocky Mountains . . . As far away as Toronto the acid raindrops would cause stinging burns wherever they fell on face or hands . . . . Ash would accumulate in Philadelphia a foot deep . . . . The whole of Manhattan Island, and an equal area besides, would open in great yawning chasms, and fiery fountains of molten lava would issue from every crack. In its deepest parts the near-molten sand would probably overtop the tallest skyscrapers, though the tip of the Woolworth tower might protrude. (From The *Valley of Ten Thousand Smokes* by Robert F. Griggs, National Geographic Society.)

Studies of the Valley of Ten Thousand Smokes have given us much information about

Fig. 7-7. Iliamna Volcano, Alaska. Note the gases which are escaping from several vents near the top of the volcano. (Photo by courtesy of the U.S. Air Force.)

Fig. 7-8. A composite volcano located in Japan. (Photo by courtesy of Japan Air Lines.)

volcanoes, their gaseous emanation, and their contents. One of the most interesting of the observations made there is that metallic minerals are dispersed in the porous tuffs, ash deposits, around the fumaroles. Magnetite, specular hematite, molybdenite, pyrite, galena, sphalerite, covellite, and other metallic minerals are found. Thus it is demonstrated conclusively that gaseous emanations can collect, transport, and deposit the metals, an important fact in the origin of ore deposits. It was also discovered that the fumaroles around Katmai yielded approximately 1 1/4 million tons of hydrochloric acid and 200,000 tons of hydrofluoric acid each year. Such acids undoubtedly play an important role in the alteration of rocks near large intrusions.

Mauna Loa and Kilauea. A diver equipped to go to the bottom of the Pacific Ocean off the Hawaiian Islands would find that the islands have been built by a succession of many thousands of overlapping lava flows. They rise from a depth of nearly 15,000 feet

below sea level to the surface and then on up to the top of the highest peak, Mauna Loa, 13,000 feet above sea level. Unlike the stratovolcanoes with their composite cones of pyroclastic materials and lavas, the activity here is almost entirely confined to the extrusion of lava which issues both from central craters and from long fissures that open up on the broad flanks of the volcanoes. Although Mauna Loa is 13,000 feet high, its profile is that of an inverted shield; for this reason it is called a shield volcano.

The lava is basalt, which rises to the surface at temperatures of 1100° Centigrade. The molten rock is not highly viscous and therefore flows rapidly, spreading out and extending the margins of the shield. Many of the streams of lava flow into the ocean where steam is generated and rises as large clouds. Basaltic lava tends to be more fluid than lavas rich in silica. As silica tetrahedra form in the silicic lavas they become connected and impede the movement of the lava as the viscosity is increased.

Fig. 7-9. Gases escaping from one of the world's largest craters, Mt. Aso, in Japan. Most of the gas is steam, water vapor, but large quantities of carbon dioxide, carbon monoxide, sulfur dioxide, hydrogen sulfide, hydrochloric acid, hydrofluoric acid, ammonia, and sulfuric acid may be present in volcanic gases. Arrow shows human figure for scale. (Photo by courtesy of Japan Tourist Association.)

For this reason bulbous masses instead of thin extensive flows tend to develop from extrusions of rhyolite and other silica-rich lavas.

The top of Mauna Loa has collapsed, forming a large caldera about 2 miles across and 1000 feet deep. Kilauea, located on the side of Mauna Loa 16 miles from the summit, has a smaller caldera. Both contain pools of lava that are almost continuously active. At times large amounts of lava pour forth. At other times only gasses bubble out of these pools.

One of the most notable eruptions in the long history of volcanic activity in Hawaii started November 14, 1959.* At that time Kilauea Volcano, of Mauna Loa, broke into eruption. There are several craters located at Kilauea. These are collapse structures formed after extrusions. The 1959 eruption started from a fissure about half a mile long in the side of the Kilauea Iki Crater. For more than 2 years seismic and tilt-meter studies at the Volcano Observatory of the U.S. Geological Survey located at Kilauea had indicated the approach of the

*The discussion of the Kilauea eruption of 1959-1960 is based on an unpublished report by Willard H. Parsons of Wayne State University.

eruptions. As lava moves beneath the ground shock waves are generated; these can be picked up and recorded at the surface. Before an eruption the upwelling of lava from depth causes the crater to be warped upward. The tilt-meter is an instrument designed to record these warps.

When the eruption started, lava poured up as a curtain of fiery molten rock half a mile

Fig. 7-10. Geologic map of Hawaii. Located here are the main craters and some of the largest lava flows which make up these shield volcanoes. (After Gordon A. Macdonald, U.S. Geological Survey, Prof. Paper 214-D.)

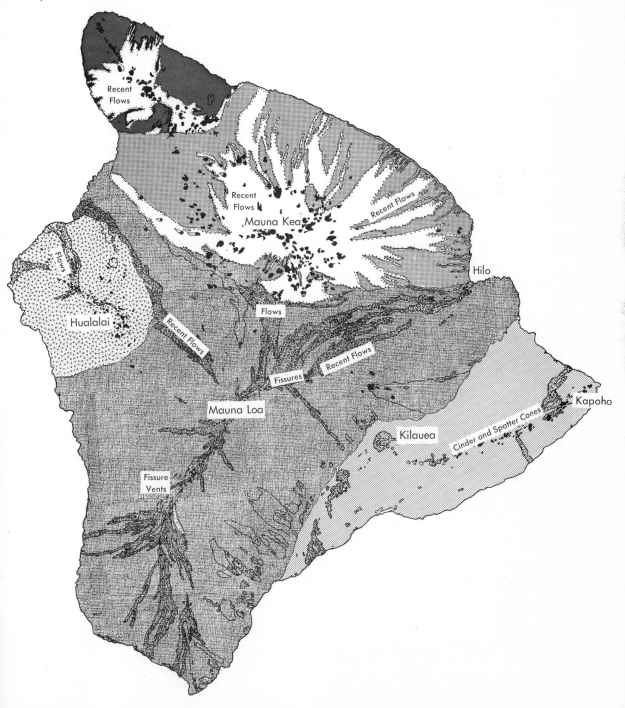

long and hundreds of feet high. As it issues from the ground the lava is over 1100° Centigrade and has a brilliant orange color. As it falls to the earth it turns a darker color as the top part of the flow cools. Some of it cools to form a glassy, porous froth of scoria or pumice. About a day after the eruptions started the outpourings became confined to a single fiery fountain. The fountain of lava from this place reached a maximum height of 1900 feet. An estimated 57 million cubic yards of lava was erupted, forming a lava lake that filled the Kilauea Iki Crater to a depth of 414 feet. On the downwind side of the eruption a cinder cone was built up more than 200 feet high.

The last eruptions at Kilauea Iki took place on December 19, but volcanic tremors continued to be recorded on seismographs, indicating the continued movement of lava underground. In the first days of 1960 the earthquakes became more intense, and finally the ground cracked open 20 miles east of the first eruption near the village of Kapoho. Lava began to pour from a fissure three-quarters of a mile long but soon became localized at one point along the fissure. A large tongue of lava flowed from this point 3 miles into the ocean, destroying the village and property along the shore. Lava in some of these flows moved somewhat like a river choked with blocks of solidified lava. It flowed at a rate of 2 to 3 miles per hour. Other flows composed of a thick cover of frozen lava blocks moved only a few feet an hour.

In the early part of February earthquakes again started at Kilauea. Tilt-meter surveys in-

Fig. 7-11. Lava flows in central New Mexico, west of Carrizozo. They are of prehistoric age, but the fact that they are so fresh indicates that they are young geologically. (Photo by courtesy of the New Mexico State Tourist Bureau.)

Fig. 7-12. Lava flows near Los Alamos, New Mexico. A huge extinct volcano crater known as Valle Grande was the source of many of the lavas found in this region. (Photo by courtesy of the New Mexico State Tourist Bureau.)

dicated that the area around Kilauea was subsiding. This marked the beginning of the close of the cycle of volcanic activity that had begun with the slow rise of magma during the past 2 years.

Ilha Nova. The Azores in the Atlantic Ocean mark the top of the mid-ocean ridge. Like the other islands of the mid-ocean belt and of the Pacific, the Azores are composed almost entirely of volcanic debris and lava flows. Many towering peaks exhibiting perfectly developed cones bear witness to the youth of the volcanic features of these islands, as do the abandoned villages destroyed by volcanic explosions and lava flows which dot the islands.

The islanders, believing it bad luck to rebuild the villages, put up new houses nearby but never on the site of a destroyed town. In September, 1957, one of the most recent episodes of the history of the islands started. Bursting forth from the sea off the tip end of the island of Fayal, a new volcano was born. Gases and steam spewed into the air as thousands of volcanic bombs shot half a mile into the sky. Steam formed a cloud extending up 20,000 feet. Within 5 days a cinder cone was built 50 feet above the water level, and before the end of a month it was 300 feet high. Then almost overnight the activity ceased, and the cone disappeared below the surface as waves broke up

the loosely consolidated ash. About a month later a jet of ash blew into the air from the site of Ilha Nova I, and activity was resumed. New eruptions of ash, dust, and bombs rapidly rebuilt the cone, and a connection was established with the main island. Activity continued into 1958, but in decreasing intensity. The island of Fayal is composed of one large volcano caldera and about nine smaller cones, all of which lie along a nearly straight line, most likely over a fault in the crust beneath through which the magma comes to the surface.

Fig. 7-14. A vertical view down into the Mauna Loa Crater. The crater is a part of the shield volcano which has collapsed and subsided. (Photo by courtesy of the U.S. Air Force.)

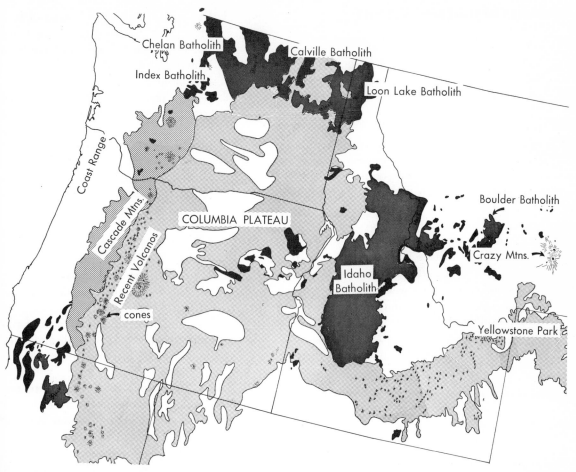

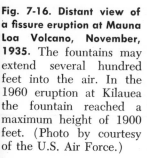

Fig. 7-15. Distribution of volcanoes, lava flows (stippled), and igneous intrusions (black) in the northwestern United States. (After the Tectonic Map of the United States.)

Fig. 7-16. Distant view of a fissure eruption at Mauna Loa Volcano, November, 1935. The fountains may extend several hundred feet into the air. In the 1960 eruption at Kilauea the fountain reached a maximum height of 1900 feet. (Photo by courtesy of the U.S. Air Force.)

SUMMARY OF VOLCANIC ACTIVITY

I. CAUSE

Volcanism is seen to be caused through the release of high pressures, which build up within magma chambers below the ground surface. Volcanic activity is one phase of the expression of igneous activity caused by the generation of magmas within the crust. Frequently the release of pressure is made possible by conduits along a fault and zones of weakness in the crust.

II WHAT COMES OUT.

A. Pyroclastic materials: These are volcanic materials that have been broken up and explosively ejected. They consist of solids broken from the walls of the magma chamber or the vent and liquids which are rapidly chilled to a solid when they are thrown into the air. The pyroclastic materials are classified according to their size and shape.

1. Blocks are the largest masses of rock blown out. Some of these are huge. A 2-ton block is known to have been blown about 2 miles during an explosion of Stromboli.

2. Bombs are composed of lava that cools and partially solidifies as it comes out of the vent. Bombs range in size, but most are shaped somewhat like a football. The ends are twisted, indicating rotation of the central liquid part of the mass after the end started to freeze.

3. Lapilli are the pea-size particles, most of which are shaped very much like the bombs.

4. Ash is the term applied to debris that is formed of particles about the size of a pin head.

5. Volcanic dust is the finest size of pyroclastic debris. It is small and light enough to be lifted high into the atmosphere.

B. Gases: The gases listed below are not always found. Some gases are extruded from all volcanoes, but which particular ones are present is variable.

1. Water vapor, or steam, is by far the most common gas. It ordinarily makes up more than 95 per cent of the total volume of gases given off.

2. Oxygen, nitrogen, and argon.

3. Carbon dioxide and carbon monoxide.

4. Hydrogen sulfide.

5. Hydrochloric acid, hydrofluoric acid, and sulfuric acid.

6. Ammonia.

C. Liquids coming from volcanoes are collectively known as lavas. All lavas contain gases. It is the escape of these gases that is responsible for the porous nature of many consolidated lavas.

1. Basalts are the most common lavas coming from oceanic volcanoes. They make up a large part of the plateau lavas such as those that cover the northwestern United States.

2. Rhyolites, composed of feldspar and quartz, are much less common. They are known only on the continents.

Fig. 7-17. Close-up of the crater of Crater Lake. The slopes are covered with debris and the small island is composed of lava. The lake occupies the collapsed part of this cone. (Photo by courtesy of the Oregon State Highway Commission.)

3. Andesite lavas are intermediate in composition between basalts and rhyolites. These lavas are not found in the central parts of the ocean basins, but they characterize extrusions around the margins of the Pacific.

III. ACTIVITY.

As we have seen, the nature of the eruptions of different volcanoes is highly varied. Several major groups are apparent. These are:

A. Violent explosions (Tamboro and Krakatoa) separated by long intervals of quiet.

B. Intermittent explosions. The pressure is frequently released, so no major eruptions occur.

C. Lava flows may start with or without accompanying explosive eruptions. Likewise gases only may be given off.

IV. FORM OF THE ERUPTIVES.

A. Those formed near a central vent: these are built when the debris and lava come from a single vent.

1. Cinder cones are the steep-sided cones composed almost entirely of cinders, ash, lapilli, and larger pyroclastic debris. The sides of the cones have a slope that is the angle of repose of the debris. The top central part of the cone is depressed to form a vent from which the debris is ejected.

2. Lava cones are those built up of lava flows. These are generally very broad and slightly convex upward if they are basalt flows. These are called shield volcanoes. If the lava is highly viscous and cannot flow far before it cools, then high bulbous forms are likely to result.

3. Composite cones are those formed when both ash and lava are extruded. The pyroclastic debris builds up the cone, and the lavas extend the margins. Mayon in the Philippine Islands is a typical example.

B. Those formed from fissure eruptions:

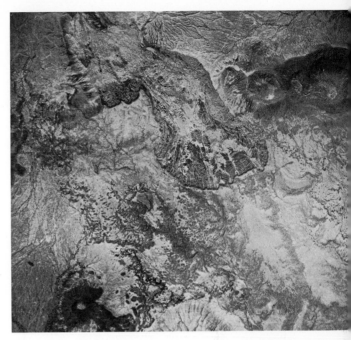

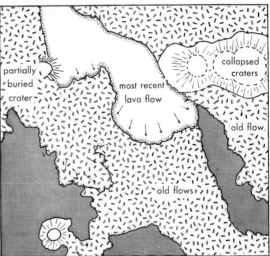

Fig. 7-18. Vertical photograph of lava flows and cinder cones in Africa. Several flows of different ages are shown. The margins of the flows and the cones are outlined on the sketch map below. (Photo by courtesy of the U.S. Air Force.)

1. Shield volcanoes are frequently the sites of fissure eruptions. Lava pours from one or more long fissures, fractures, or faults during the eruption. The eruption of Kilauea in 1959-1960 included this type of activity as well as central eruptions.

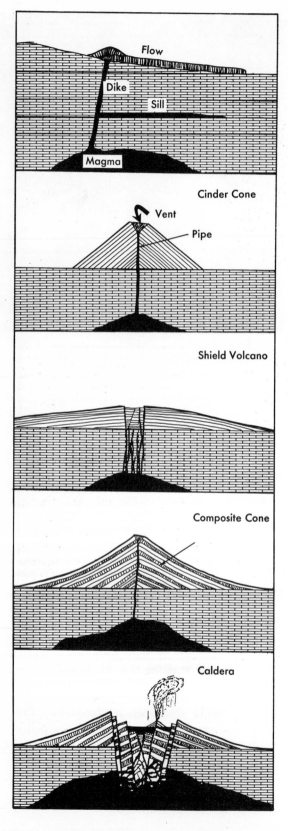

2. Flood basalts. These are extensive extrusions of lavas, notably basalts, which sometimes cover great areas. Basalts of this nature issued from fissures in the northwestern United States at a number of times during the Cenozoic Era, the last 70 million years. These cover large parts of Oregon, Washington, northern California, and Idaho. Similar extrusions are found in the Deccan of India.

C. Subsidiary features include those small features associated with volcanoes and lava flows. All of these are widespread.

1. Fumaroles are the "smoke holes" from which volcanic gases issue. They are common near volcanoes and shallow intrusions. Many of them are found in Yellowstone Park, which is thought to be underlain by a cooling magma. A large part of these gases may come from vaporized ground water instead of from the magma.

2. Solfataras are fumaroles from which sulfur gases escape. The sulfur may build up deposits of sulfur crystals around the edge of the hole.

3. Spatter cones are the small cones formed on lava flows where breaks occur in the cooled surface of the flow, allowing hot lava and gases to be blown out. These are blown through the holes by the pressure of the gases that are constantly coming out of the liquid lava as it cools.

4. Collapse features: Calderas are formed when the top of a volcano subsides or collapses into the space vacated by extrusion of material from below the surface. The central part of the cone may subside along a complex system of faults and fractures, leaving a large depression on the top of the cone. Some calderas are many miles in diameter. Commonly smaller cones are built up within the collapsed portion.

Fig. 7-19. The form of various types of eruptives.

REFERENCES

DALY, R. A., 1933, *Igneous Rocks and the Depths of the Earth:* New York, McGraw-Hill Book Co., 508 p.

GRIGGS, F., 1922, *The Valley of Ten Thousand Smokes:* Washington, National Geographic Society, 341 p.

GROUT, F. F., 1932, *Petrography and Petrology:* New York, McGraw-Hill Book Co., 522 p.

SHAND, S. J., 1947, *Eruptive Rocks,* 3rd ed.: New York, John Wiley & Sons, 488 p.

TURNER, F. J., and VERHOOGEN, J., 1960, *Igneous and Metamorphic Petrology,* 2nd ed.: New York, McGraw-Hill Book Co., 694 p.

WAHLSTROM, E. E., 1947, *Igneous Minerals and Rocks:* New York, John Wiley & Sons, 367 p.

WILLIAMS, HOWEL, 1941, Calderas and Their Origin, Univ. Calif. Dept. Geol. Sciences Bull., v. 25, p. 239–346.

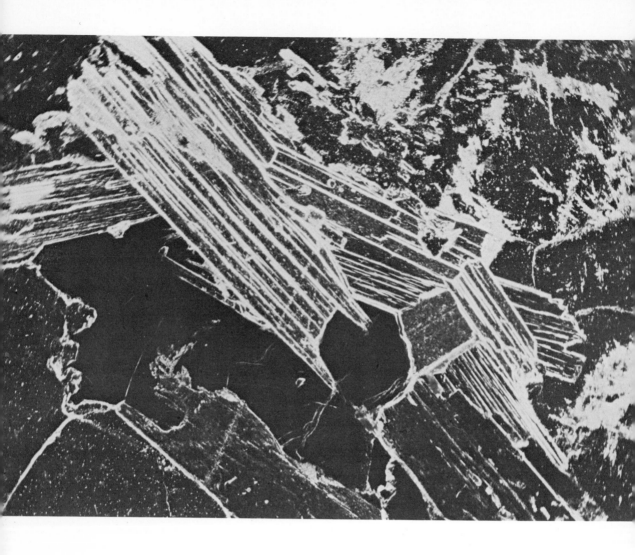

8   Igneous Rocks

If you had studied geology under Aristotle, you would have been taught that stones grow in the earth and on its surface through the influence of the rays of sunlight. According to his ideas these rays penetrating into the earth cause exhalations that bring about new combinations of elements and give rise to various kinds of stones. Although such an idea may seem somewhat far-fetched to us today, it was held by most philosophers until the end of the sixteenth century. Andreas Baccius had the same idea in 1603 when he wrote:

"Gems are the most precious products of nature and must be generated from highest source. They come to birth like gold itself through the action of the heavens and the stars. They also draw their virtues from the stars. The earth being situated immovable at the centre of the universe has all the heavenly powers concentrated upon it as at a focus." (Adam's *The Birth and Development of the Geological Sciences*)

One of the most interesting theories of the origin of rocks was that of the "rock seed," a theory that was widely taught in the sixteenth and seventeenth centuries. According to these theories there are three kingdoms of nature—living animals, plants, and the mineral kingdom. Of these the animals are the most alive, plants somewhat less so, and minerals only barely alive. But, like all living matter, the minerals and rocks have to be born and grow from seeds. These seeds originate in the earth's interior from rain water, which first is filtered from the surface down to the interior where flames are constantly burning. There the waters pick up various fluids and start back up toward the surface. On the way, when a suitable place is found, the fluids set up a process somewhat like fermentation; the result is the production of a female element with which the fluids, which are male, unite and create a seed that will eventually develop into a rock, mineral, or fossil. Certainly you will not find the modern theories on the generation of rocks any more involved or confusing, although they may show somewhat less imagination.

Nature of magma

The name "igneous" means born from fire. It is applied to those rocks that have originated in and on the earth's crust from the solidification of molten masses of rock, called magma. In the largest sense the name "igneous" is applied both to those rocks that pour out of volcanoes and those that slowly crystallize at depth under a deep cover of surficial rock. These two groups make up a large portion of the crust of the earth. If we consider the bulk of all the rocks down to a depth of 10 or more miles it is on the order of 90 per cent igneous rock.

The lavas that flow out of volcanoes in and around the Pacific Ocean and the Mediterranean Sea give us an excellent opportunity to study one of the principal types of magmas, that known as basaltic magma. (See the description of basalt later in this chapter.) Other types of magma may never come to the surface of the earth in a molten form for us to examine first hand, but much can be learned from the exposed portions of those igneous rocks, which crystallized deep in the earth and were subsequently uplifted and laid bare by erosion.

Magmas consist of mixtures of solids, fluids, and dissolved gases. Essentially they are very hot silicate melts containing large quantities of water and varying amounts of highly reactive fluids and gases in solution. These reactive fluids include such things as hydrochloric acid and hydrofluoric acid. Although the compositions of different magmas undoubtedly vary, many are very close to the following composition:

Chemical Composition

SiO_2	59	per cent
Al_2O_3	15	
Fe_2O_3	3	
FeO	3.5	
CaO	5	
Na_2O	3.8	
M_9O	3.5	
K_2O	3	
H_2O	1	
TiO_2	1	
P_2O_5	.3	
MnO	.1	
CO_2	.1	

Mineral Composition

Feldpars	59.5 per cent
Pyroxene and Amphibole	17.
Quartz	12.
Mica	4.
Others	8.

Plus water and some highly reactive fluids.

How hot is a magma? We have no way of finding out just how hot a magma may become within the earth, but we can observe the temperature of those that flow to the surface. Temperature measurements have been made at many places, notably at stations set up near Katmai Volcano in the Valley of the Ten Thousand Smokes in Alaska, and on the flanks of Mauna Loa in the Hawaiian Islands. Direct measurements made in basaltic magma show that it has a temperature of 1100° Centigrade as it flows out on the surface. Since it must have been forced up from a considerable depth it most certainly has cooled off some from its temperature at the point of origin. By means of a number of "geologic thermometers" we can trace the cooling history of the magma once it reaches the point of beginning to crystallize. What do we mean by geologic thermometers? In a sense every mineral is a thermometer because each begins to melt at a certain temperature, called the fusion temperature, and each one begins to crystallize out of a melt of the proper composition at a certain temperature just as ice begins to solidify or crystallize at 0° Centigrade. Some minerals are better thermometers than others, however, for we find that some will crystallize only in a narrow range of temperatures, while others will crystallize at almost any temperature below a certain level.

Viscosity. Basaltic lava breaking through the side of a volcano will flow like a stream of fire, carrying along ash and blocks in it like ice in a river. Yet, in places, lavas of granitic composition are known to form large bubble-like masses. The basaltic magma flows like so much heavy motor oil, while the granitic magma behaves like the proverbial molasses in January. An answer to this riddle is found in the composition of the magmas. The essential component of igneous rock-forming minerals is the silica tetrahedron. These are more abundant in the granitic magma, which contains more silicon and oxygen, than in basalt, and they have a strong tendency to form chains, rings, or sheets that slow down the movement of the magma. Another important factor is the amount of water in the melt. Although basaltic mag-

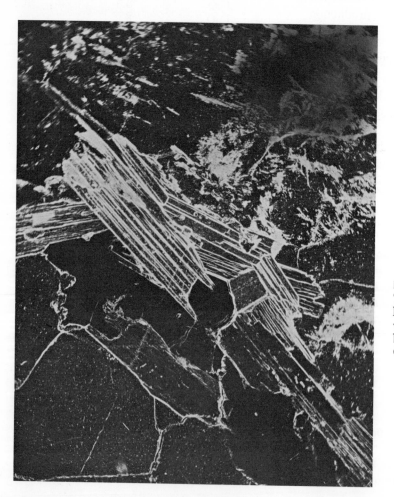

Fig. 8-1. An igneous rock, granite. This microphotograph, greatly enlarged, shows the crystals of which granite is composed. (Photo by courtesy of Bausch & Lomb Co.)

mas are usually more fluid than granitic magmas, the latter are highly fluid when the water content is high, and then they too flow rapidly.

GENERATION OF MAGMA

Having just been introduced to one of the seventeenth-century philosophic views on the generation of stones you may wonder what improvements we have made in the theories since that time. Presently most people conceive of the origin of magmas as either:

1. A liquid residuum from an originally molten earth, which sporadically breaks through to the surface or to near-surface levels.
2. A liquid that is generated by partial or complete fusion (melting) of a part of the solid crust or of the nearly completely crystalline material that makes up the outer portion of the earth's interior.

The first of these is a popular conception although it leaves us with some important unanswered questions:

1. Was the earth actually molten when it originated? There is considerable evidence supporting the theory that the earth originated from cool solid particles.
2. How would a magma manage to come all the way to the surface from that part of the earth's interior which is thought to be in a fluid state? The distance is on the order of 1800 miles, and this alone would appear to be an obstacle of considerable magnitude in moving even the most fluid magma to the surface.

It seems more logical to assume that most of the magmas that come to the surface and that cut into or intrude near-surface rocks were generated within a few miles or at most a few hundred miles of the surface.

We have no way of making direct observations of the formation of a magma. Thus we must rely on our knowledge of the materials involved and the general processes acting in and on the earth. First, what conditions are necessary to bring about melting of a rock or mineral? We know that two things influence melting—temperature and pressure. No mineral will remain solid after the temperature reaches its fusion point under a given pressure. On the other hand, the higher the pressure is, the higher the fusion point is. The temperature range for fusion of basalt under atmospheric pressure is 900° to 1100° Centigrade. This has been directly observed and also checked experimentally by melting rocks and minerals in the laboratory. The confining pressure on rocks within the earth is great, and it increases with depth, so in order to generate a magma in the crust the temperature must either be raised high enough to reach the fusion point of the rock under the great pressure, or the pressure on already very hot rocks must be reduced in some way in order to reach a lower fusion point.

With this understanding of the conditions that must be met we can review some of the processes most likely to produce these conditions:

A. Increase of Heat:
   1. Large quantities of radioactive minerals are known to exist in the earth's crust. If these are more concentrated at depth than they are near the surface, the temperatures generated by their decay and resultant release of energy might be sufficient to melt rocks locally.
   2. The amount of frictional heat produced when two surfaces move over one another depends on the texture of those surfaces and on the force pushing them together. The surfaces in the earth that are known to move are called faults, breaks in the solid crust. At depth these must be forced together by great pressures resulting from the weight of the rocks pressing against and down on them. Thus this seems to be a most likely possibility for the generation of magma. It should not be difficult to test this hypothesis simply by determining if faults and magmas are commonly associated. The answer is yes;

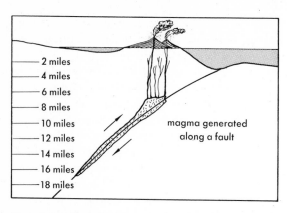

2 miles
4 miles
6 miles
8 miles
10 miles
12 miles
14 miles
16 miles
18 miles

magma generated
along a fault

Fig. 8-2. Hypothetical cross section showing the generation of magma by the frictional heat along a fault. Temperatures increase with depth at a rate of about 1 degree centigrade per 100 feet near the surface. Thus rocks at a depth of several miles are normally hot, but not hot enough to melt.

faults often are intruded by magma. But this is only partially conclusive proof, for it may be argued that the magma was intruded long after the break in the crust occurred and that it simply followed a line of easy access through the crust. More substantial evidence is found in the frequent association of volcanic activity, earthquakes, and belts of mobility in the

Fig. 8-3. Hypothetical cross section showing the generation of magma by the release of confining pressure. Part of the weight of the column of rock over the magma is supported by the sides of the arched structure. Magma will form under these conditions only if the rocks at depth are very hot. The effect of lowering pressure is to reduce the fusion temperature.

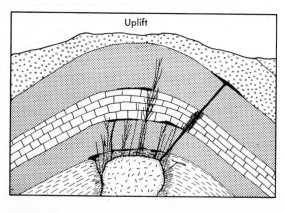

Uplift

crust in which deformation and faulting are concurrently going on. The margins of the Pacific Ocean form such a belt. Here earthquakes and faulting movements in the crust frequently precede the eruption of volcanoes. Nevertheless these three phenomena—faulting, igneous activity, and earthquakes—are closely associated and most certainly are causally connected.

3. The upward movement of hot gases from the supposedly liquid interior of the earth might raise temperatures near the surface to the fusion point. There is no experimental or field evidence to substantiate this problematical view.

4. Exothermic chemical reactions are those interactions of elements and compounds in which heat is evolved. There is a possibility that these may generate magma, although few geologists consider this probable.

B. Decrease of Pressure:

Before a decrease in confining pressure could be effective in melting parts of the earth's interior, temperatures would already have to be very high (i.e., in excess of the temperatures of molten rock at the surface, 900° Centigrade) since the effect of the high pressure is to raise the fusion point. So, decreasing pressure alone would not be sufficient to produce molten rock. It would, however, make possible the melting of rocks that were relatively close to the fusion point. Pressure within the earth may be reduced through arching of the crust. The site of most igneous activity at the present time is in what we have called the belts of mobility of the earth's crust. These are places where extended mountain ranges stand high or are rising under pressures from within the earth. Two effects are produced by this uplift which are favorable to the release of pressures at depth under the mountains. One is that, as the mountains rise higher, the forces of erosion cut into them at accelerated rates, removing great quantities of material from them. Secondly, this uparching may act somewhat like any structural arch in a building where part of the weight of the central portion is supported by the flanks or sides.

CRYSTALLIZATION OF A MAGMA

Note the appearance of the minerals in a typical igneous rock as shown in Fig. 8-4. This photograph is greatly enlarged to show the interrelations of the various minerals making up the rock. Careful examination will lead you to the conclusion that the minerals did not all form at the same time. You will notice for example that:

1. Some of the crystals are much larger than others.
2. Some are euhedral (perfect geometric forms), while others are subhedral or anhedral.
3. Some small minerals are included (completely surrounded) within other minerals.

Try to imagine what conditions within a magma might produce each of the above effects. The larger crystals must have been formed in the early stages of crystallization when there was plenty of room for them to grow and when there was an abundance of the elements needed for their crystal structure. Secondly, the euhedral crystals probably formed before subhedral and anhedral crystals. The first-formed crystals had space to grow into perfect forms, but those crystallizing later had to fit into the spaces left in the crystal mesh before the process of solidification was complete. It should be obvious that any mineral that is included within another one formed before the including mineral. Using these techniques it is possible to make a very good estimation of the order of crystallization in an igneous rock.

A great many laboratory studies have been made of the crystallization of certain igneous rocks and minerals. From these we know at what temperatures most minerals begin to crystallize. It is not a difficult matter to melt a certain quantity of a given mineral and then

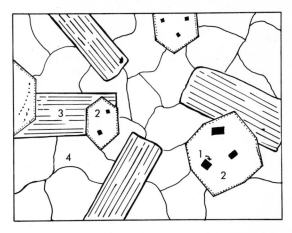

Fig. 8-4. An enlarged section through an igneous rock. This section demonstrates how the sequence of crystallization may be determined. In general larger crystals form before small ones, euhedral crystals form before anhedral or subhedral crystals, and enclosed crystals form before the minerals which enclose them.

cool it slowly and note the crystallization. It is not so simple, however, to approximate the actual condition within magmas, because magmas are not simple melts containing only the necessary elements in the proper amounts to form a certain mineral. Magmas are much more complex. They were generated by the melting of a mass of rock that contained a number of minerals each of which has certain elements within it. Once melted, these elements lose all connection with the original minerals of which they were a part, and they are free to form new compounds with other elements. The new minerals that are going to result from crystallization will depend on such factors as:

1. The composition of the magma.
2. The rate at which the magma is cooled.
3. The impurities present.
4. The presence of any solid nuclei (small fragments of minerals).
5. The events during crystallization of the magma which bring about differentiation of the constituents.

Bowen's reaction series

One of the most important of the laboratory studies made on the complex history of the

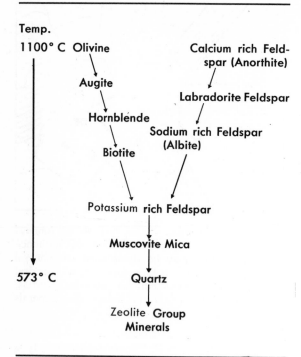

Temp.

1100° C Olivine   Calcium rich Feld-
                          spar (Anorthite)

    Augite

                  Labradorite Feldspar

    Hornblende

          Sodium rich Feldspar
          (Albite)

    Biotite

    Potassium rich Feldspar

    Muscovite Mica

573° C   Quartz

    Zeolite Group
    Minerals

Fig. 8-5. Bowen's Reaction Series.

crystallization of a magma is that of Dr. N. L. Bowen. He studied the crystallization of and the reactions which take place in a basaltic

Fig. 8-6. Change of state. A solid, such as crystal form **A**, may change to a different form of the same material, crystal form **B**, by an increase of temperature. The solid will melt if the temperature continues to rise, and eventually the liquid will boil to form a gas on further heating. Likewise a solid may go into the gaseous state by variation of the temperature or pressure conditions. A generalized scheme for these changes is shown.

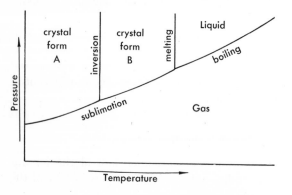

magma as it cooled. Fig. 8-5 is a diagrammatic representation of the reactions he observed. At a temperature of about 1100° Centigrade the first signs of crystallization started to take place. The minerals that began to appear were: olivine, the pyroxene augite, and calcium-rich plagioclase feldspar. As soon as the first solids form in a magma the original composition of the melt is changed. Bowen found that each of these early formed crystals tended to react with the elements of the melt and to be altered to other minerals. As the temperatures decrease the solid olivine reacts with the melt to form hornblende. By the time the magma reaches a temperature of 700° Centigrade, therefore, an initially large olivine crystal may have only a nucleus of olivine left which is surrounded by a shell of hornblende. At still lower temperatures the hornblende reacts with the magma to form biotite mica. Likewise the calcium-rich plagioclase feldspar reacts with the melt to form increasingly richer sodium plagioclase feldspar. By the time the magma has been reduced in temperature to 573° the mineral quartz is formed, and as the temperatures start into the lower ranges toward 200° such minerals are sericite, chlorite, epidote, and zeolites may be formed through reactions between the nearly solid igneous rock and the solutions or residues of the melt.

The physical chemistry of natural rock melts poses an interesting and challenging problem. The principles of the crystallization of systems containing the elements of one-, two-, and even three-component minerals are fairly well understood, but imagine the complexity of trying to unravel these processes when the number of variables begins to reach 10 or 12. The nature of the relations may be illustrated by an example using a two-component system composed of a rock containing 25 per cent anorthite minerals and 75 per cent diopside minerals. The temperature of the magma is raised well above the melting point of either anorthite or diopside, and then allowed to cool slowly. As the temperature drops it will eventually reach a point at which the first solid appears. This temperature is a unique one for a magma of the particular composition 25 per cent anorthite and 75 per cent diopside. The solid formed is a crystal of diopside. As this solid grows, what happens to the net composition of the melt? It is shifted toward more anorthite, less diopside. The temperature necessary to crystallize this composition is slightly lower, so more solid forms, again diopside, and again the composition of the remaining melt shifts, and likewise the temperature of crystallization is lowered. This process continues until a certain temperature is reached, called the eutectic. At this point both diopside and anorthite may both crystallize so from this point on the relative amounts of the two minerals in the melt do not change as crystallization continues until the whole melt is a solid. The resulting rock is one composed of large euhedral crystals of diopside, which formed early and which are embedded in a groundmass of small crystals of diopside and anorthite, the last things to crystallize.

Rate of crystallization; texture

The rate at which a magma cools has much to do with the resulting rock and particularly with the texture of the rock. Texture as used here refers to the size, shape, and arrangement of the minerals in the rock. Extremes in cooling rates are seen if we stop to compare for a moment the crystallization of a magma that is extruded from a volcano and flows rapidly down the flanks of the cone and into the sea (as it does in the islands of the Pacific) with crystallization of a magma that is intruded 10 miles beneath the surface and cools perhaps over a period of tens of thousands or even millions of years.

Crystal nuclei. It has been found that very pure melts, devoid of any solids, may be cooled below the temperature at which they should crystallize if the cooling proceeds without agitation or any other disturbance. If, while this super-cooling is taking place, the melt is agitated or particularly if small mineral grains of solid impurities are introduced, crystallization will start immediately. The mineral fragments usually act as seeds on which the minerals will begin to grow. The most favorable nuclei are fragments of the minerals that would ordinarily be crystallizing out of the melt at its temperature. Nevertheless, it is obvious that the presence of these fragments aids the formation of crystals and, therefore, plays a part in the rate of crystallization. Nuclei will form spontaneously even from a pure melt, but the rate or the ability of certain minerals to form the initial grain or crystal seed differs. The rate of cooling plays an important role in that this determines how long a time there is for a given crystal to grow. A crystal grows by having the necessary ions or elements come to its margin and become attached by one of the types of bonding we have already discussed (ionic, covalent, metallic). After a crystal begins to grow it almost immediately pulls to it from the immediate vicinity those ions or elements of the type required for its structure. This leaves atoms and ions around it that cannot fit into its crystal structure. Thus time is required for other necessary ions and atoms to be brought to the crystal. This is accomplished by convection within the melt or by having the crystal move through the melt.

Keeping these two variables (rate of cooling and rate of production of crystal nuclei) in mind, consider what happens in a magma that is cooling very slowly and that contains only a small number of available nuclei. The rock that is to result eventually from crystallization of this magma will be one composed of few, but very large crystals. As the rate of cooling and rate of nuclei production increase we expect many medium-sized crystals and a maximum of small crystals. As the rate becomes very high and the number of nuclei begins to decrease, the rock will become one with few crystals large enough to see. Finally, as the rate of cooling becomes extremely fast the rock is in effect frozen. It cools so fast that only a very few or no crystals at all have time to form. Such a rock is a glass. It contains no ordered crystalline structure. Indeed, it is an amorphous mass.

Porphyry. One of the most striking types of igneous textures is that represented in a rock known as a porphyry. An igneous rock is called a porphyry when it is made up of large crystals (at least large enough to be seen by the naked eye, which are euhedral or nearly

Fig. 8-7. Textural variations in igneous rocks. Left, from top to bottom: Porphyry composed of fine groundmass and large crystals; a coarse-grained granite; a fine-grained felsite; a porous, vesicular rock called scoria. Right, top: graphic granite; bottom, obsidian, natural glass. (Photos by courtesy of the U.S. National Museum.)

perfectly formed, embedded in a groundmass of very small crystals or glass. (When crystals are too small to be identified by the naked eye they are called aphanitic.) The large crystals in the porphyry are called phenocrysts. The origin of this texture is easily understood in the light of the principles just outlined. The large crystals form while the magma is cooling slowly at depth in the earth. Then the cooling rate is changed as the magma is forced upward toward the surface or to the surface where the cooling rate is much faster, and the remainder of the magma cools rapidly, giving rise to small crystals or, if cooling is very fast, to glass.

Magmatic differentiation

There are many types of igneous rocks. If you can identify the minerals that make them up and know the chemical elements in those minerals you will recognize that the rocks differ in composition as well as in texture. Such differences are frequently noted within a single mass of igneous rock all of which obviously crystallized from a single magma. Some of the differences are of a gradational nature, with the composition of one rock being only slightly different from that of nearby ones. Others may be greatly different in composition. How do these variations come about? Although we are unable to observe the processes within a real magma it is possible to postulate some of the processes that almost certainly must play a part in bringing about this differentiation within the magma. Of the more important ones we will consider:

1. Crystallization differentiation.
2. Gravity separation.
3. Filter pressing.
4. Mixing of magmas.
5. Liquid immiscibility.
6. Assimilation.

Crystallization differentiation. This process, also known as fractional crystallization, is very broad in scope. It includes all factors that might tend to bring about a separation of the magma into two phases (a solid and a liquid), re-

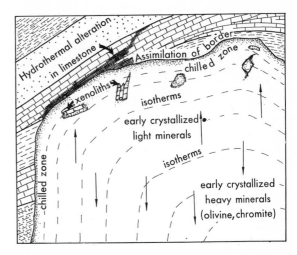

Fig. 8-8. Magmatic differentiation. Many different types of igneous rocks may originate from a single magma. The differences arise from rates of cooling, settling of early crystallized heavy minerals, contamination of the margins of the magma by the assimilation or melting of country rock, and other processes.

Fig. 8-9. The Palisades sill of New Jersey. This is a section through the sill. The Triassic sandstones and shales into which the basalt sill was intruded are shown at the top and bottom. Near the bottom of the sill the early formed olivine minerals are found. Being heavier than the melt they sank to the bottom; thus the sill became differentiated.

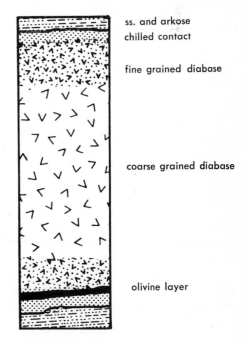

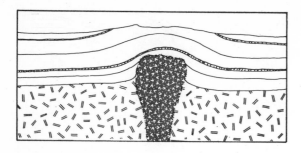

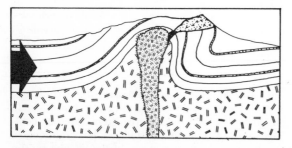

Fig. 8-10. Differentiation of a magma through filter pressing. At the top a magma which has been intruded into a sedimentary sequence is shown partially crystallized. As the region becomes compressed the liquid part of the magma is squeezed to the top as the crystal mesh is compacted. At the bottom the liquid has been pressed off into fractures and faults above the original magma.

sulting, after crystallization is complete, in two or more different types of rocks. This may be accomplished by complete or partial isolation of the liquid from the solid, or the migration of certain constituents of the magma into zones where they become concentrated. An example of this will serve to illustrate. Near the margins of a magma, cooling is much faster than it is within the magma chamber. As the margins cool, there forms a sort of insulating mat for the rest of the magma. Because cooling is proceeding more rapidly in one part of the chamber, ions may migrate toward that part either by diffusion or by convection within the melt. As certain of these ions are incorporated in the crystals forming at the margins, the net composition of the magma is changed, and differentiation has been effected.

Gravity separation. If the first crystals to form in a magma as it begins to crystallize are heavier or lighter (higher or lower density) then the melt, they will tend to sink or rise

through the melt and become segregated either at the bottom or as a raft of floating minerals near the top of the magma chamber. This may give the resulting igneous rocks a banded appearance near the top or bottom of the intrusion. Olivine, the first mineral to crystallize from a basaltic magma, is heavy and is frequently found concentrated near the bottom of basaltic intrusions such as the Palisades sill along the west shore of the Hudson River in New Jersey. This process may also account for some ore bodies. Chromite is another early forming high-density mineral, and it is known to occur near the bottom of a number of large intrusions as layers, for example, in the Stillwater complex of Montana and the Bushveld complex of South Africa.

Filter pressing. One process that may aid or follow initial fractional crystallization is filter pressing. As crystallization proceeds, a point is eventually reached at which the once-molten mass has become a sort of mesh of crystals loosely interlocked and connected. Surrounding these crystals and in the pore spaces left we find the residual liquids. If the chamber should become subjected to strong earth pressures, such as those that might have played a part in the generation of the magma, then the chamber could become deformed. If there is any way for the residual liquids to escape, they are likely to be squeezed off from the solid crystal mesh, and become isolated from the already solid part of the mesh. When this last remaining liquid solidifies it will be quite different from the earlier formed rocks in composition and possibly in texture also.

Mixing of magmas. It is possible that some of the diverse igneous rocks do not represent the systematic crystallization of a single magma. At some stage in cooling, a magma may be intruded by another magma of a different composition. Thus all the rocks formed after this time would have a strikingly different composition from those formed earlier.

Liquid immiscibility. One liquid is said to be immiscible in another if it will not mix with it or will do so only to a very limited degree. Such a mix is water and oil. Oil will not mix with water, and the two become separated by the difference in their specific gravity. The same may occur in a magma, with parts being immiscible during the initial stages of cooling or at some later stage when the composition has been changed by the removal of certain constituents to form crystals.

Assimilation (modification of a magma by the digestion of its margins). Magmas are all very hot, but some are much hotter than others, and the difference may reach several hundred degrees Centigrade. If two magmas, one 800° Centigrade and one 1200° Centigrade, were intruded into the same type of country rock (the name country rock may be applied to the intruded rock regardless of its exact composition), the effects at the margins might be very different. Any minerals in this particular country rock that melt at relatively low temperatures (quartz melts at 573° Centigrade) will melt around the margins of the magmas. But what will happen to the minerals that begin to melt at 800° Centigrade? One magma would cause the melting of these, the other would not. The very hot magma might cause pure melting of a thick zone surrounding the magma chamber. This new melt would mix with the magma and alter its composition, particularly around the margins. Even partial melting will cause a change in the composition of the magma.

Remember our discussion of Bowen's reaction series; in it the melt reacted with the minerals that formed earlier at a higher temperature. Now, if some of these same minerals are present in the country rock, they too will react with the melt just as in Bowen's reaction series. These reactions are exothermic—that is, they proceed with the production of heat and not the absorption of it. They too will alter the composition of the margins of the magma and lead to differences in composition of the igneous rocks eventually formed.

After considering the great variety of processes tending to bring about compositional and textural variation in magmas and therefore in the igneous rocks forming from them we must agree that it would be much more surprising to find a large intrusive cooled from a single magma that was all the same igneous rock than it is to find a great variety of rocks formed from the same magma.

Classification of igneous rocks. Two major features of igneous rocks have been stressed, their textural and compositional variations. Our classification of the igneous rocks is based on these two variables. Classifications are set up in an attempt to simplify the orderly arrangement of things, whether they be minerals, rocks,

Fig. 8-11. Classification of igneous rocks.

		Oversaturated			Saturated			Undersaturated	
		Quartz	Quartz and Feldspar		Feldspars			Mafic Minerals Predominate	
			Orthoclase	Plagioclase	Orthoclase	Na rich Plagioclase	Ca rich Plagioclase		
Deep intrusions	coarse grained phaneritic	Vein Quartz	Granite		Syenite	Diorite	Gabbro	Peridotite	
		←————————— Porphyry (mixed textures) —————————→							
Extrusions and shallow intrusions	fine grained aphanitic		Rhyolite	Dacite		Andesite	Basalt	Olivine Basalt	
	glass		Pumice			Scoria			
		←——— Pitchstone ———→							
		←——— Obsidian ———→							

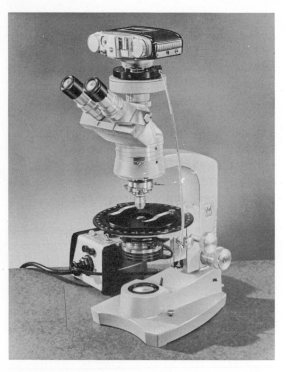

Fig. 8-12. A petrographic microscope. This instrument is used to study thin sections of rock. The rock is first ground to a thickness of .03 mm. At this thickness light is transmitted through all non-metallic minerals. By noting the way the light behaves on passing through the minerals of the thin section, the minerals can be identified. (Photo by courtesy of the American Optical Company.)

Fig. 8-13. A thin section of the igneous rock, diabase, as seen through a petrographic microscope. (Photo by courtesy of Bausch & Lomb Co.)

fossils, or something completely unrelated to science. If you understand the basis for a classification it will greatly simplify learning the relations between the things classified. Given any particular composition, it is possible to have a number of very different-looking rocks produced from it. For example, a certain magma may cool slowly at depth, yielding a coarsely crystalline rock with large crystals of feldspar, quartz, mica, and pyroxene. This rock is called granite. The same magma might cool rapidly near the surface to form a very dense, finely crystalline, light-colored rock, which we would call a felsite. If the same magma came to the surface, poured out, and cooled very rapidly it might become a black glass called obsidian. The coarse crystals alone do not make a rock granite, for gabbro and peridotite are also coarsely crystalline, but they are of a very different composition. Having decided on a basis for the classification we are confronted with certain problems of making consistent estimates of composition and texture. In regard to the textures we recognize four types:

1. Aphanitic: crystals too small to be seen by the unaided eye.
2. Phaneritic: crystals large enough to be seen with the unaided eye. These are subdivided into coarse, medium, and fine-grained textures.
3. Porphyritic: large euhedral crystals in a fine-grained groundmass.
4. Glassy: texture of glass.

Estimates of the composition are not so easy. In the first place we recognize that the word composition may be interpreted in several ways. First it might mean the bulk chemical composition of the rock, the amount of each element present. Secondly, we might mean the amounts of each mineral present in the rock. Unfortunately it is not possible to distinguish all minerals visually. This can ordinarily be done with a microscope especially designed for this purpose, called a petrographic microscope. The rock to be studied is cut, using a diamond saw, and then a small section of it is ground and polished until it is about .03 mm thick. At this thickness light can pass through the non-metallic minerals in the thin section, and this light can be studied. The way it behaves is a guide to the identification of the mineral. Work of this nature is done in optical mineralogy and petrography. Although these first two methods of classification are very important, neither is simple enough for the use of the geologists who are working in the field and who must pick up rocks and tentatively identify them until it is possible to make more careful laboratory studies. This field system is one that can be readily used by elementary students. It consists of identifying the igneous rocks by the principal mineral constituents and the relative amounts of each. Study the chart of Fig. 8-11, showing the classification. You will note that the presence, amount, and type of feldspar is a major diagnostic factor. This reflects the abundance of feldspar in igneous rocks. It is the most common igneous rock-forming mineral, next in importance is quartz, then the dark minerals pyroxene and amphibole.

STRUCTURE OF INTRUSIVE IGNEOUS BODIES

A. DISCORDANT TYPES (those whose margins are not coincident with structures that existed prior to the intrusion):
   1. Batholiths. These are the largest intrusive bodies. In surface area they range in size anywhere from 40 square miles to many thousands of square miles. There is little information regarding their structure at depth, but they appear to extend at least a few miles down, and some may go down to great depths (10 or more miles). Most batholiths are found in belts of deformation within the earth's crust. Most are granitic in composition, composed primarily of coarsely crystalline rocks. Within the United States some of the largest are the Boulder batholith of Montana, the Sierra Nevada batholith in California, and the Idaho batholith.
   2. Stocks. A stock is simply a small batholith. It is an intrusion that has less than 40 square miles of surface area.
   3. Dikes. These are plate-like masses of

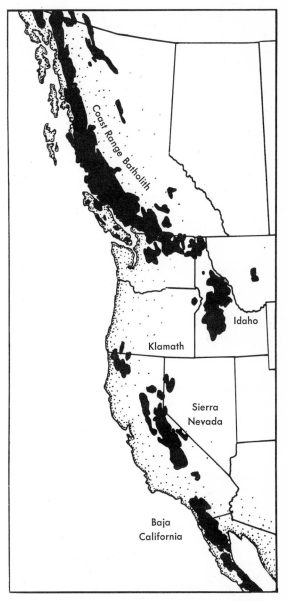

Fig. 8-14. A map of large batholiths located in the western part of North America. Most of these are of Jurassic age. Ancient batholiths are exposed in the Rocky Mountains and in the Canadian Shield of central Canada.

igneous rock that cut across the structure of the rocks they intrude. Some dikes extend for many miles; a few exceptional ones may be traced as much as several hundred miles. Their thickness is also highly variable, ranging from only a few inches up to thousands of feet.

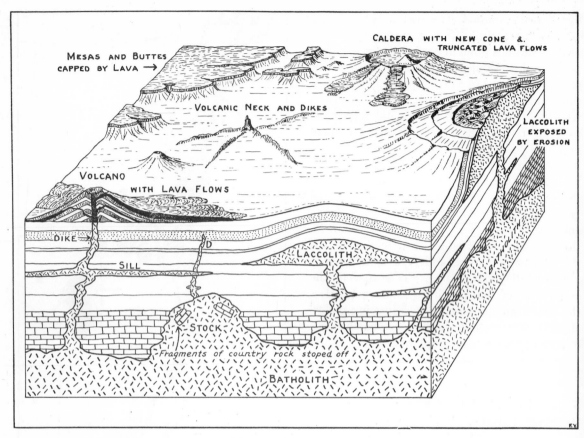

Fig. 8-15. Occurrence of igneous rocks. (After Frederick Young, Hunter College in New York City.)

Fig. 8-16. An early Precambrian batholith in the Canadian Shield. (From a map by K. R. Dawson.)

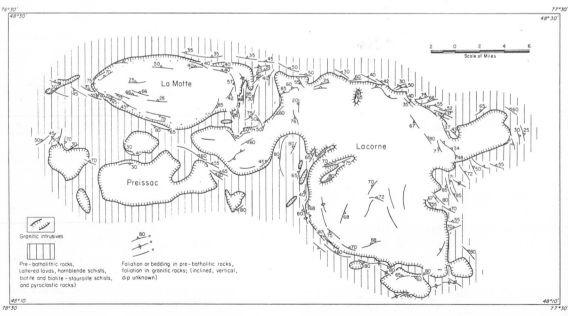

Fig. 8-17. Intrusions exposed in Canada. The light-colored rock is an intrusive. The large oval-shaped body is a stock. The region is cut by several dark-colored dikes and the light-colored rock has been intruded along fractures and as sills. (Photo by courtesy of Royal Canadian Air Force.)

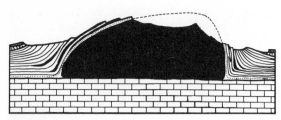

Fig. 8-18. A cross section through Mount Hillers in the Henry Mountains of Utah. (After G. K. Gilbert.)

B. CONCORDANT TYPES (those in which the intrusive's boundaries are controlled by and parallel to pre-existing structures):

1. Sills. A sill is a plate-like mass of igneous rock similar to a dike, but instead of cutting across rock-unit boundaries the sill conforms to them. A sill's thickness is relatively thin compared with its extent. Sills may be flat, arched, even folded in structure.

2. Laccoliths. Like a sill, laccoliths conform to earlier structure, but are not of uniform thickness. A laccolith is thickened near the center, and this thickening usually causes the sedimentary rock units into which it has been intruded to be folded or arched up over it.

3. Lopoliths. A body similar to a laccolith except that the thickening has taken place downward instead of upward. This is made possible by the collapse of some

Fig. 8-19. Columnar structure in lava flows exposed in a cliff near Tower Falls in Yellowstone Park. (Photo by E. W. Spencer.)

columnar joints in lava flow

gravels

old flow

of the strata below the lopolith into the magma chamber, filling the space left when the magma moved out.

IDENTIFICATION OF IGNEOUS ROCKS

A. PHANERITIC INTRUSIVE ROCKS

Granite. A coarse- to medium-grained equigranular rock composed of potassium feldspars (orthoclase and microcline), quartz, and with some biotite mica and hornblende, usually present in small amounts. Many other minerals may be present but in small amounts. These include: black specks of magnetite, honey-yellow crystals of sphene, red grains of garnet, as well as others that are less common.

Graphic granite. Rocks of granitic composition that have a particular texture consisting of an intergrowth of feldspar and quartz in such a way that the quartz has a geometrically regular pattern.

Granite pegmatite. A very coarse-grained granite. In some the crystals attain dimensions measured in feet rather than inches. A granite pegmatite is of the same composition as granite. It contains microcline feldspar, quartz, and mica (biotite or muscovite). In many instances a great variety of very rare minerals may be present.

Orbicular granite. A rare granitic rock containing large oval-shaped orbicules or nodules. The origin of this textural variety of granite is still undecided.

Syenite. A coarse- to medium-grained equigranular rock composed primarily of orthoclase feldspar. It contains no quartz. There is usually some hornblende, biotite, and pyroxene present.

Diorite. A coarse- to medium-grained rock composed of plagioclase feldspar and biotite, hornblende, or pyroxene. Small quantities of quartz may be present. The amount of dark minerals ranges from an eighth to three-eighths of the total.

Gabbro. A rock composed of coarse- to medium-grained crystals mainly of pyroxene, hornblende, and biotite. The amount of these exceeds the amount of feldspar, all of which is plagioclase. The mineral olivine is usually present, and quartz is absent. Most gabbros are dark because the dark minerals predominate. They are equigranular. It is not uncommon to find gabbro pegmatites. Like the granite pegmatites, these are simply extremely coarse-grained equivalents of the gabbro.

Peridotite. A dark, coarse-grained, equigranular rock containing a large quantity of olivine and either pyroxene or hornblende, but no quartz and no feldspar.

Dunite. A rock composed completely of the mineral olivine.

Fig. 8-20. A cross section of one of the lava flows which make up the Watchung Mountains of New Jersey. At the base is Triassic sandstone. The lava flow may be divided into several structural layers. The bottom is composed of hexagonal columnar structures. Above these the columns become somewhat less well defined. Near the top is a massive layer of basalt and pillow lava which is usually formed where lava is extruded under water.

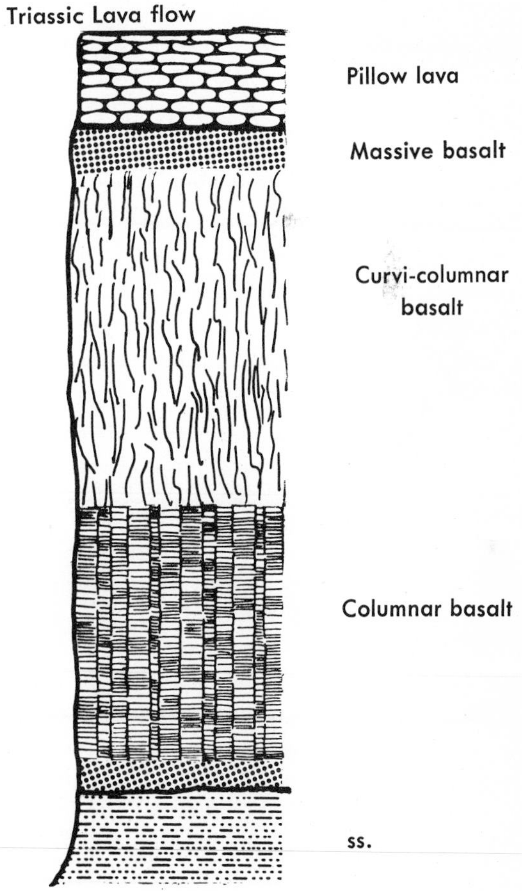

Triassic Lava flow

Pillow lava

Massive basalt

Curvi-columnar basalt

Columnar basalt

ss.

Fig. 8-21. The Giant's Causeway, Northern Ireland. This structure is composed of basalt which is fractured to form columnar structures. Similar structures make up the columns at Devil's Tower. (Photo by courtesy of the British Information Service.)

Pyroxenite. A dark coarsely crystalline rock composed mostly of pyroxenes.

Hornblendite. An igneous rock of coarse texture and nearly equigranular fabric composed mostly of hornblende.

B. APHANITIC INTRUSIVE ROCKS

Felsite. A general term applied to igneous rocks of very fine-grained texture and light color indicating a granitic composition. If large crystals are present in a stony felsitic groundmass it is called a felsite porphyry. The colors of the felsites may range from white, gray, pink, yellow, brown, to purple and light green.

Basalt. The dark-colored equivalent of the felsite. Basalts are dark because they contain large percentages of hornblende, pyroxene, biotite, oblivine, or other dark minerals. The texture is of a very fine grain. Basalt is often an extrusive igneous rock and is frequently filled with

cavities left by escaping bubbles of gas.

Dolerite (diabase). Rocks that are intermediate in texture between basalts and gabbros.

C. GLASSES

Obsidian. A glassy equivalent of granite or felsite, a solid, natural glass containing no crystals. Its appearance is in every way that of artificial glass. Most obsidian is black, but it can also be green and brown. It breaks with an unusual fracture, conchoidal, which is shaped like a shell. The natural glasses frequently contain round or spherical bodies of white, gray, or red color. They have a radiating fibrous structure inside composed of feldspar and silica. These bodies are called spherulites and form from the rapid crystallization of the glass. Another feature found in the natural glasses is the collapsed remains of glass bubbles (lithophysae). They formed as gases escaped from the glass. The bubbles broke, and the hot glass flowed back down but did not completely melt again.

Pitchstone. A variety of obsidian with a luster like that of a resin instead of glass. Pitchstone differs in composition from obsidian in that it contains 5 or more per cent water. Obsidian contains less than 1 per cent. Colors include black, gray, red, brown, and green.

Pumice. An extremely vesicular glass; it is a glassy froth. Colors include white, gray, yellowish, and brownish. Some varieties are almost fibrous in texture and luster. The cavities are very small and delicate. The light color is an indication of the siliceous composition.

Scoria. A dark-colored vesicular glass. The texture of the scoria is much coarser than that of pumice. The cavities were formed by escaping gases. The dark color indicates that

the composition of these glasses is much closer to that of the gabbros and diorites.

Fragmental volcanic rocks

The basis for the classification of the volcanic fragmental rocks is primarily one of size. All of them are materials ejected from volcanoes in a very hot solid state or as liquids which cooled before hitting. All of this material is known as pyroclastic debris.

Bombs: pieces larger than 32 mm in diameter, about the size of a baseball. Usually the bombs are twisted, showing that they were very hot and partially fluid when ejected.
Blocks: large solid pieces of igneous rock blown out of the volcanoes.
Lapilli: pyroclastic pieces in the size range

Fig. 8-22. Shiprock, New Mexico. This volcanic plug of lava once occupied the pipe of a large volcano which has been eroded away leaving only the erosion-resistant plug and dikes which radiate out from the pipe. (Photo by courtesy of the New Mexico State Tourist Bureau.)

of 32 mm to 4 mm. These also show
the twisted ends characteristic of the
bombs.

Ash: the particles in the size range of 4
mm to about 1/16 mm in diameter.

Volcanic dust: the particles smaller than
1/16 mm in diameter.

Tuff. A volcanic rock composed of the accumulation of large quantities of volcanic dust
and ash. It may also contain lapilli.

Agglomerate. The layers of volcanic pyroclastic debris that are composed of a great assortment of the sizes listed above.

Volcanic breccia. A rock composed of
angular fragments of bombs, blocks, and lapilli,
cemented in a matric or groundmass of ash,
dust, and lapilli. The volcanic breccia may also
contain fragments of rocks other than the volcanic and igneous rocks. It may contain anything through which the escaping lava and
gases moved and had an opportunity to dislodge on its way to the surface.

REFERENCES

BOWEN, N. L., 1928, *The Evolution of the Igneous Rocks:* Princeton, Princeton University Press, 334 p.

DALY, R. A., 1933, *Igneous Rocks and the Depths of the Earth,* 2nd ed.: New York, McGraw-Hill Book Co., 508 p.

GROUT, F. F., 1932, *Petrography and Petrology:* New York, McGraw-Hill Book Co., 522 p.

KNOPF, ADOLPH, 1955, Batholiths in Time, p. 685-702 in Poldervaart, Arie, Editor, Crust of the Earth: Geol. Soc. America, Spec. Paper 62, 762 p.

TURNER, F. J., and VERHOOGEN, J., 1960, *Igneous and Metamorphic Petrology,* 2nd ed.: New York, McGraw-Hill Book Co., 694 p.

TYRRELL, G. W., 1926, *The Principles of Petrology:* London, Methuen & Co., Ltd., 349 p.

WAHLSTROM, E. E., 1947, *Igneous Minerals and Rocks:* New York, John Wiley & Sons, 367 p.

WILLIAMS, H., TURNER, F. J., and GILBERT, C. M., 1954, *Petrography:* San Francisco, W. H. Freeman Company, 406 p.

9 Sedimentary Rocks

You are probably more accustomed to seeing and handling sedimentary rocks than any other kind. They cover about three-quarters of the land surface of the earth and are spread almost continuously across the ocean floors. What are sedimentary rocks? Specifically the term sediment applies to anything that settles out of suspension in water, but it applies more generally to particles that settle out of water, wind, or ice as well. When these sediments become consolidated to form a hard solid rock

they are termed sedimentary rocks. Such a definition places no restrictions on the source, texture, or composition of the sediment.

The sands and gravels found on the bottoms of streams settled out of the water; the sands, silts, or cobbles that make up the beaches you have seen were laid there from water; muds on lake bottoms; decaying plants and mud in swamps; salts covering the ground in deserts; the sands, dust, and ashes transported by the wind; and the less common

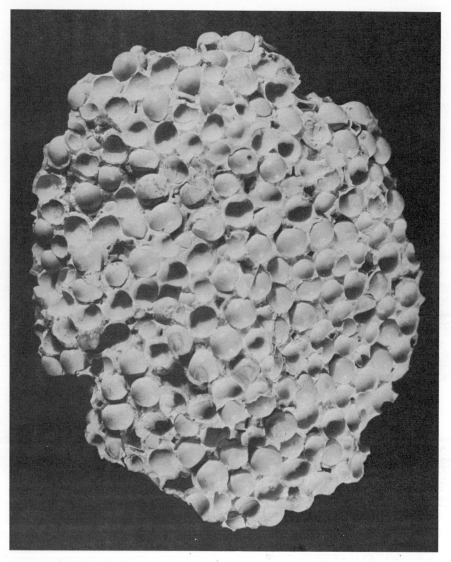

Fig. 9-1. Oölitic limestone from Carlsbad, Bohemia. (Photo by courtesy of the U.S. National Museum.)

debris that melts out of the margins of glaciers are all sediments. If conditions prove to be favorable for their preservation they may become sedimentary rocks. But actually most of the sediments you see on land are not very likely to be preserved for any extended periods of time. The forces of erosion are continuing to act upon them, and they are likely to be transported again toward the sea where the chances of burial and preservation are much greater.

SOURCE OF SEDIMENTS

The particles of soil, rocks, and minerals that make up sediments are mostly derived from the breakdown or decay of rocks of the earth's crust. Some sediments are composed in part of meteoritic particles from outside the earth, other sediments are derived through volcanic action from sources deep in the earth, but the great majority of the sediments and sedimentary rocks that form the shallow veneer over the face of the earth simply represent a reworking of the materials in the earth's crust by the hydrosphere (waters), atmosphere, and biosphere with which they are in contact.

Products of decay

What sort of particles are those produced by the decay and disintegration of the crust, and therefore freed to become available to form the sediments? Principal among these are: clastic particles, ions, colloids, and organic matter.

Clastic particles. The term clastic means "broken off." Clastic particles are the fragmental materials such as sand and gravel. These represent the mechanical disintegration of pre-existing rocks. It should be emphasized that a clastic sediment may consist of fragments of a sedimentary rock which originally formed from ions, colloids, or any other type of rock. Fragmental sediments have not been completely broken down either mechanically or chemically in the process of their decay.

Ions. These charged particles are formed through solution of minerals in water. When many minerals dissolve they break down into their component ions. The process of solution may have been aided by the presence of acids or alkalies in the water. Solution is accelerated by mechanical breakdown of the material that is being dissolved. Since solution takes place at the surface of a solid, the greater the exposed surface area the more rapidly solution can take place. Given a certain volume of a mineral in a single piece, it is possible to increase the surface area of that piece by breaking it into smaller and smaller pieces. Once a solid has gone into solution, either it is available for the formation of a sediment by direct chemical precipitation or it may be removed from the solution by animals or plants that use it to build their skeletons or shells. These in turn may become sediment after they die.

Colloids. This term refers to a particular size of matter—anything in the range of 10^{-5} to 10^{-7} cm in diameter. Colloidal particles make up mud or clay. These particles are so small that we cannot distinguish them individually even with a high-power microscope.

Fig. 9-2. Models of four Protozoans, single-celled animals. The shells of these animals are found covering large parts of the sea floor. They are composed of calcium carbonate which the animals took from sea water to build their shells. The shells shown here are greatly magnified. In actuality they are about the size of pin heads. (Photo by courtesy of the Chicago Natural History Museum.)

Fig. 9-3. A single grain of sand greatly magnified and seen in polarized light. (Photo by courtesy of Bausch & Lomb Co.)

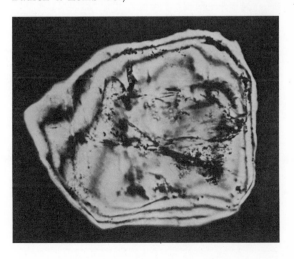

If we stir this mud or clay in water until the clay particles move through the solution in suspension then we will begin to see a separation of the larger aggregates and particles from the colloids. The heavier and larger aggregates will settle out, but the colloids of clay will remain in suspension and move more or less at random through the solution. The dimensions of colloids approach atomic sizes, but they are about 10 times or more the size of an atom. Colloids have several unusual characteristics.

They will not diffuse through a membrane, and they do not affect the freezing point, boiling point, or osmotic pressure of the solution in which they are dispersed. And we find that they are charged electrically either positively or negatively. Matter may be brought into the colloidal state either by comminution from a larger size or by precipitation or condensation from smaller sizes. Many sediments are formed from the deposition of colloids.

Organic matter. This term is used in a

Fig. 9-4. Diatoms. These are the siliceous remains of marine plants which are tremendously abundant in the oceans. Their remains are an important constituent of marine deep water sediments. (Photo by courtesy of the U.S. National Museum.)

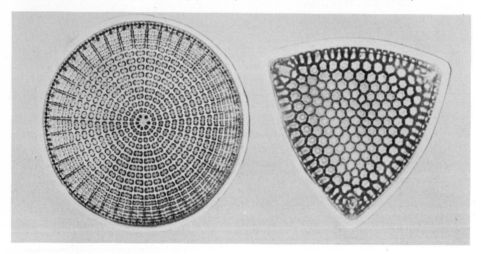

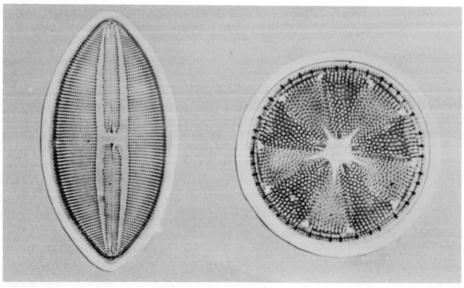

Fig. 9-5. Enlarged view of grains of sand. Note the variations in size, rounding, and composition. (Photo by courtesy of Bausch & Lomb Co.)

Fig. 9-6. Conglomerate. This is the name applied to a consolidated gravel. The pebbles of which this hard rock is composed are clearly visible. (Photo by courtesy of the U.S. National Museum.)

Fig. 9-7. Conglomerate of shells. This is an organic deposit composed of the calcite shells of various marine invertebrate animals. The mixture is called coquina. (Photo by courtesy of the U.S. National Museum.)

very general sense to include the remains of plants, which may be converted into coal, the excrement and any waste products of the life processes of organisms, and the solid parts of the animal itself, which may become part of the sediment. Some sediments are made almost wholly of such remains of plants and animals. Others can be identified as the excrement of organisms, and there is considerable evidence to suggest that organisms play a role in the precipitation of certain constituents from solution, but the exact way in which this is accomplished is still unknown.

STRATIFICATION

One of the most characteristic features of sedimentary rocks is the layering or stratification that usually results from the various processes of sedimentation. Consider for the moment a lake in which sediment is accumulating. If this lake is fed by streams, then coarse sediments may enter the lake at these inlets. This sediment will fan out into the lake. The finest particles may be evenly distributed throughout the lake, but heavier particles are dropped near the inlets. The fine sediments would tend to form a thin layer over most of the lake bottom, but they would be mixed with coarse sediment near the mouths of the streams. Any change in the type of material being brought into the lake by the streams would tend to give rise to variations in the layers deposited, and this would in turn cause layering or stratification to become apparent.

Fig. 9-8. Dog Canyon, near Alamogordo, New Mexico. Stratification or bedding is one of the most common features of sedimentary rocks. The layering is caused by variations in color, composition, texture, porosity, and other physical properties of the layers in the sequence. (Photo by courtesy of the New Mexico State Tourist Bureau.)

Stratification may be the result of variations in any of the characteristics in the following list:

1. Composition of different layers.
2. Color of layers.
3. Texture of the layers.
4. Porosity.
5. Structure of the layers.

The layers are referred to as strata or beds if they are thick. They are called laminae if they are very thin. The plane separating different layers is called a bedding plane.

Not all sedimentary rock units are comparable to the lake deposits described above; however, the continental shelves and the ocean basins are the places where most sediments are deposited, and in these places plate-like sedimentary units are deposited which cover many thousands of square miles. Some of these are very constant in thickness and composition. Others vary greatly both in composition and thickness, but stratification is almost invariably present.

Fig. 9-9. A massive layer of sandstone exposed in a cliff in New Mexico. Such strata are commonly found to extend for many tens or even hundreds of miles. They reflect very continuous conditions of sedimentation at the time they were formed. (Photo by courtesy of the New Mexico State Tourist Bureau.)

Fig. 9-10. Sand deposits in the channel of Canadian River, near Muskogee, Oklahoma. The texture, composition, and structure of sediments are indicators of the environments in which they formed. (Photo by courtesy of the U.S. Department of Agriculture.)

ENVIRONMENTS OF DEPOSITION

Although most sediments are ultimately laid down in the ocean basins or around the margins of the oceans, there are many other places where sediments accumulate, and even within the oceans there are many variations in the environment. These environmental factors usually affect the texture, composition, or structure of the sediments that form. Thus it is possible to demonstrate that some of the hard consolidated sedimentary rocks now exposed on the flanks of mountain ranges thousands of miles from the ocean originated in the ocean. It is sometimes even possible to tell how deep the water was, and approximately the temperature of the water. This subject will be discussed in detail in your study of Historical Geology.

There are three major groups of sedimentary environments. These are marine, transitional, and continental environments. Some of the important subdivisions of each are:

MARINE ENVIRONMENT.
　　Shallow water (neritic).
　　Intermediate-depth water (bathyal).
　　Deep water (abyssal).

Fig. 9-11. Sediments composed of boulders and cobbles of volcanic rocks in a stream on the flanks of Mt. Hood. Sediments such as these are not ordinarily preserved for very long periods of time, but are washed downhill. Most sedimentary rocks are ultimately deposited in the oceans. (Photo by E. W. Spencer.)

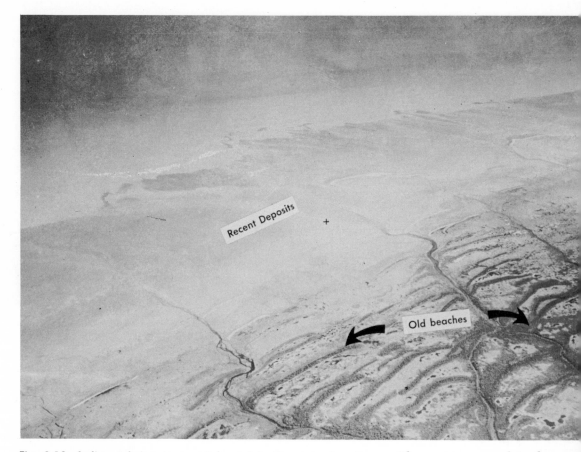

Fig. 9-12. Sediment being transported out into the ocean by streams. The oceans accumulate the grea quantity of sediments washed into them each year from the erosion of the continents. Even within th ocean different types of marine environments are reflected in the nature of the sediments formed These are used by geologists to reconstruct ancient geography. (Photo by courtesy of the Royal Canadia Air Force.)

TRANSITIONAL ENVIRONMENTS.
Deltas.
Lagoons.
Beaches.

CONTINENTAL ENVIRONMENTS.
Deserts.
Glacial environments.
Streams.
Lakes.
Swamps.
Caves.

The characteristics of the deposits formed in each of these environments will be discussed as we consider the natural processes acting in each.

CLASSIFICATION OF SEDIMENTARY ROCKS

Because of the diversity of origins, tex tures, compositions, and occurrences of sedi ments they may be classified in many ways The classification we select should have a many of the following characteristics as pos sible:

1. It should relate the rock to its mod of origin or genesis.
2. It should employ easily recognizabl criteria (should not require specia laboratory study or equipment).
3. It should contain little ambiguity (tha is, it should not be possible to put single rock in more than one category)

Problem of mixtures

One problem almost always incurred in attempting to make exact classifications of sedimentary rocks is that many of them are mixtures of two or more sediments. By far the most common sedimentary rocks are sandstone, made of sand, limestone, composed of calcite in various forms, and shale, consolidated mud.

One hundred per cent pure limestones, sandstones, and shales are rare. Most limestones have a small amount of sand or mud in them, most sandstones contain either calcite or mud impurities, and most shales are partially limestone or sand, or both. An exact technique of representing the amounts of each of the constituents of a rock is sometimes needed in sedimentary-rock studies. Such a technique con-

Fig. 9-13. Classification of sedimentary rocks.

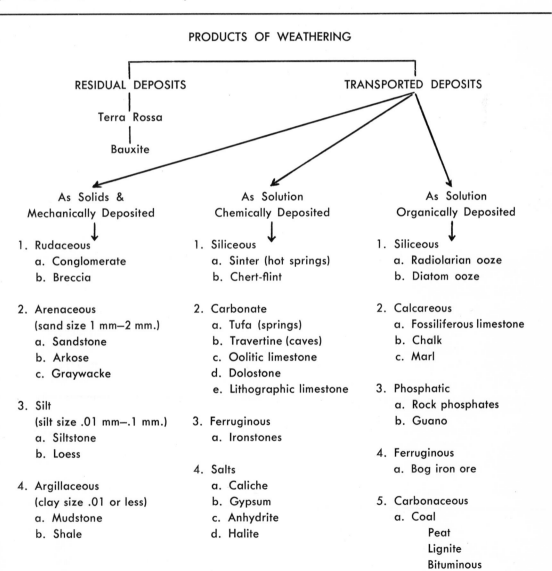

PRODUCTS OF WEATHERING

RESIDUAL DEPOSITS

Terra Rossa

Bauxite

TRANSPORTED DEPOSITS

As Solids &
Mechanically Deposited

1. Rudaceous
   a. Conglomerate
   b. Breccia

2. Arenaceous
   (sand size 1 mm—2 mm.)
   a. Sandstone
   b. Arkose
   c. Graywacke

3. Silt
   (silt size .01 mm—.1 mm.)
   a. Siltstone
   b. Loess

4. Argillaceous
   (clay size .01 or less)
   a. Mudstone
   b. Shale

As Solution
Chemically Deposited

1. Siliceous
   a. Sinter (hot springs)
   b. Chert-flint

2. Carbonate
   a. Tufa (springs)
   b. Travertine (caves)
   c. Oolitic limestone
   d. Dolostone
   e. Lithographic limestone

3. Ferruginous
   a. Ironstones

4. Salts
   a. Caliche
   b. Gypsum
   c. Anhydrite
   d. Halite

As Solution
Organically Deposited

1. Siliceous
   a. Radiolarian ooze
   b. Diatom ooze

2. Calcareous
   a. Fossiliferous limestone
   b. Chalk
   c. Marl

3. Phosphatic
   a. Rock phosphates
   b. Guano

4. Ferruginous
   a. Bog iron ore

5. Carbonaceous
   a. Coal
      Peat
      Lignite
      Bituminous

The classification we will use adequately fulfills the requirements set forth above. It recognizes that most of the sediments ultimately are derived from weathering or decay of the crust. The decayed material either remains as a residue in the place where it originated, or it is transported to another locality by water, wind, ice, or downslope mass movement. The material that is moved is carried either as a solid or in solution. Its deposition is eventually brought about through some mechanical process such as settling from suspension if it is carried as a solid. Those materials that are transported in solution as ions are either chemically deposited, as by precipitation, or their deposition is brought about by organisms that may either cause them to be deposited directly or use the material for their own structures, in which case it is deposited as a part of the organism when the organism dies. It is most satisfactory to classify the sediments carried as solids according to their size (their most obvious and easily measured characteristic). Sediments that originate from chemical deposition and from organisms are conveniently classified first, according to their chemical compositions, and secondly, according to special features that are of either textural or genetic significance.

Fig. 9-14. Sand dunes. Sand dunes such as these are sometimes consolidated into hard sedimentary rocks. (Photo by courtesy of the New Mexico State Tourist Bureau.)

sists of separating the various constituents of a rock mechanically or chemically and then plotting them on a triangular diagram.

Textures

One of the easiest ways to learn to identify sedimentary rocks is to learn the textures which are characteristic of or frequently associated with each type of sediment. The word texture refers to the size, shape, packing, and fabric of the components of the rock. Two principal groups of our classification are the materials transported as solids and those transported as solutions or in solution. The first of these, the clastic sediments, have different textures from the chemically derived sediments.

Fig. 9-15. Travertine deposits of calcium carbonate. These deposits make exotic forms here in Carlsbad Caverns. (Photo by courtesy of the New Mexico State Tourist Bureau.)

Fig. 9-16. Medial moraine. Tongues and sheets of ice are important sources of sediment in the high latitudes at the present time. As the ice melts, sediment transported in and on the ice is dropped out. (Photo by courtesy of the U.S. Air Force.)

Clastic textures

The clastic rocks are fragmental. Thus the size of the fragments is the most apparent and easily applied method of identifying them. There is no natural grouping of sizes in nature. Everything from colloids only a minute fraction of a centimeter in diameter up to boulders hundreds of feet across can be found, and every intermediate size is known. The difference in size between the smallest and largest fragments is extreme. To make analysis of sediments relatively easy, a system of sizes has been arbitrarily selected. This scale, known as the Wentworth classification, defines the limits of each type of clastic particles.

Boulder anything above 256 mm in diameter
Cobble 64 mm–256 mm
Pebble 4 mm–64 mm
Granule 2 mm–4 mm
Sand 1/16 mm–2 mm
Silt 1/256 mm–1/16 mm
Clay 1/256 mm or less

Shape of clastic particles

The shape of the particles in a clastic sediment may be used as a means of estimating the distance the particles have traveled, or it may give some idea of their mode of origin. The more common shapes are spheroidal, disc-bladed, and roller or prismatic. Each of these may have well-rounded or angular edges. More-rounded particles have in general been transported farther.

Surface texture. From the nature of the surface of the grains of sand in a sandstone it may be possible to determine if it was transported by wind or water. When it is carried by the wind the grain becomes frosted as though subjected to a sand blast, while water-transported grains show little frosting. Pebbles carried by a glacier are striated—they have

fine grooves across them. Thus it may be possible to answer questions of the origin and history of a sediment from detailed observations of its texture.

Arrangement of particles. This may give some clues to the history of the rock. For instance, bladed or disc-shaped cobbles or pebbles in a stream are likely to be flipped over by

Fig. 9-17. Tufa, hot spring deposits, being formed in Yellowstone Park. (Photo by courtesy of the Union Pacific Railroad.)

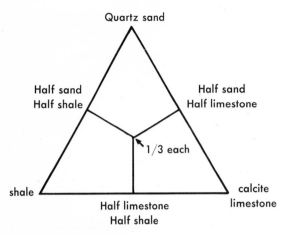

Fig. 9-18. Most sedimentary rocks are mixtures of two or more constituents. The most common are mixtures of sand, lime, and clay. A triangular diagram such as this one may be used to classify such mixtures. Every point within the triangle corresponds to a particular rock. The points correspond to pure rocks. The outside boundaries are mixtures of only two constituents. Points inside the triangle would correspond to mixtures of three constituents.

the current until they lie inclined upstream. Thus this arrangement can help you determine the direction of flow in a stream long since dis-

Fig. 9-19. Cape Perpetua. The ocean is the ultimate site of deposition for most sediments. Isolated beaches of sand dot this rugged shoreline in Oregon. (Photo by courtesy of the Oregon State Highway Dept.)

appeared if the channel is found and it contains particles of this size and shape.

Porosity. This term means the percentage of the rock that is occupied by voids. The porosity of a rock may be of great importance since it determines what quantity of fluids, such as petroleum or water, may be stored in the rock. The amount of porosity in a rock depends on such factors as:

1. The way the particles are packed together.
2. Their size and shape.
3. The number of different sizes that occur together. (This point is important because small particles may fill the voids left between larger ones.)

Permeability. This property of sediments is a measure of the ability of the rock to transmit liquids. It is not enough for a rock to be porous; the pores must be interconnected, if we are to pull or drain the liquid contents out of a rock unit.

Nonclastic sedimentary textures

Nonclastic textures form as a result of deposition through chemical reactions. The crystalline texture is one of interlocking aggregates of crystals. The crystals may be small, medium, or large, or they may even exhibit a mixture of sizes somewhat like the igneous porphyries. The crystals may exhibit certain definite shapes, (equidimensional, fibrous, or scaly, for example). It is not ordinarily possible to distinguish those formed by inorganic chemical reactions from those deposited through reactions caused by organisms.

To the inexperienced eye it is often more difficult to distinguish the textures of nonclastic sedimentary rocks from igneous rock than it is to distinguish them from clastic textures. This is not surprising when you consider the similarities in the mode of origin of igneous and chemically deposited sediments. Both form through processes of crystallization from solutions. They differ primarily in that the igneous rocks are formed at very high temperatures, while the sediments are formed at temperatures normal to the surface of the earth. Naturally the minerals formed are very different ones, but the pattern of crystallization is similar. In addition to direct crystallization from a solution, many sediments are recrystallized from gels or after the sediment is a solid.

Formation of the crystalline textures

Most of the crystalline textures are formed from direct precipitation from a saturated solution. The crystals grow from many centers and spread until they form an interlocking crystal framework or mosaic. Commonly the centers of the crystals are small clastic particles of irregular shape and size. A second mode of formation for the crystalline sediments is through the process of recrystallization. Here a reorganization and growth of crystals in a solid take place. Usually part of the rock is slightly dissolved by solutions moving along the boundaries of individual crystals. The dissolved substance is carried along, and it may eventually crystallize as part of another crystal. In the process many of the small particles or masses of a mineral are dissolved, and a few larger crystals grow.

Textures of rocks deposited as colloids. When colloids coagulate they form a gelatin-like mass. This gelatinous mass may lose some of the water in it and eventually harden to form an amorphous (lacking crystalline structure) mass. This amorphous substance is not very stable, and it may be changed into a crystalline mass. When and if crystallization of a hardened mass of colloids does take place, the mass tends to become a fibrous form first, but it may later become granular by recrystallization. Some of the textures of common colloidal deposits are: nodular, oölitic, and spherulitic. Oölites are small, nearly spherical bodies between 1/4 and 2 mm in diameter. Larger bodies are called pisolites. In section one can see that the oölites are made up of a series of concentric spheres. Within any spherical shell either a fibrous radial structure may be apparent, or it may be finely laminated. Spherulitic texture is characterized by small spherical bodies with radial structures originating at the center and extending out to the mar-

Fig. 9-20. Remnant of continental debris. This boulder conglomerate is part of the sediment derived from the Alps as they began to rise higher and became subjected to increased erosion. (Photo by courtesy of the French Cultural Services.)

gins. Nodules or small pellets are of nearly oval or spherical shapes without internal radiating or concentric structures.

DESCRIPTIONS OF SEDIMENTARY ROCKS

Mechanically deposited sedimentary rocks

RUDACEOUS (coarse-grained fragmental or clastic rocks)

1. *Conglomerate.* The name is applied to a consolidated gravel sediment commonly mixed with varying amounts of sand, silt, and mud. The fragments that make up a conglomerate may be composed of any other rock (igneous, metamorphic, or sedimentary). An appropriate prefix may be added to indicate the size of the major constituents of the rock, i.e., as pebble conglomerate or boulder conglomerate. The fragments in a conglomerate are rounded usually as a result of rolling in a stream or repeated tossing and impacts in waves along a coast.

Fig. 9-21. Beach deposits. This view of one of the sandy beaches along the western coast of the United States is typical of this sedimentary environment. You can see in the foreground that the sand has a structural feature in it which would make its place of origin apparent. When the sand becomes hardened it is called beach rock. Note also the ripple marks in the sand. Ripples may form either in wind-blown sand deposits or in the water where there is a current or wave action. (Photo by E. W. Spencer.)

2. *Breccia*. Breccia differs from a conglomerate in that the fragments are angular instead of rounded. In other respects it is like the conglomerate except for its origin. A breccia might form anywhere a rock is broken up but not rounded. Breccias occur in volcanic vents where the sides of the vent or pipe are broken up by explosions in the volcano. They might form in the collapse of the roof of a cave, or from the fragments of rock you see on steep slopes of mountain valleys, where brittle rock units are folded and break up, or when a fault causes mechanical breakdown of its walls.

ARENACEOUS (sand-dominated rocks)

1. *Sandstone*. Using the literal meaning of the term we must consider as a sand-

stone any rock composed of fragments of the size range 1/16 to 2 mm regardless of composition. We ordinarily think of sand as quartz sand because most sandstone is largely composed of quartz fragments. But many other minerals may dominate sands. In the Antarctic there are sand dunes composed of fragments of ice, in Italy some beaches are made up of sand composed of olivine derived from the volcanic rocks, and in the White Sands National Park the sand dunes are composed of gypsum.

2. *Arkose*. This arenaceous rock is made up largely of a mixture of quartz sand and feldspar fragments. It may contain small angular rock and mineral fragments. Arkose looks something like a granite and is ordinarily thought to be derived from the decomposition of a granite. Frequently arkose is red or pink, colors derived from the oxidation of iron-bearing minerals.

3. *Graywacke*. This term is not exactly defined. It has been used in many different ways by different geologists. In general it applies to impure sandstones and is made up of quartz and feldspar fragments, and small fragments of igneous, metamorphic, and sedimentary rocks. One common association is ash and volcanic dust with quartz and feldspar fragments. The color is most commonly gray, which comes from a slate-like matrix. This matrix is composed of a mixture of mica, chlorite, and quartz. The importance of graywackes comes from their widespread occurrence in the mobile belts around the earth. They make up a large percentage of the total volume of sediments.

SILTY ROCKS

1. *Siltstone*. This is a consolidated rock composed of clastic particles in the size range of 1/16 to 1/256 mm in diameter. Rocks composed of a large amount of silt are much less common than are sandstones or shales. Much of the silt is probably mixed in shales, which may

contain up to 50 per cent silt. Layers of siltstone are generally thin and hard. Unlike sand, a silt particle is usually angular, and most siltstones contain a large amount of platy minerals such as micas, but a microscope is needed to see most of the constituent minerals.

2. **Loess.** This is a special type of silt. It is a light-buff unconsolidated silt. It is unstratified, composed of angular particles, and can stand in very steep cliff faces. When cut along roads, as in the Mississippi Valley, it is stable in vertical cliffs. The particles of loess are very well sorted; they are almost all the same size, averaging from .01 mm to .05 mm. It is fine enough to be a wind-blown deposit in many places where it occurs

in the Mississippi Valley. It may have come from lakes formed at the margins of the continental ice sheets that have covered parts of North America in the last 100,000 years.

ARGILLACEOUS (A term applied to all rocks composed of clay or having a high percentage of clay in them. Note that the term is used as an adjective modifying other rock names when they have some clay in them.)

Shale. One of the most common sedimentary rocks, shale is consolidated mud and clay. It often contains sand (arenaceous shale) or lime (calcareous shale) in large amounts. Shale has an earthy odor when breathed upon, and this is often a useful identifying char-

Fig. 9-22. Mud cracks. This is a view of a lake bottom which has dried out. The mud layers on the lake floor have cracked open and curled. Such features are sometimes found in ancient consolidated rocks. Their presence is an indication that the place where they were deposited was once subjected to alternate wetting and drying. (Photo by E. W. Spencer.)

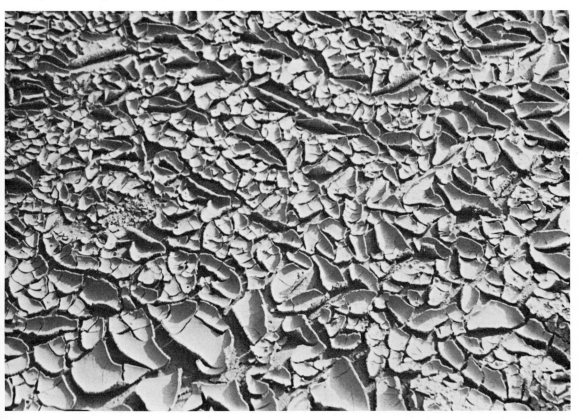

acteristic. The manner in which a shale breaks is characteristic. It is fissile—that is, it breaks or splits easily along nearly parallel planes. Other important properties are its slight permeability and porosity, the particle size, less than 1/256 mm in diameter, and its composition. Shales are composed of clay minerals, quartz, sericite, chlorite, feldspar, calcite, and small quantities of many other minerals.

Chemically deposited sedimentary rocks

SILICEOUS DEPOSITS (containing silica)

Many of the siliceous sediments are colloidal deposits; other are formed through chemical processes. Some of the siliceous deposits are laid down directly from water, while others are formed through processes of recrystallization in sediments during

Fig. 9-23. Ancient mud cracks. These cracks were filled with sandy mud which is now eroded to stand out. (Photo by E. W. Spencer.)

the consolidation. There are few reliable criteria by which these two modes of origin can be positively identified. The most common occurrences for siliceous deposits are as nodules or concretions in layers of limestone. Many of these nodules of siliceous material contain fossils at their centers, showing that they are of a secondary origin.

1. *Chert* (flint). The most common of the siliceous sedimentary rocks is a dense, hard rock. Its colors range from white through gray to black. Chert is a form of quartz, SiO_2. It has the same hardness, 7, a conchoidal fracture, and semivitreous luster. Chert occurs in other sediments as pebbles.

2. *Siliceous sinter.* This is a chemical sediment formed at mineral springs. It consists of silica, is white or light-colored, and porous. That formed around the vents of geysers is known as geyserite.

CALCAREOUS DEPOSITS (largely composed of calcium carbonate, calcite)

It must be noted that many of the calcareous sedimentary rocks are or may be classed as organic rocks. The calcareous rocks include all limestones. Calcium and carbonate ions are both present in large quantity in sea water. Under the proper conditions the water becomes saturated with these ions, and limestone is deposited as a precipitate. Favorable conditions include:

1. Warm water, which can hold large quantities of ions in solution.
2. High rate of evaporation, as at the equator, where the ions become concentrated near the surface as the amount of water decreases.
3. Agitated water in which precipitation is encouraged.

Under such conditions precipitation is expectable, and if the water is agitated then oölites are likely to form. Their concentric structures grow as they move in the agitated water while successive layers of $CaCO_3$ are deposited on them.

Except for the particular structures

Fig. 9-24. Ancient cross bedding. Cross bedding of this sort is formed where large quantities of sand are available. These deposits were laid down in sand dunes, but similar deposits might form in running water where the current suddenly decreases and the sand is dropped to slide down a slope. (Photo by E. W. Spencer.)

that characterize the various forms of limestone, they are similar. All contain calcite as the dominant mineral constituent. Siliceous limestones, arenaceous limestones, and argillaceous limestones are all known and are common. Limestones tend to have many of the physical properties of their main constituent, calcite. They have a hardness of about 3, and they effervesce when hydrochloric acid is poured on them.

1. *Travertine* or *tufa*. These are limestones formed by the evaporation of spring and stream waters containing calcium carbonate in solution. Tufa, a surficial spring deposit, forms in hot and cool springs and in running water. It is a spongy, porous, fragile rock with an earthy texture. The deposits frequently contain branches, twigs, and other debris that fell into the water.

Travertine is formed in caverns by the evaporation of the waters that percolate through the rocks above the cavern and emerge in the cave along fractures, or as springs. It is a dense, banded deposit.

2. *Caliche*. This limy deposit forms in the soils of semiarid regions underlaid by rocks composed of carbonate. Capillary action draws the ground waters, in which calcium carbonate is in solution, to the surface where they evaporate, leaving the deposit as a cement in the soil or as thin layers.

3. *Dolomite* (dolostone). A sugary-textured dense gray rock which does not effervesce in dilute acid, dolomite is a calcium magnesium carbonate $(Ca,Mg)CO_3$. Most dolomites are probably formed during recrystallization of calcareous sediments. The calcium and magnesium ions are nearly the same size so that it is possible for the magnesium ion to replace a calcium ion in the calcite structure. One reason for thinking the dolomites are recrystallized limestones is that the dolomites have a porosity that is almost exactly equal to the difference in the size of the slightly larger calcium ion and the magnesium ions. Dolomitized fossils have been found, but no animal is known to construct its shell

Fig. 9-25. Clay concretions which formed in a clay strata. The peculiar shapes of such concretions are hard to explain. Often the concretions contain a fossil in the center suggesting that they formed after the rock was initially deposited. Many are formed through the effect of water in the sediments. (Photo by the U.S. National Museum.)

of dolomite. Dolomite occurs irregularly as patches through limestones. Dolomitized oölites have been found, but no dolomite oölites can be found anywhere in present-day sediments.

FERRUGINOUS DEPOSITS (iron-bearing sediments)

Since iron is one of the most common although small constituents of all rocks, the groups studied here must be restricted t those in which iron makes up a large pa of the rock—that is, at least 10 per cent c more.

1. *Bedded siderites.* These rocks, whic are mined as iron ore in the Gogebi range in Minnesota, contain an associa tion of siderite ($FeCO_3$) and chert. I this area both the siderite and the che are thought to be direct chemical pre cipitates.

2. *Iron-silicate sediments.* The mineral chamosite and glauconite are two sil cate · minerals that contain iron. Th chamosite occurs in mudstones and lime stones. Its origin is still in questior Glauconite (iron-potassium silicate) i forming on the sea floor today. It i commonly known as greensand an looks very much like other sands excep for its color. Glauconite is a colloida deposit laid down where streams carry ing colloids, formed through weatherin of iron minerals exposed on the conti nents, enter the sea. Sea water is a electrolyte and neutralizes the charge on the colloids, making it possible fo them to settle through the sea water t the bottom where they form aggregate or granular masses.

3. *Sedimentary hematites.* Many of thes are oölitic hematites, and some provid important iron ores, such as the Clinto iron ores mined and used at Birming ham, Alabama. Some of these are com posed of fossil fragments that have beer replaced by hematite. In others th oölitic ores have cores of quartz grain around which layers of hematite wer deposited.

SALTS (deposits formed from concentrated solu tions of brines)

Three salts are of particular impor tance. These are halite (common tabl salt, sodium chloride), and gypsum an anhydrite, which are calcium sulfates These, along with some less common salts are precipitated in a sequence from se waters that become saturated. Such satura tion of sea water with salts may occur when a portion of the sea becomes cut off, leaving an isolated body of water which slowly evaporates. Similar conditions hold for inland bodies of water such as Great Salt Lake.

Experiments in the evaporation of sea water that contains about 3.5 per cent by weight of dissolved solids give the following sequence:

1. Iron oxide and $CaCO_3$ are precipitated when half the water is evaporated.
2. Gypsum forms when one-fifth of the original volume is left.
3. Halite, NaCl, begins to crystallize next.

4. Finally, sulfates and chlorides of magnesium, and potassium chloride form.

The most impressive thing about this sequence is the amount of water that must be dissolved before most of the salts begin to precipitate. Sedimentary formations of halite and gypsum are often several hundred feet thick. Such thicknesses would require evaporation of tremendous quantities of water. It is generally supposed that these bodies of water were inland seas, which became restricted and cut off from the oceans or were only occasionally connected with the oceans, at which times new supplies of water were introduced.

Fig. 9-26. Ripple marks. Such marks are formed by current action and by the oscillation of water in waves. These two types are easily distinguished by their profile. The current ripples are asymmetrical in profile (see insert), while the oscillation ripple marks are symmetrical. Note that the pointed crest of the oscillation ripples point upward, making them an excellent criterion for determining the top of strata containing them. Where the earth's crust has been deformed the strata are not all right side up. (Photo by E. W. Spencer.)

Organically formed deposits

SILICEOUS DEPOSITS (those composed of large amounts of silica)

1. *Radiolarian oozes*. The radiolarians are a group of single-celled animals, which construct skeletons of silica. These are built into beautifully intricate structures. The radiolarians live in the seas where they float in the upper parts of the ocean. When they die, the remains sink to the bottom. These accumulate in large quantities and may form a large part of the sediment in areas where rates of sedimentation are very slow, and particularly where the water is deep. Calcareous shells tend to dissolve in the cool temperatures and high hydrostatic pressures found in the deep seas, but silica is stable; so, the remains of radiolarians may accumulate.

2. *Diatoms*. These are siliceous plants, also of microscopic size. They have many different shapes from rod-like to spherical and circular. The plants inhabit the oceans in tremendous numbers. They float in the surface waters and may become concentrated in large quantities. Each diatom contains a droplet of oil, which may be the principal source of most petroleum. The rock formed from the remains of these plants has an earthy appearance and texture. It is loose, fine, white powdery rock, resembling chalk.

CALCAREOUS DEPOSITS (containing calcite or calcium carbonate)

1. *Fossiliferous limestone*. Most of the limestones are of organic origin. We include here primarily those limestones formed from the shells of marine animals. These shells are composed of the mineral calcite, which the animal is able to take from the sea-water solution in which he lives and build into the marvelous structures that house the soft parts of the animal. You can see the cleavages of calcite in the broken fragments of many shells. Most of us have seen beaches almost covered by shell and fragments broken by wave action. These shells accumulate in quantity in the oceans and shallow seas and eventually become cemented by calcite, silica, or some other material being precipitated in the water. The term fossiliferous limestone is applied to a limestone composed of shells. If one particular type of shell makes up most of the rock it may go by some special name.

2. *Chalk*. This is a fossiliferous limestone composed of the shells of protozoans (single-celled animals) and particularly one which has a globular-shaped shell called *Globigerina*. Chalk is white, light weight, and has the property of being so soft that it will easily mark most things it is rubbed on.

3. *Marl*. This name applies to mixtures of shells and shell fragments with mud and sand. It is an impure limestone usually found in a semiconsolidated state, held loosely together.

PHOSPHATIC DEPOSITS

The two organic sources for phosphate are bones and bird excrement. Neither is very common. The deposits of bird excrement, guano, are confined to a few islands where birds have lived in large numbers for long periods of time. The bones are the remains of land animals and are rarely found in large enough quantities to be called rocks.

FERRUGINOUS DEPOSITS

Deposition of ferric oxide and ferrous sulfide may be brought about by certain bacteria and perhaps by algae. The iron bacteria can extract the iron from solution and deposit it around their cells. Others may perform the function of gathering the materials, which are then directly precipitated. The accumulation of bacteria casts and the precipitated granules forms a rock called bog iron. As the name suggests, it is deposited in bogs, swamps, or marshes.

CARBONACEOUS DEPOSITS (containing large amounts of carbon)

The important rocks of carbonaceous composition and of organic origin are the coal formations. Coal does not have a definite mineral composition and should not be classified as a rock unless we accept the idea that any naturally occurring solid that makes up a large part of the earth's crust is a rock.

REFERENCES

DUNBAR, C. O., and RODGERS, JOHN, 1957, *Principles of Stratigraphy:* New York, John Wiley & Sons, 356 p.

GROUT, F. F., 1932, *Petrography and Petrology:* New York, McGraw-Hill Book Co., 522 p.

HEEZEN, B. C., THARP, MARIE, and EWING, MAURICE, 1959, *The Floors of the Oceans. 1. The North Atlantic:* Geol. Soc. America, Spec. Paper 65 (122 p. and map in color)

KRUMBEIN, W. C., and SLOSS, L. L., 1951, *Stratigraphy and Sedimentation:* San Francisco, W. H. Freeman and Company, 497 p.

PETTIJOHN, F. J., 1957, *Sedimentary Rocks,* 2nd ed.: New York, Harper & Bros., 718 p.

SHROCK, R. R., 1948, *Sequence in Layered Rocks:* New York, McGraw-Hill Book Co., 507 p.

TRASK, PARKER, Editor, 1939, *Recent Marine Sediments—A Symposium:* Tulsa, Am. Assoc. Petroleum Geologists, 736 p.

TWENHOFEL, W. H., 1932, *Treatise on Sedimentation,* 2nd ed.: Baltimore, The Williams & Wilkins Co., 926 p.

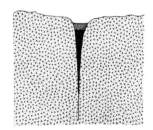

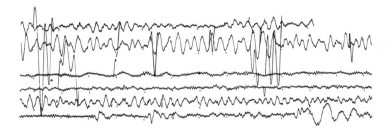

III   FRAMEWORK OF THE EARTH

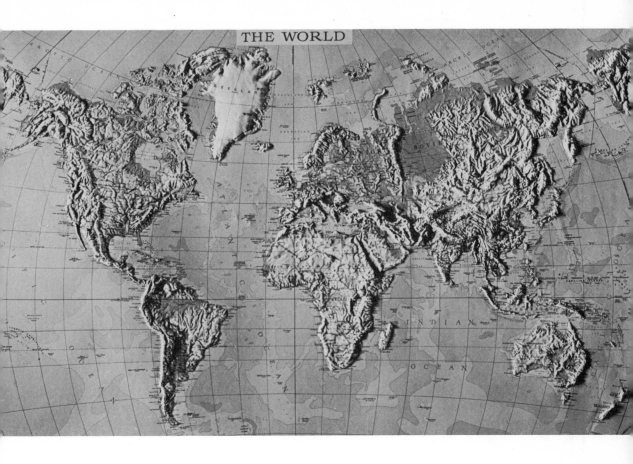

THE WORLD

10   Major Divisions of the Crust of the Earth

Because we are most intimately associated with the surficial parts of the crust of the earth it takes on added significance for us. This is the part of the earth with which we are most familiar and from which we must work in obtaining knowledge about the interior below us and the gaseous layers above. The phrase "crust of the earth" evokes an image of an earth consisting of a hardened external layer of rock underlain by a liquid interior, and this view has been widely accepted. Some people even believed that there is a fiery interior, but these beliefs have given way to a more enlightened point of view. One of the most active parts of

earth science today is concerned with the relation of the earth's interior to the crust. Through seismology, studies of the gravitational and magnetic fields of the earth, and even through deep drilling, data are being accumulated which can be used to improve our understanding of this relationship.

No liquid interior is postulated to exist within 1800 miles of the surface of the earth because shear waves set up by earthquakes can be propagated through the earth's interior to that depth, and shear waves travel only through rigid substances. Geophysical studies show that the interior is made up of a number of nearly

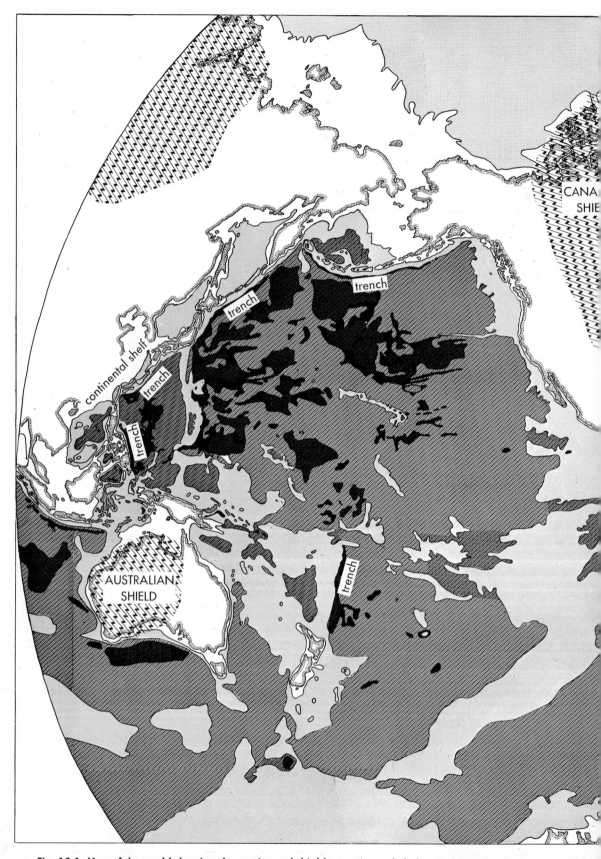

Fig. 10-1. Map of the world showing the continental shields, continental shelves (white), depths between 100—1

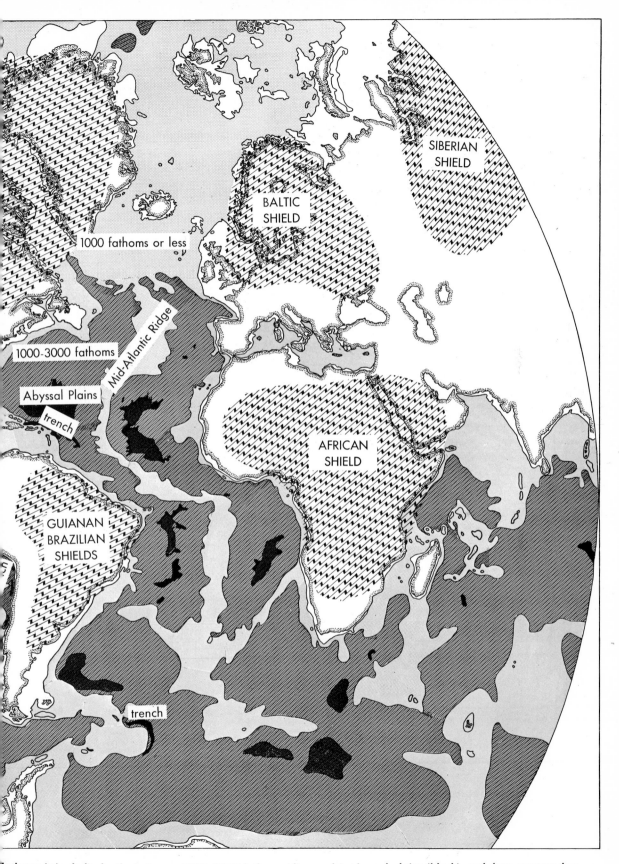

SIBERIAN SHIELD

BALTIC SHIELD

1000 fathoms or less

Mid-Atlantic Ridge

1000-3000 fathoms

Abyssal Plains

trench

AFRICAN SHIELD

GUIANAN BRAZILIAN SHIELDS

trench

fathoms (stippled), depths between 1000—3000 fathoms (diagonals), abyssal plains (black), and deep sea trenches.

concentric shells of matter within which the physical properties vary with depth. However, between the shells, properties vary considerably. That is, the variations in physical and chemical properties are not continuous, or gradational across boundaries between the shells. These boundaries, with their marked changes in physical properties, are called discontinuities. Most of them have been discovered through seismic studies. It is found for instance that the velocity of certain shock waves (earthquake waves) gradually increases with depth. Then the velocity suddenly changes within a very short distance at some particular depth. For deep discontinuities it is usually found that a similar change occurs at the same depth throughout the world. What would give rise to such a discontinuity? The most obvious answer is that there has been a change in one of the physical properties of the material through which the waves are moving. In particular, we know that changes in the elastic constants for

a rock will cause the velocity of shock waves to change also. Then what would bring about such changes? At least two possibilities are considered. One is that the composition of the rock might change. The discontinuity may simply mark the contact between two very different rock types. This is true of the seismic discontinuities found at shallow depths where it is possible by drilling a well to find out what causes the discontinuities. But it is not feasible to drill far into the interior. Even if wells are completed into the subcrust they will not go far toward the center of the earth. A second consideration for the cause of discontinuities at depth is the possibility of phase changes in the rocks. We commonly think of three phases of matter—solid, liquid, and gaseous. Within the solid state the same atoms may be packed differently to give different types of solids of the same material. Such changes can be induced by high pressures, and we know that pressures on the rocks are extremely high in the earth's

Fig. 10-2. Crustal structure. The thickness of the crust of the earth is shown for a number of locations. Note the great thickness under continents as compared with the thickness under ocean basins. The solid black represents part of the mantle beneath Moho. (From G. P. Woollard, Trans. Am. Geophysical Union, v. 36, No. 4.)

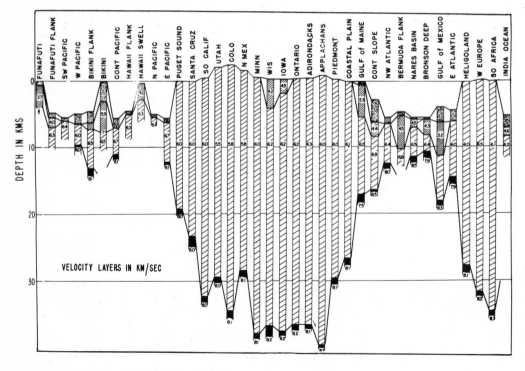

interior. Some of the discontinuities could mark the zones within which changes in phase of this type might occur.

Moho

Of the many seismic discontinuities known, none is better documented than one named for its discoverer, Mohorovičić. The discontinuity is usually called Moho, or M for short. This seismic discontinuity is generally accepted as the base of the crust of the earth. Thus the crust of the earth is defined as the outer portion of the lithosphere between the ground surface and the Moho. Moho is recognized by the sudden increase from about 6.5 to 8 km per second in the velocity of the compressional shock waves. It almost certainly marks a sudden change in the type of rock. As this book goes to press plans are being made to drill a well through the crust to the Moho and into the mantle of the earth. The findings of this great experiment in geology will be extremely important in substantiating or refuting the currently held ideas about the Moho which are based on information obtained by indirect methods.

The Moho is not found at the same depth under oceans and continents. Although investigation of its exact depth throughout the world is far from complete, there is enough information to suggest a general pattern. The Moho is at greater depths under the continents than it is under the oceans, and it is deeper under mountains than it is under the plains. It appears then that the configuration of the underneath side of the crust of the earth is almost a mirror image of the surface.

GROSS FEATURES OF THE EARTH'S CRUST

In the chapters that follow, the processes that cause erosion of the earth and those that are responsible for maintaining parts of the crust high in spite of erosion will be discussed in some detail. Before turning to the details of this balance between upheaval and erosion, let us get firmly in mind the major framework of the crust, its main subdivisions, and their general characteristics.

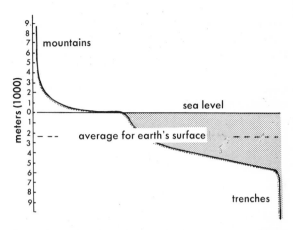

Fig. 10-3. The distribution of elevations in various parts of the earth. The vertical scale is elevation. The horizontal scale is surface area of the earth.

The most obvious as well as the most fundamentally important divisions of the crust are the continents and the ocean basins. These differ in many respects and are separated by zones of transition which have characteristics that are different from those of either the continents or the ocean basins. Among the most striking differences are the following:

1. Continents average almost half a mile of elevation above the level of the modern-day seas, but ocean floors average almost 3 miles beneath the surface of the waters. Thus there is about a 3 1/2 mile difference in surficial elevation between the two.

2. The thickness of the crust is strikingly different in oceans and on continents. Under the oceans the crust is between 8 and 10 km thick, counting the ocean water also, and it is about 20 km thick on the continents, reaching a maximum under some mountains where it may be 40 km thick.

3. The crust under the oceans has a bulk composition that differs from that of the continents. The continental crust is made up of rocks of granitic composition (note that a section of mixed limestone, sandstone, and shale has a granitic composition). These rocks are rich in the elements silicon and aluminum, and the abbreviation sial (si for silicon and al for aluminum) is often used to denote this type of composition when no more specific information is known or when this is unimportant. Almost

the entire continental crust is thought to be sialic, but the oceanic crust contains only a thin layer of sialic material if any at all. The minerals of the oceanic crust are those that make up basalt. They are rich in silicon and magnesium (abbreviated sima).

4. The products of igneous activity are different in that extrusions and intrusions in oceans tend to be basaltic in composition, and those in and on the continents tend to be more granitic (andesites) in composition. The extent of this difference is partially dependent on how many of the granite batholiths known on contients are really of igneous origin and how many of them are metamorphic rocks.

5. Even the processes of erosion and deposition are strikingly different as a result of the different properties of the fluids directly in contact with the lithosphere on continents and under oceans. The fluids, of course, are the atmosphere and the hydrosphere.

6. In general the continents may be considered the sites of the most rapid erosion, while the ocean basins are primarily sites of deposition.

7. A greater variety of factors play roles in the changes due to erosion and decay of rocks on continents than in oceans.

While the oceans and continents have many striking differences there are some respects in which they are rather similar. Each has broad plain areas that are nearly flat. Both have high mountain ranges that extend for thousands of miles. We do not yet know if there is a fundamental difference between the types of mountains in oceans and on continents. Just as there are high mountain peaks such as Everest 30,000 feet on continents, there are deep-sea trenches nearly 37,000 feet deep in the oceans. Thus both peaks and trenches have extremes of relief that make up a relatively small amount of the total area.

Fig. 10-4. Physiographic map of the world. This plastic relief map shows elevations greatly exaggerated. (Photo by courtesy of the Aero Service Corporation.)

There may be other differences and similarities with which we are presently unfamiliar. Study of the oceans has been a challenge to man for centuries, but these efforts have, until recently, been largely in vain. The problems of studying the ocean floors and the suboceanic crust are great, and these have had to await the development of techniques making the investigations possible. Not only is study of the oceans inherently more difficult, it is also more time-consuming and expensive than investigations on land. Most of the earth's surface is covered by water, and only a relatively small number of geologists are directly concerned with investigations of the oceans. The importance of this work is now being emphasized, and more attention is being given to these problems than ever before.

It is possible to make further subdivisions of the crust of the earth. Such a procedure could be extended to include a vast number of unique crustal segments, but for the purposes of general discussions at least six types of crustal segments must be recognized. These six are:

1. The continental shields.
2. The young folded mountain belts.
3. The shelf-like continental margins.
4. The island-arc systems.
5. The deep oceanic crust.
6. Mid-ocean ridges.

CONTINENTAL SHIELDS

Within the boundaries of each continent there are large areas of exposures of very old rocks formed during that portion of geologic time known as the Precambrian. The term "shield" is applied to those areas of Precambrian exposed at the surface or shallowly buried which has not been folded or complexly deformed since the end of the Precambrian, a little over 500 million years ago. Since the areas have not been strongly deformed within the last half billion years, they are considered stable. They have not been stable always, for structural evidence of old mountain systems is still found in every shield. Undoubtedly they were strongly deformed at one time perhaps 1

or more billion years ago. The important thing about them is that, unlike most of the surrounding continental masses, they have not been deformed since the end of the Precambrian. Certainly Precambrian rocks must underlie the rest of the continents, but they have apparently yielded to deformation more than the shields.

The Precambrian rocks are very complex. Because they are old there has been more opportunity for them to become deformed and for more alteration of them to take place. This alteration has been twofold—degradation, removal of material brought on by erosion and weathering, and metamorphism, caused by heat and pressures. Most of the Precambrian rocks and all of the earlier Precambrian rocks have been metamorphosed. Large portions are granitic in composition, and, although some of these are now known to be granitized sedimentary rocks (rocks altered to granitic composition and texture), others may be of igneous origin. This is one reason for the current importance of the problem of the origin of granite.

The largest shield areas are:

1. The Canadian Shield, covering most of the central part of Canada and down into the northern United States. The central part of the United States is covered by a few thousand feet of sediments, but large parts of it have been relatively stable since the Precambrian and should be considered as somewhat similar to a shield area.
2. The Baltic Shield, located in northern Europe and including the area of Sweden, Finland, and most of the Baltic Sea.
3. The Central African Shield, located in the southern and central parts of Africa.
4. The Brazilian Shield, which makes up most of the area of Brazil.
5. The Australian Shield, located in the western part of that continent.
6. The Angara Shield of northern and eastern Siberia.

The exact margins of the shields are not easily determined. Extensive drilling into the Precambrian, often referred to as the "base-

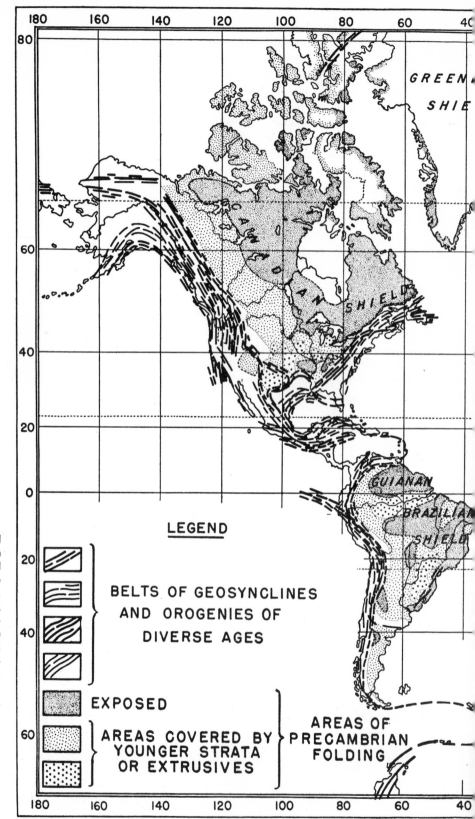

Fig. 10-5. The folded mountain belts which have been deformed within the last five hundred million years. Compare this with Fig. 10-4 to determine which of these folded mountain belts are still physiographically high. (From L. G. Weeks, Am. Assoc. Petroleum Geologists, Bull., v. 36, No. 11.)

LEGEND

BELTS OF GEOSYNCLINES AND OROGENIES OF DIVERSE AGES

EXPOSED

AREAS COVERED BY YOUNGER STRATA OR EXTRUSIVES

AREAS OF PRECAMBRIAN FOLDING

ment" or "basement complex," would be necessary in order to determine the extent to which it has been involved in later deformations. There are many areas that have not been extensively deformed since the Precambrian, but in which the Precambrian is buried by considerable thicknesses of younger sediments. Such areas are not known as shields although there is much evidence of stability.

Shields, like all parts of the continents, are subject to erosion. The net long-term tendency is for more rock to be removed from their surfaces. As a result of their long-term stability they contain very few mountains. Most of them are well above sea level, but the physiography is that of gently rolling hills and isolated physiographic features etched out by long years of erosion on rocks of different resistance.

Their stability is marked by the absence of volcanism, active deformation, or earthquakes within their boundaries. Considered from the point of view of stability they resemble some of the deep plains of the ocean basins.

YOUNG FOLDED MOUNTAIN BELTS

These are segments of the crust of the earth which have exhibited mobility since Precambrian time. Obviously the term "young" is used in a strictly relative sense. Only geologists or astronomers would ordinarily think of anything half a billion years old as young. As the name suggests, these segments are elongate in shape and characterized by folding of at least those rock units in the uppermost part of the crust of the earth. The term "elongate" is hardly sufficient to describe some of these belts, which are as much as several thousand miles long and 100 to 200 miles wide. The term mountain belt also requires some explanation since it is not here restricted to those belts of mountains which are physiographically high mountain ranges today. The highest mountain on the earth today may be completely eroded down to a relatively flat surface within a period of 20 to 30 million years. Obviously, then, high mountains of the past half billion years may not be high ranges today. Once the crust of the earth is disturbed and deformed into a folded mountain system,

however, the structures brought into existence at that time leave a relatively permanent imprint in the crust, and although the top part of the mountains are eroded off, the lower and marginal structures may be preserved indefinitely.

The age of the deformation in these belts varies considerably. Some belts have been deformed several times since the Precambrian; others have experienced only one major deformation. The most recently deformed mountains are those that stand as high mountain systems today. Older ones are lower mountains physiographically, and the oldest ones may not show in the topography at all.

The term "belt" implies a long system of mountains, but we are used to thinking of mountains in terms of their geographic names and not as genetically continuous belts. The following are some of the more important mountain systems:

1. The Rocky Mountain system extends northward through western Canada and into Alaska, and southward through Mexico, continuing southward as the Andes along the western margin of South America into the Antarctic.

2. The Blue Ridge and Appalachian folded belt of the eastern United States is covered by younger rocks at its southern end in Alabama, but it extends northward into the New England States. An older mountain system overlapped the northern part of this range. It continued into and along the eastern border of Canada and is probably continuous across the northern part of Greenland and southward into Scotland and Norway.

3. The highest and most complex system of mountains today is that of which the Himalayas are a part. It extends from Indochina northward through China across Tibet and the northern part of India. The Kunlun Mountains of Russia are a part. Westward the system is made up of the Caucasus Mountains between Turkey and Russia, the mountains of Greece, the Alpine system, and

extensions from it into North Africa, the Atlas Mountains, and into Spain, the Pyrenees Mountains.

4. The last major folded belt is that including the Ural Mountains and the island of Novaya Zemlya. This belt probably extends across to northern Greenland, but it is largely covered by water and ice in the Arctic.

The folded mountain belts are and have been undoubtedly closely associated with many natural processes and phenomena which have contributed to their history as belts of mobility. Some generalizations may be made from comparison of the structures, rock types, configurations, and associations of all these belts:

1. They are long, relatively narrow, and run more or less continuously for great distances across the face of the earth.
2. Single periods of deformation have involved a large part of the system's total length, but sometimes the same belt has been deformed several times.
3. The belts are not straight. They are usually curved and may almost double back on themselves. Thus, taken as a whole, the belts are irregular.
4. Igneous activity must play an important role in their history because most of the batholiths, which are known definitely to be of igneous origin, are found within them and the island-arc belts. Igneous granite, other intrusives, and extrusives are common in these belts.
5. Erosion takes place most rapidly on the higher parts of the earth's crust, and transportation downward is facilitated by the steep slopes. This lays bare the central parts of the mountains. Here the rocks are mostly metamorphic and igneous. The extensive alteration of the rocks, metamorphism, is indicative of the depth to which the rocks found there had been buried before the deformation. It also may reflect the high temperatures and pressures to which the rocks have been subjected. The metamorphic rocks are most common in the central parts of the ranges or systems and tend to be scattered or nonexistent toward the margins.

6. In every folded-mountain belt we find that the individual strata tend to thicken toward the center of the belt. That is, before deformation into a mountain system occurred, the total thickness of the sediments and sedimentary rocks in these belts was much greater than it was on the margins.
7. Most of the strata in these belts are marine sedimentary rocks mixed with variable amounts of volcanic ash. Since these strata were laid down in a sea, just as their thinner continuations to either side of the belt were, their greater thickness must mean that the belt subsided as the strata were deposited. Thus before the belt of mobility was uplifted and folded it had already shown signs of this mobility by its subsidence. The amount of this subsidence is on the order of 50,000 feet or more in many cases. This can be determined by measuring the thickness of the sections of rock in the present-day mountains and comparing this with the thickness of the same rock units outside the belt.

Fig. 10-6. Cross sections through parts of three folded mountain belts. The section at the top is across the Appalachian Mountains, that in the center is across the Jura Mountains, and that at the bottom is typical of the Himalayas and Alps.

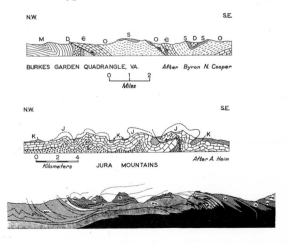

8. Structurally these belts are characterized by long folds or systems of folds in the crust. It is frequently possible to trace the folds from the margins of a belt, where there are few folds or merely broad arches, into zones of increasingly intense deformation. These may culminate in the formation of huge folds tens of miles across, which have been forced over into a recumbent position just as you might push a fold in your napkin until it lies flat. Faults are also prominent in these belts. The strata break and slip sometimes for many miles along these faults. Both high- and low-angle faults are found. These represent part of the accommodation of the crust locally to the stresses which were acting in the crust at the time of the deformation. More attention will be given to this aspect of the folded-mountain system when we consider their origin. (See Diastrophism.) The folded-mountain systems differ in details. Some typical cross sections of these mountains are illustrated.

CONTINENTAL MARGINS

The continental margins mark the zone of transition from crustal structure of the continents to that of the deep-ocean basins. The structure of the continents is not perfectly uniform, nor are all ocean basins identical, but we have seen that some generalizations can be made concerning such things as the depth to the Moho, the composition of the rocks, and the average elevation. These appear to hold true for all continents and oceans. And in this sense the continental margins are zones of change from high elevations to great depths for the crustal surface, the change from great depths of the Moho under continents to its shallow depth under oceans, and from sialic to simatic compositions for the crust.

Regardless of what criteria are chosen for the purposes of classifying the continental margins we find there are several different types. Some margins are characterized by the island-arc systems, which are of sufficient importance to be considered as a separate crustal segment. Other margins are the sites of very young folded-mountain belts. Most of the remaining continental margins are characterized by shallow shelf-like extensions from the land which slope off into the deeper water at some distance from shore. This is the most common type of continental margin.

Based on the configuration of the ocean floor the continental margins are usually found to have three parts:

The continental shelf.
The continental slope.
The continental rise.

The continental shelf is a shallow, gently sloping surface of very low local relief. The shelf has a slope of about 1 in 1000, so slight that you would not perceive its slope at all if you were standing on it. The outer margin of the shelf is rarely more than 600 feet or 100 fathoms deep, and it may be less. The edge of

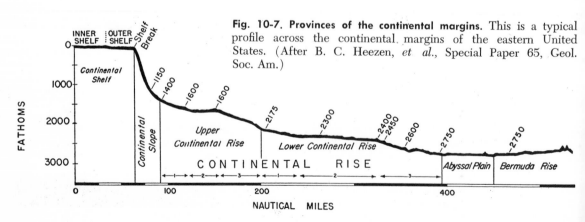

Fig. 10-7. Provinces of the continental margins. This is a typical profile across the continental margins of the eastern United States. (After B. C. Heezen, *et al.*, Special Paper 65, Geol. Soc. Am.)

he shelf is marked by a sharp increase in the
slope of the bottom. This sudden increase takes
place at different distances from shore. The
width of the shelf ranges anywhere from as
little as a few miles to more than 200 miles.
On the west side of Florida the shelf is as wide
as the state. It is sometimes difficult to distinguish the shelf of a continent from a marginal
sea on the continental block itself, such as the
Gulf of Maine or the Gulf of St. Lawrence,
although the latter is usually somewhat deeper,
and its bottom has greater relief. The shelves
and such marginal seas are extremely important geologically because they are the sites of
deposition for large quantities of the material
eroded from the high continents. They provide
the first catchment areas next to the continents, and in them most of the clastic sediments are trapped. Because there is an abundant supply of food and sunshine, the shallow
waters provide excellent places for living organisms. For this reason the shelves also receive large quantities of sediment deposited by
the organisms. Most of these sediments are limestones.

The continental slope is the physiographic
province usually found adjacent to the shelf.
The continental slope is steeper, 3° to 6°, as
compared with the 1:1000 of the shelf, but the
slope is still hardly enough to be detected visually. The vertical dimensions of most diagrams showing the continental margins are exaggerated so much that the slopes appear much
steeper than they are. Remember that they too
are gently sloping surfaces. In spite of their
shallow slope the ocean floor drops from a
depth of about 100 fathoms to a depth of 800
to 1800 fathoms before the slope gives way to
the next physiographic province. The slopes
vary in width but are generally much narrower
than either the shelf or the rise.

The continental rise is the name given to
the province between the slope and the deep
flat part of the ocean basins. Usually a marked
decrease in slope occurs at the beginning of the
rise, but there may be no change whatsoever.
The rise ranges from a few feet to more than
100 miles in width and is characterized by
slopes between 1:1000 and 1:700, or almost as
gentle as the continental shelf.

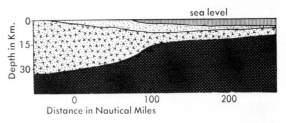

Fig. 10-8. **Cross section across the continental margins near Cape May, New Jersey.** (Worzel and
Shurbet.)

Since the margins of the continents mark
the transition zones of crustal structure it is
extremely important that we find out as much
as possible about the structure of the rocks beneath them. The physiography of a region,
whether it be on the surface of the continent
or beneath the sea, reflects not only the structure of the crust but also and sometimes primarily the effects of erosion and deposition.
The question then is: What does the continental margin look like in cross section? To find
the answers to this question geophysical studies
have been made. These have included measuring the magnetic field, noting the seismic activity of the margins, and utilizing artificially
induced shock waves.

The continental margins outside the belts
of the island arcs are not seismically active.
Very few earthquakes are found within the
provinces of the continental margins except
along island arcs.

Studies of the magnetic field of the earth
are used to detect the presence of anomalies in
the field. An unusually high reading for the
magnetic field provides a clue to the presence
of rocks with magnetic properties. Studies of
this nature have revealed some high anomalies
over the continental shelf, which are interpreted
as buried volcanoes. Anomalies have also appeared along the continental slope, and they
may be related to the transition zone between
the continental and oceanic crust. The continental rise is marked by the absence of magnetic anomalies.

Perhaps the most important information
about the structure of the margins comes from
artificially induced shock waves. These are set
up by detonating TNT on the surface of the

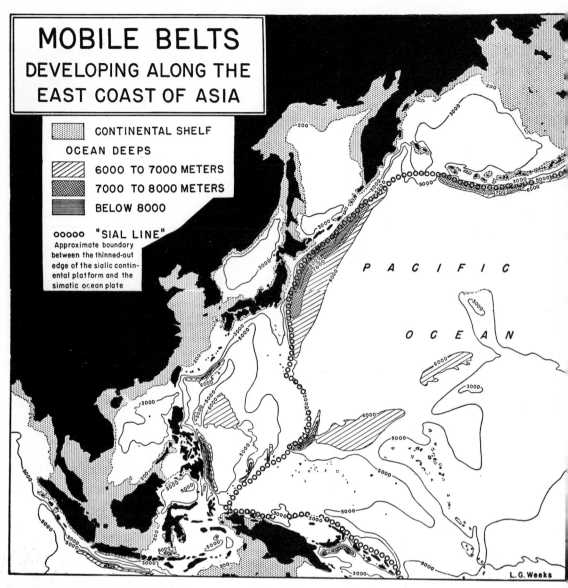

Fig. 10-9. Mobile belts and island arc systems of the western Pacific. (From L. G. Weeks, Am. Assoc. Petrol. Geol., Bull., v. 36, No. 11.)

water. The shock waves travel down through the ocean into the sediments and are reflected back from each discontinuity between different rock types. The reflected energy is picked up on the surface of the water by a string of "geophones," which are sensitive to certain frequencies of vibration. The time required for the shock wave to travel from the surface to a particular discontinuity and be reflected back to the surface is a function of the depth to that

discontinuity. Thus by measuring the time carefully it is possible to determine the depths. Other studies may be made with the shock waves that are refracted along the boundaries between rock units. Profiles of the marginal crust reveal three things in general:

1. A thick lens-shaped body of sediment and sedimentary rock beneath the continental rise.

2. A discontinuity in crustal structure at the base of the slope.
3. A wedge-shaped mass of unconsolidated sediments beneath the continental shelf.

ISLAND ARCS

One of the most interesting segments of the earth's crust is that made up of the arcuate volcanic islands, the island arcs. Undoubtedly this is the most active of the various segments of the crust. While the shields, continental margins, ocean floors, and even the young folded mountains and the mid-ocean ridge have been relatively stable for long periods of time, the island arcs are the site of greatest instability found anywhere on earth. Here more than any other place processes involving the crust are in action at the present time. The island arcs make up a portion of the continental margins. Most of them are located in the Pacific Ocean where they almost form a rim around the entire northern, western, and southern margins. Others are located in the Atlantic, especially in the Caribbean Sea. Note the locations shown on the map, Fig. 10-9. The largest arcs include:

1. The Aleutian Islands arc, extending from Alaska to Kamchatka.
2. The Kurile Islands arc (Kamchatka to Japan).
3. The Japanese arc.
4. The Philippines arc.
5. The Indonesian archipelago, Sumatra through Java to North Guinea.
6. Solomons Islands arc.
7. New Hebrides arc.
8. New Caledonia arc.
9. Kermadecs and Tonga Island arcs.
10. Sandwich Islands.
11. West Indies arc.

The general features of the island arcs are well known to us. Their pattern on a map is so striking that even the most casual observer must note the peculiar arcuate arrangements of the islands in these belts. Large earthquakes are common in these active belts, and this in itself has provided an excellent means of study of the crustal sections near the arcs. Many studies have been made of the gravity field over the arcs, and like other geophysical studies the results have been most impressive. The weakest link in our chain of knowledge about the arcs comes from a lack of basic geologic field studies. This is understandable because most of the islands are located in the tropics, they are covered by jungles and thick lava flows, and their margins are usually fringed by reefs.

Many of the unique features of the arcs are found to be common to all arcs. These include:

1. Shape: The islands form an arc that extends for 100 miles or more. These arcs are almost invariably convex toward the deep-ocean basin. Most of the arcs end where they intersect a second arc.
2. Location: All arcs are marginal to continents. They are situated just at the contact of the continental crust and the oceanic crust. That this is the case in the Pacific is shown by the difference in the composition of lavas coming out of volcanoes on the islands, which is andesite (intermediate between rhyolite, the composition of granite, and basalt), and out of those of the central Pacific, which are basalts. The line separating these compositional differences is called the Andesite Line. On the continental side the lavas are always andesitic; on the other side they are always basaltic.
3. Deep-sea trenches: These contain the greatest depths found anywhere in the oceans. The trenches are elongate furrows up to 38,000 feet below sea level. They are long, very narrow, and deep. Some of the trenches have flat floors similar to the abyssal plains. The trenches are all located on the deep-ocean side of the islands.
4. Large negative gravity anomalies are found invariably over the deep-sea trenches. The negative anomaly means that the force of gravity over the trench is less than would be predicted for a theoretical homogeneous earth. There-

fore there is a mass deficiency in the section of the earth beneath the anomalies.

5. All island arcs are the sites of volcanic activity. Most of the arcs appear to be made up largely of volcanic rocks near the surface, and although volcanic activity is not confined to them they are the most active zones of volcanism on earth today.

6. The world's belts of greatest seismic activity parallel the arcs. Almost all of the very deep-seated, 700-km earthquakes occur in the arcs. Shallow quakes are also heavily concentrated along the arcs. If the positions of the earthquakes epicenters and their depths are plotted it is found that the deepest quakes are on the continental side and that the more shallow quakes line up in the vicinity of the bottom of the trenches. This line of quake foci is inclined about 50° toward the continents and is generally thought to be a major fault over which ocean basins and continents are moving in relation to one another.

7. The largest and youngest batholiths are found in the arcs.

Fig. 10-10. The distribution of volcanoes and intermediate depth earthquake zones in the Pacific. Notice how closely these conform to the deep sea trenches and the island arc systems. (From L. G. Weeks, Am. Assoc. Petrol, Geol., Bull., v. 36, No. 11.)

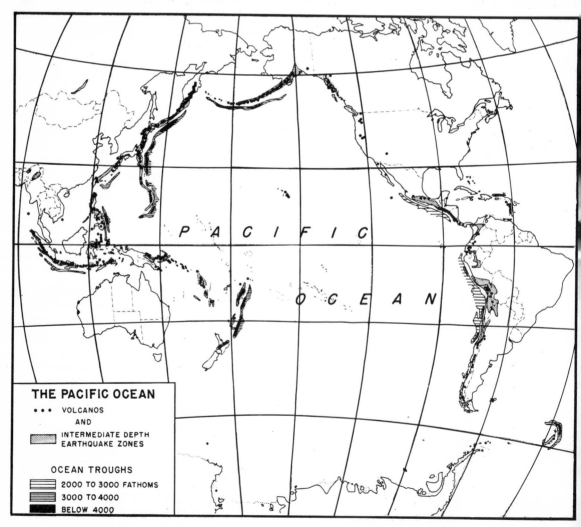

THE PACIFIC OCEAN

• • • VOLCANOS
AND

INTERMEDIATE DEPTH
EARTHQUAKE ZONES

OCEAN TROUGHS

2000 TO 3000 FATHOMS

3000 TO 4000

BELOW 4000

8. There is no evidence of the Precambrian basement of metamorphosed gneisses, which dominate the shields and which are exposed in the core of the folded mountains.

9. The arcs are the sites of active deformation within the crust. They may be the initial stages of the formation of mountain systems.

10. Most of the arcs are not directly connected with the continents. They are separated by seas which in several cases are more than 100 miles wide. The seas are relatively shallow.

Our attention will return to the island arc again when we consider one of the most baffling and yet intriguing problems of the earth —the origin of the continents and the cause of repeated upheaval of the crust.

THE DEEP OCEANIC CRUST

The continental rise slopes gradually to depths of about 1800 fathoms. At about this depth the floor of the ocean basin is found. At least three major sections can be recognized on the basis of topography. They are the abyssal floor, the oceanic rises, and the seamounts.

The abyssal floors or plains are more or less the mid-ocean counterparts of the great plains of the North American Mid-continent. They are flat—much flatter, in fact, than the plains of Kansas, Oklahoma, or the Dakotas. Abyssal plains have been found in all oceans. However, they do not necessarily occupy the central parts of the ocean. In the North Atlantic there are four plains, two on either side of the Mid-Atlantic Ridge. They are found off coasts which do not have marginal trenches such as those of the island-arc systems. The abyssal plains have relief amounting to a few feet, they are irregular in shape, and are found in a great range of sizes up to several hundred miles across. The margins of the abyssal plains are frequently marked by the presence of greater relief consisting of isolated hills which project up above the extremely flat surface around

them. These may well represent a topography being slowly buried in the plains.

The oceanic rises are large areas that are not part of the mid-ocean ridges or the isolated seamounts. They rise a few hundred fathoms above the level of the surrounding abyssal floor. Such rises are found around Bermuda and in the South Atlantic, Indian, and Pacific oceans.

Seamounts are isolated mountain-shaped rises in the oceans. Seamounts usually protrude more than 500 fathoms above the ocean floor and they may extend to the surface where they project through as islands. Seamounts are found on the oceanic rises and on the mid-ocean ridges as well as the abyssal floors. Most seamounts appear to be the remnants of volcanoes. Some are still active. Most have the general shape of volcanoes, and their sides are covered by ash and volcanic debris.

The abyssal plains and the oceanic rises are seismically inactive. With the use of the same geophysical techniques already described, the crustal sections has been obtained in these provinces. It is essentially composed of:

a. A layer of water 1800 fathoms deep.
b. Between 1/2 and 1 km of unconsolidated sediment and sedimentary rocks.
c. Oceanic crustal rocks 3 to 4 km thick.
d. The Moho discontinuity.

MID-OCEAN RIDGES

The mid-ocean ridge is one of the longest and most continuous features of the crust of the earth. The existence of a Mid-Atlantic ridge has been known for many years, but its true structural extent under the oceans was discovered only recently, in 1958. This ridge runs the length of the North Atlantic, South Atlantic, the Indian, and across the South Pacific oceans. It is more than 40,000 miles long.

The Mid-Atlantic Ridge is the best-known part of the mid-ocean ridge. Only a few years ago the general conception most people had of the bottom of the ocean was that of an extensive flat, almost featureless plain dotted here and there by isolated volcanoes. The changes

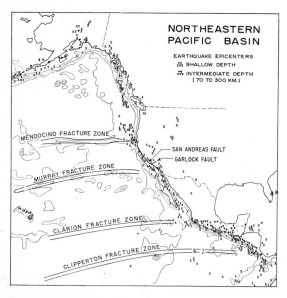

Fig. 10-11. Major rift zones in the floor of the Pacific Ocean. Some of these may be traced far out into the Pacific. (After H. W. Menard.)

in this idea have been brought about mainly by the development of the echo-sounding methods of determining depth. The instruments used in these methods are now perfected to the point of measuring the depth accurately within a few feet, and they are capable of making almost continuous soundings along the track of the ship carrying them. The recording of depths is made on a piece of paper mounted on a rotating drum. A sound wave is sent out from the ship, and the time required for it to be reflected back to the ship is a measure of the depth of the water. The instrument is equipped to send and receive these sounds, and to record the interval of time between them. It is a fascinating experience to watch the picture of the bottom of the ocean unfold before your eyes as your ship makes its way across the Atlantic. In crossing from New York to England or France you would see first the nearly smooth continental shelf, then the break as you passed over the edge of the slope. This smooth surface slowly gives way to a gentler continental rise and finally the smoothness of the abyssal plain. As you approach the middle of the ocean the bottom becomes much more irregular, and small peaks of mountains begin to make their clear impression on the record.

Finally the rise becomes quite striking, and you realize that you are sailing across a mountain range that would appear higher than the Rockies if you could see it. The islands of the Azores represent the top of this range. Once the ridge has been crossed, the bottom deepens again to the level of the abyssal plains, and then the picture is reversed as you approach the western European coast.

The most unusual feature along the Mid-Atlantic Ridge is the presence of a rift valley that runs along the crest of the ridge throughout most of its extent. This shows up as a notch or cleft on most profiles. The valley is frequently as much as 1000 fathoms lower than the peaks on either side of it, and the two sides are 20 to 30 miles across. This rift appears to be a down-dropped section of the crust bounded on either side by faults. This feature exists not only on the crest of the Mid-Atlantic Ridge; there is positive evidence of its existence at many places along the mid-oceanic ridges, and it is possible that this rift zone follows the mid-oceanic ridges around the world. If it does, it may be of profound significance since a rift of this sort could be created by having the crust of the earth pulled apart in tension. It is too early now to know what more detailed work will reveal concerning this recent discovery.

Unlike the continental margins and the deep oceanic basins, the mid-ocean ridge is the center of much seismic activity. When the epicenters of earthquakes occurring in the oceans are plotted they form two striking patterns. One is associated with the island arcs, and the second is a very narrow zone along the crest of the mid-oceanic ridges. Many of the epicenters fall in or on the edges of the rift valley along the crest of the ridge.

The rocks dredged and cored and exposed along the Mid-Atlantic Ridge are basic igneous rocks and volcanic rocks most of which are basaltic in composition. The samples include such rocks as olivine, gabbro, serpentine, basalt, and diabase. The same is true of the rocks dredged from the flanks of mountains in the Pacific. They are largely basic igneous and volcanic rocks.

The crustal structure of the Mid-Atlantic

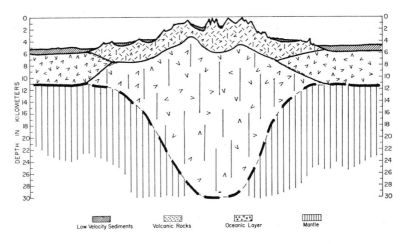

Fig. 10-12. A generalized structure section across the Mid-Atlantic Ridge. (From Ewing & Ewing, Geol. Soc. America, Bull., v. 70, No. 3.)

DEPTH IN KILOMETERS

Low Velocity Sediments   Volcanic Rocks   Oceanic Layer   Mantle

Ridge is known only through scattered seismic profiles. In general it consists of:

a. 1/2 km of sediment.
b. 3 km of rock with velocity of 5.1 km/sec, about that of basalt.
c. A substratum of velocity 7.3 km/sec.

The most significant distinction between this and other sections of the oceanic crust is the substratum with velocity 7.3 km/sec. This velocity is intermediate between the crustal rocks typical of the oceans (6.7 km/sec) and that of the mantle (8.1 km/sec), below the Moho. Remember, then, it is the appearance of the jump to 8.1 km/sec that is taken as the lower boundary of the crust. The question then arises as to why the velocity is lower under the mid-ocean ridges. The explanation offered by Professor Ewing of the Lamont Geological Observatory of Columbia University is that there has been an intermixing of the subcrust and the lower part of the crust under the ridge, brought about by intrusion and vulcanism.

Origin of the ridge. Only since the late 1950's have attempts been made to understand the mid-ocean ridges. Our researches are still in the vital stage of accumulation of knowledge, factual data with which to judge the hypothesis regarding its origin. But even now some hypotheses of its origin have been advanced. These may be enumerated, although there is not yet enough information available to allow us to evaluate their real importance completely.

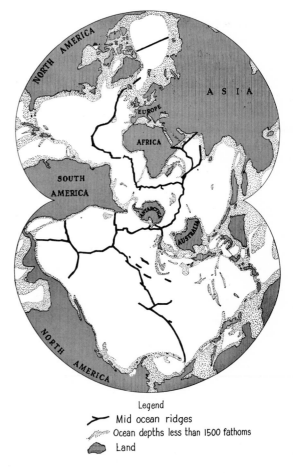

Fig. 10-13. The mid-ocean ridges. To view the Pacific Ocean invert the page. This ridge is continuous for about forty thousand miles. It is a few hundred miles wide and from 10,000 to 30,000 feet high above the ocean floors. Near the crust of this ridge there is a fault scarp along which the crust is ruptured and pulled apart slightly. (From J. T. Wilson, *Am. Scientist*, v. 47, No. 1.)

Legend
Mid ocean ridges
Ocean depths less than 1500 fathoms
Land

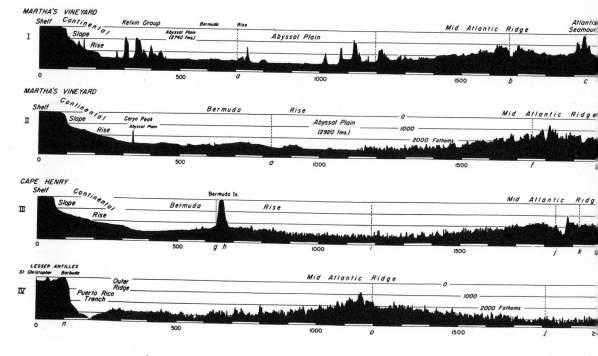

1. The ridge may be a folded mountain system; however, there is presently no evidence to support this idea.
2. It is mainly a high pile of volcanic debris and lava flows.
3. It now appears that the crest has been faulted to form the rift valleys, and it

may be similar to the rift valleys of east Africa.
4. If the notches observed are, as they appear to be, rifts, then we must seek an explanation for this origin. Were these rifts caused by horizontal extension of the earth's crust, or were they caused

Fig. 10-15. Structure cross section of the Puerto Rico Trench. This section is based on geophysical studies of the Eastern Caribbean region. The breaks between different layers represent changes in the elastic properties of the rocks and probably in the composition of the layers. (After Officer, *et al.,* 1959. Reprinted with permission from *Physics and Chemistry of the Earth,* v. 3, 1959, Pergamon Press, Inc.)

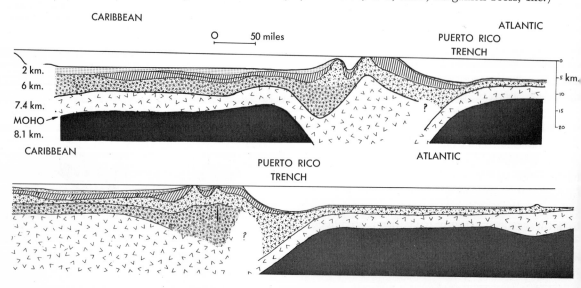

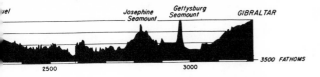

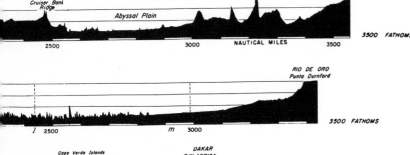

Fig. 10-14. Profiles of the Atlantic Ocean sea floor. Note the great vertical exaggeration of the scale, 40:1. (From B. C. Heezen, et al., Special Paper 65, Geol. Soc. Am.)

by uplift and tensional stresses across the top of the upfolded mass?

5. A potential cause of uplift might be the absorption of water by the subcrustal rocks. The effect of this would be the formation of serpentine rocks, which can swell. This volume increase might cause such an upbulge in the crust, and also create tension across the crest of the bulge.

REFERENCES

BAILEY, E. B., 1935, *Tectonic Essays, Mainly Alpine:* Oxford, Clarendon Press, 200 p.

BORNHAUSER, MAX, *Gulf Coast Tectonics:* A.A.P.G., v. 42, No. 2

BUCHER, W. H., 1933, *The Deformation of the Earth's Crust:* Princeton, N.J., Princeton University Press, 518 p.

DALY, R. A., 1940, *Strength and Structure of the Earth:* New York, Prentice-Hall, 434 p.

HEEZEN, B. C., THARP, MARIE, and EWING, MAURICE, 1959, *The Floors of the Oceans. 1. The North Atlantic:* Geol. Soc. America, Spec. Paper 65 (122 p. and map in color)

HOWELL, B. F., JR., 1959, *Introduction to Geophysics:* New York, McGraw-Hill Book Co., 399 p.

JACOBS, J. A., RUSSELL, R. D., and WILSTON, J. T.,

1959, *Physics and Geology:* New York, Mc-Graw-Hill Book Co., 424 p.

KING, P. B., 1951, *The Tectonics of Middle North America:* Princeton University Press, 203 p.

KLEMME, H. D., *Regional Geology of Circum-Mediterranean Region:* A.A.P.G., v. 42, No. 3, Pt. 1, p. 477

KUIPER, G. P., Editor, 1953–, *The Solar System:* 6 vols., Chicago, University of Chicago Press (v. 1, 1953, v. 2, 1954, v. 3-6 in press)

MASON, BRIAN, 1958, *Principles of Geochemistry,* 2nd ed.: New York, John Wiley & Sons, 310 p.

OFFICER, C. B., et al., March, 1957, *Geophysical Investigations in Eastern Caribbean:* Geol. Soc. America, v. 68

OFFICER, C. B., *Southwest Pacific Crustal Structure:* Trans. A.G.U., v. 36, No. 3

POLDERVAART, ARIE, Editor, 1955, *The Crust of the Earth:* Geol. Soc. America, Spec. Paper 62, 762 p.

SHEPARD, F. P., 1959, *The Earth Beneath the Sea:* London, Oxford University Press, 275 p.

SVERDRUP, H. U., JOHNSON, M. W., and FLEMING, R. H., 1942, *The Oceans, Their Physics, Chemistry, and General Biology:* New York, Prentice-Hall, 1087 p.

TRUMBULL, JAMES, *Continents and Ocean Basins and Their Relation to Continental Shelves and Continental Slopes,* U.S. Geol. Survey, Bull. 1067, February, 1958 (first paper)

WILSON, J. T., 1959, *Geophysics and Continental Growth:* Am. Scientist, v. 47, p. 1-24

11   The Interior of the Earth

The interior of the earth poses many problems for those who would try to unfold its secrets. A knowledge of it is fundamental to an understanding of the origin of the earth, the causes of mountain formation, the development of deep trenches in the ocean basins, and the nature of other planets. In short, processes in the earth's interior have controlled directly or in-

directly the development of most of the features within the crust and on the surface of the earth. Yet there are few opportunities to make direct observations of the interior. A few wells drilled by petroleum companies have penetrated between 20,000 and 25,000 feet of the earth's crust. But these barely scratch the outermost layers. It is a distance of 3959 miles from the center of the earth to the surface. The deepest wells penetrate about one-thousandth of this distance.

The interior of the earth is often defined as that part of the planet that lies below a depth of 10 miles. When this definition was formulated the interior was visualized as being composed of concentric shells of material, the outermost shell being the crust. In recent years our concept of the crust has changed. Now the lower boundary of the crust is defined by the depth at which there is a sharp break or discontinuity in the velocity with which shock waves are propagated through the earth, the Moho.

Direct observations

As indicated earlier, plans are being made to drill a hole through the crust of the earth into the mantle below. The project is known as the drilling of the Mohole, and if it is successfully completed it will be the first hole to penetrate the Moho. There are many formidable problems facing those directly involved in this project. Because the crust is so thick under the continents there is little chance of drilling through it. The hole must be put down someplace in the deep-ocean basin where the crust is relatively thin. Such places as the deep-sea plain off Puerto Rico or in the Pacific south of the southern California coasts are the most likely places; the latter has been selected and special drilling techniques will be necessary.

The deepest well that has been drilled before 1960 is about 26,000 feet deep. This is approximately the depth the Mohole must be drilled in the ocean basin in order to penetrate the crust. The deep well mentioned above is in the Gulf Coast, and because of the thick accumulation of sediments there it is only about a quarter of the way through the continental crust.

Our best opportunities to study rocks that have been buried at great depths in the crust are found in the cores of the folded-mountain belts. These belts are great upbuckles in the crust. The stratified layers of sedimentary rocks near the surface are folded and faulted. The lower old metamorphic and igneous rocks are likewise deformed and uplifted high above sea level. Once this mass of crust is elevated, erosion of it is accelerated, and the younger units are cut away exposing successively older beds and then the core of the Precambrian "basement complex." It is possible to approximate the depth of burial of any part of the core by measuring the thickness of the sedimentary rock units overlying it and then the depth to which erosion has cut into the older metamorphic rocks. If the youngest sedimentary strata are marine sediments they were deposited at or below sea level. At that time the oldest unit was buried at a depth equal to the thickness of all of the intervening strata. On this basis we can say that the rocks exposed in the Blue Ridge Mountains of the eastern United States were covered by a thickness of more than 35,000 feet of sediments in the Permian Period. Even this great depth is less than half the distance to the Moho under the mountain range. Thus the interior is not exposed even in the deeply eroded folded-mountain belts.

The best evidence of the nature of the interior that can be obtained through direct observation is found where materials from below the Moho have been intruded into the crust of the earth, or in places where deep-seated volcanism brings lavas and blocks up to the surface from below the Moho.

The existence of these intrusions has been recognized for many years. Professor H. H. Hess of Princeton University summarized the origin and nature of these intrusions in 1937 at the International Geological Congress in Russia. These intrusions are composed of peridotites (a general term for essentially nonfeldspathic plutonic rocks consisting of olivine, with or without other mafic minerals. The other mafic minerals may be amphiboles, pyroxenes, or micas). Peridotites are often altered by hot waters to rock serpentine ($Mg_3Si_2O_5(OH)_4$, synonymous with asbestos). Not all peridotites are formed by intrusions from below the crust. A great many of them are formed when magmas intruded in the crust began to cool. Among the first minerals to crystallize from a magma are olivines, amphiboles, and pyroxenes. These early formed minerals then settle to the bottom

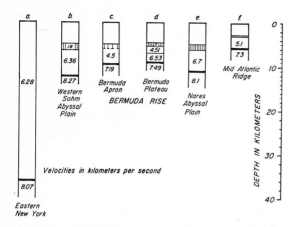

Eastern
New York

Velocities in kilometers per second

DEPTH IN KILOMETERS

Fig. 11-1. Crustal sections in various parts of the Atlantic Ocean. Note particularly the great difference in the thickness of the crust under eastern New York as compared with other sections in the ocean. (From B. C. Heezen *et al.*, 1959.)

of the magma chamber and form a layer or body which on further cooling becomes peridotite. Such a rock is called a magmatic differentiate, formed by differentiation of the molten rock. These peridotites can be distinguished from those intruded deep in the crust. They differ in texture; the differentiated peridotites have nearly perfectly formed (euhedral)

crystals of olivine in a groundmass of pyroxene. The two types also differ slightly in their mineral content. The chemical ratio of certain constituents (MgO/FeO) is higher in the peridotite found in the mountain belts, and they differ in their association with other types of rocks. (The deeply intruded types are usually associated with radiolarian cherts and spilitic lavas.)

These deeply intruded peridotites are located in the central parts of the complexly folded mountain belts such as the Alps. Since the core of the folded belts now exposed through erosion by glaciers, weathering, and running water has been uplifted great distances, it is probable that the peridotites which were intruded at the beginning of the deformation came from below the Moho. There are two minor exceptions to the association of these peridotites with alpine-type mountain systems:

1. They appear throughout the earliest Precambrian rocks such as those exposed in Southern Rhodesia and the Canadian Shield.
2. They are found on some fault scarps in the oceans where peridotitic rocks are thought to occur a few kilometers below the sea floor.

11-2. Ground fractures. These fractures opened in the ground near a fault scarp which resulted from the Montana earthquake of August, 1959. (Photo by E. W. Spencer.)

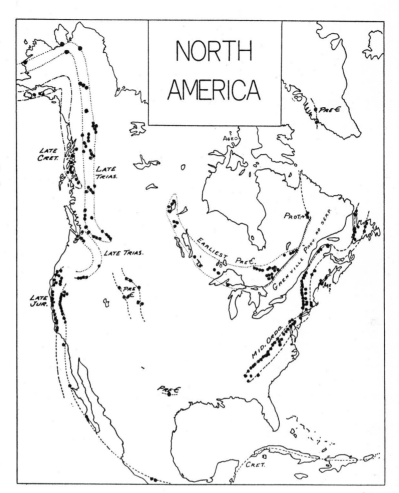

In the alpine belts the peridotites occur in two belts about 120 miles apart which extend the length of the mountain system. So close is the relationship between these peridotites and the alpine type of mountain belt that the presence of such peridotites showing a similar alignment in the earliest Precambrian rocks is used as an indication of the probable existence of an old alpine-type mountain system which has been almost completely destroyed by erosions, metamorphism, and subsequent deformation.

The Cortlandt complex

One of these peridotite bodies is located near the town of Peekskill, New York, on the Hudson River and along the axis of the Appalachian mountain system. This belt of the crust was deformed toward the end of the Ordovician Period. A long and extensive mountain range rose from the shallow seas which had covered the eastern United States for about 150 million years. Remnants of this mountain chain remain today, but in the millions of years that have elapsed since that time most of the materials of that range have been carried away to be deposited in the inland seas, which existed in the central United States during the later Paleozoic, or in the Atlantic Ocean. Erosion has stripped the younger rocks exposing the core of the range. Magma was intruded into a sequence of sedimentary rocks that were being altered to metamorphic rocks such as schists, marbles, and gneisses. Because no fossils have been found in these metamorphic rocks their age is uncertain, but they appear to be metamorphic equivalents of sediments

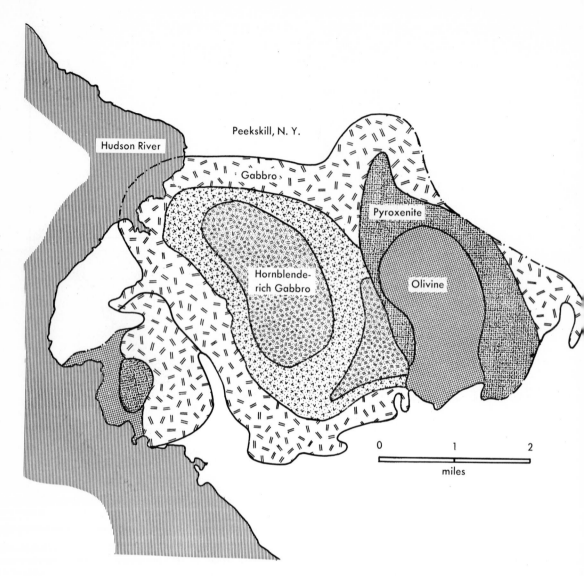

Fig. 11-4. Map of the Cortlandt Complex. The complex is mapped on the basis of variations in the mineral composition of the rocks of which it is composed. (After S. J. Shand.)

located nearby which can be dated by fossils as Cambrian and Ordovician in age.

Seventeen different types of igneous rocks such as peridotite, norite, gabbro, and diorite are found within the complex. These rock species are everywhere connected by transitional forms into the closest relationship, and they must have been derived from a common magma. Early mapping revealed the oval shape and dimensions of the intrusion. Later, more intensive investigations of the structure, petrology, and geophysical studies were made. One of

these was a map of the orientation of the small platy or elongate minerals, lenses, and bedding in units of sediment around and within the igneous mass. These blocks are xenoliths, blocks of the walls of the intrusive that were caught in the molten rock as it was injected. The map showing all these features gives a clear impression of the direction and the flowing motion of the magma. A pattern of frozen eddy currents caused by convective overturning within the liquid rock as it began to cool and crystallize is seen.

The peridotites and associated rocks within the intrusion are more dense than the country rock of schists which surrounds them. With this knowledge, studies of the force of gravitational attraction over the body were made. Where the magnitude of the gravitational pull is greatest the dense rocks must be thick. When the pull is less, the intrusion must be thinner. This technique has been used to obtain estimates of the depth and shape of the intrusion where it cannot be seen in exposures (Fig. 11-5).

The Cortlandt complex is a good example of one of the peridotite intrusions characteristic of alpine mountain systems, but it is an even better example of the way in which geologists have pooled their specialized knowledge to obtain a coherent picture of as many aspects of this natural phenomenon as possible. Williams recognized the body as an intrusion, Shand devised a means of mapping units of the intrusion, Balk showed the internal structure of it, and Steenland and Woollard have provided an understanding of its shape in depth. The results of their work are presented in part in the illustrations.

Volcanic extrusions

Other than the intrusions of peridotite in folded-mountain belts, blocks of peridotite and lavas extruded from deep-seated volcanoes offer the only means of determining directly the composition of the rocks below the crust (in the outer mantle). The Moho is at a much shallower depth under the deep-ocean basins than it is under continents, making it more likely that rocks melted below the crust would find their way to the surface beneath the deep oceans rather than to the surface on the continents. This has actually happened. There is a distinct difference in the composition of the lavas extruded from volcanoes in the Pacific basin from those coming out around the margins of the Pacific. The lavas in the deep ocean are composed of olivine basalt, while those of the boundary zone are andesite or rhyolite. "This suboceanic crust constitutes an environment within or beneath which olivine-basalt magma is generated . . . . Xenoliths of peridot-

ite might be interpreted as derivatives of a peridotite layer within the crust . . . ." (Turner and Verhoogen, 1951).

SEISMOLOGY

Most of what is known about the interior of the earth is obtained through the exacting work of seismologists. Unlike most other major branches of natural science, seismology (the study of earthquakes) dates back less than 100 years. The first effective records were not obtained until the latter part of the nineteenth century, and the application of seismology to the exploration for oil and other natural resources did not occur until after World War I. Japanese scientists have carried on much of the work on earthquake waves in hopes of finding a way to predict the occurrence of earthquakes which have taken such heavy tolls of life and property in Japan and other Asian countries. Most earthquakes are caused either by failure of the rocks of the crust and mantle or by explosions of volcanoes. The sudden impulses generated in quakes expand and distort rocks near the fault or the explosion, and they are propagated through the interior of the earth and along its surface because the materials of which the earth is composed are highly elastic. These impulses or shock waves travel with different velocities through rocks with different elastic properties. Part of the energy of a wave may be reflected or refracted where it comes to the contact between different types of rocks. Many of these waves are intense enough to go through or completely around the earth. The job of the seismologists is to devise a means of

Fig. 11-5. An hypothetical cross section through the Cortlandt Complex. (After Robert Balk, 1948.)

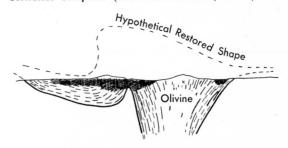

Fig. 11-6. A fault scarp formed during the Montana earthquake of 1959. When the crust of the earth breaks, shock waves are generated which may be transmitted through and around the earth. (Photo by E. W. Spencer.)

Fig. 11-7. Landslides, a side effect of severe earthquakes. This slide of thirty-five million cubic yards of debris was set off by an earthquake in Montana in 1959. (Photo by courtesy of the U.S. Geological Survey.)

Fig. 11-8. Tilted lake basin. As a result of faulting, this lake basin, Hebgen Lake, tilted, leaving these docks six feet out of water. (Photo by courtesy of the U.S. Geological Survey.)

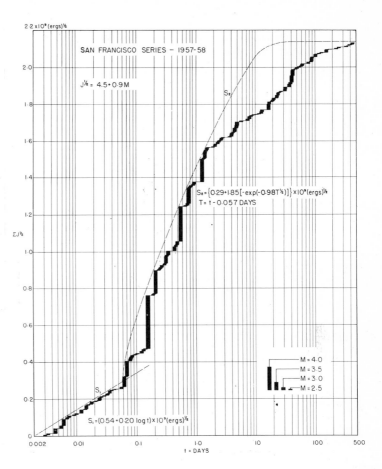

Fig. 11-9. A graph depicting the elastic rebound which follows a major earthquake as a series of aftershocks. (By courtesy of the California Division of Mines.)

In the figure:

SAN FRANCISCO SERIES – 1957-58

$J^{1/4} = 4.5 + 0.9M$

$S_2 = \{0.29 + 1.85[-\exp(-0.98T^{1/4})]\} \times 10^9 (\text{ergs})^{1/4}$
$T = t - 0.057 \text{ DAYS}$

$S_1 = (0.54 + 0.20 \log t) \times 10^9 (\text{ergs})^{1/4}$

M = 4.0
M = 3.5
M = 3.0
M = 2.5

vertical axis: $\Sigma J^{1/4}$, $2.2 \times 10^9 (\text{ergs})^{1/4}$

horizontal axis: t = DAYS

detecting the waves, to recognize the different types of waves, and to interpret their significance. The extent of their success in this difficult task marks one of the great achievements of the human mind.

Causes of earthquakes

Faults. The outer parts of the earth are not stable. Locally, at least, the earth comes under compressive stresses or is stretched and pulled apart under tension. Materials of the earth, being elastic, can withstand a certain amount of stress without deforming permanently, but if the stress is continued for a long period of time, or if it is increased in magnitude, the rocks will first take a permanent deformation or strain and eventually rupture. A fault is a break or fracture in the materials of the earth along which there has been displacement. They abound in rocks exposed at the sur-

face of the earth. When the rupture occurs, rocks on either side of the fault tend to return to their original shape because of their elasticity, and an elastic rebound occurs. It is this rebound that sets up the seismic waves. Of course, the magnitude of the faulting is highly variable. Some faults are nothing more than slight displacements in the minerals of a rock. Others extend for hundreds or thousands of miles across the surface of the earth and show accumulated displacements amounting to many miles. The San Andreas fault in California is one of the longest faults exposed at the surface of the earth. A movement along it was responsible for the San Francisco earthquake of 1906. The crust was visibly rent for a distance of 270 miles, and displacements in that zone amounted to as much as 20 feet. The movement along the fault was primarily a horizontal shifting, with minor vertical displacement. That this fault has been active for a long period of time is shown by the displacement of streams and other physiographic and geologic features. All of these features are offset to the right on opposite sides of the fault.

Macelwane (1947) summarizes the character of the majority of the slight earthquake shocks as follows:

"1. The area of greatest intensity often lies along a known fault zone;
2. They occur far from any volcano;
3. Even in the neighborhood of an active volcano they are often not correlated with any particular sign of volcanic activity;
4. They often associate themselves in groups in which the center of intensity of successive earthquakes migrates parallel to a fault zone."

Volcanic earthquakes. In general the earthquakes associated with volcanoes are more localized both in extent of damage and in intensity of the waves produced than are those associated with faulting motions. In some regions, particularly in the circum-Pacific belt, volcanic activity and active faulting are closely associated. Nevertheless it is possible to distinguish some earthquakes as being caused by activity due to volcanic phenomena not associated with major breaks in the crust of the earth. A shock may be produced by any of the following mechanisms:

1. Explosion of the volcano upon the release and expansion of gases and lavas.
2. Faulting within the volcano resulting from pressures in the chamber of molten rock.
3. Collapse of the center of the volcano into the space formed by the extrusion of gases and molten matter.

Kwanto earthquake

One of the greatest earthquakes on record occurred about 50 miles from Tokyo, Japan, on September 1, 1923. Estimates of the loss of as many as a quarter of a million lives have been made. The earthquake occurred shortly before noon, and much of the damage was caused by fires which swept through the ruins just after the quake. These fires were started because so many families were cooking at the time of the quake. Buildings collapsed and ignited, and water mains were broken making the extinguishing of the fires impossible. Half a million buildings were shaken down in the region around Sagami Bay, and much of this damage was concentrated in the heavily populated cities of Tokyo and Yokohama. Hydrographic resurveys of the bay made shortly after the quake revealed changes in the shape and depth of the bottom of the bay of such magnitude that most geologists attribute part of the change to errors in the earlier survey. If the figures of both surveys are taken at face value some areas of the bay were lowered more than 650 feet, and other areas were raised more than 800 feet. Even allowing for errors in surveying, the magnitude of the changes was exceptionally great. Most of the sediments in the bay came from eruptions of the famous volcano Fujiyama. It is likely that these unconsolidated sediments shifted or slumped during the earthquake. Waves on the surface of the bay attained a height of 35 feet during and shortly after the earthquake, and more than 1000 aftershocks of minor intensity followed the main quake, which lasted only a few minutes.

Assam, India

The earthquake which occurred in the range of mountains south of the Himalaya Mountains and north of the Bay of Bengal in 1897 is probably the most violent in recorded history. The quake occurred when the mountains, which are formed of large blocks of the crust that have been tilted along faults, were shifted northward and uplifted as much as 35 feet in some places. Faults that opened in the surface were traced for more than 20 miles into the jungle. Drainage of some streams was stopped; lakes formed, and large areas flooded. In other areas lakes and swamps were drained. Many fissures opened in the ground. Almost all masonry buildings in the mountains were leveled. The region of complete destruction covered nearly 9000 square miles. Extensive damage was done in an area of 150,000 square miles, and the quake was felt over an area of 3/4 million square miles.

Katmai

This volcano is located on the Aleutian Peninsula and is one of many volcanoes that make up the Aleutian island arc, so called because of the arcuate pattern formed by these volcanic islands. Similar systems of islands are common around the western margin of the Pacific. Katmai exploded in 1912 after a long period of dormancy. The eruption could be heard as far south as Juneau, which is 750 miles away. The explosive activity continued for 3 days. Immense clouds of ash and volcanic dust blown up by the explosions settled around the volcano covering the ground with several feet of ash. Dust from the eruption covered the ground for hundreds of miles and the shocks were strong enough to be recorded in Europe.

Madison Canyon earthquake, Montana

On the night of August 17, 1959, the region west of Yellowstone Park was shaken by one of the five most intense earthquakes ever recorded in the United States. This quake could be felt from the plains of the Dakotas to the State of Washington. In the immediate vicinity of the epicenter people were thrown out of bed, and vibrations of the ground were so intense that it was impossible to walk during the first shocks. For days after the first shocks the ground motion was periodically resumed. Ground motion was great enough to set off many landslides, including the disastrous Madison Canyon slide. This quake was caused by faulting motion. Displacements of as much as 20 feet occurred along a fault system which can be traced for more than 20 miles. The faults are associated with the borders of the Madison Mountain Range, which has been uplifted along these and other faults in the past. Thus, although this particular movement is the first in recorded history in this locality, it was probably preceded by a great many previous movements, some of which date back many

millions of years to the time when this part of the Rockies was first deformed in the Cretaceous Period. Unlike the movements along the San Andreas fault in California, which are horizontal displacements, these faults were displaced vertically. The mountain block rose 20 feet. At the same time a large reservoir, Hebgen Lake, was tilted. During the movements large waves formed on the lake; the margins of the lake slumped into the edge of the lake; and before movement ceased one side of the lake had been lowered and flooded by the lake, while the other side was uplifted and left dry.

Chilean earthquakes of 1960

At 6 A.M. on May 21, 1960, a sharp earthquake was felt in the region around Concepción, Chili. Considerable property damage was

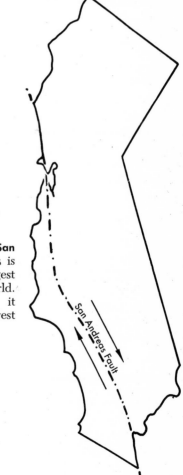

Fig. 11-10. The San Andreas fault. This is one of the longest faults in the world. Movements along it have shifted the west side northward.

caused by this movement and most of the people in the region affected were so frightened that they ran out of their houses. This quake which was later determined to have originated at a depth of 50 kilometers was followed by small aftershocks for all of the next day. Then on the next day at 3 P.M. a second sharp shock came and was followed fifteen minutes later by the most severe shock of what was to be a long period of violent earth movements. The center of this shock was almost 300 kilometers south of Concepción, but it affected an area 150 kilometers wide and 1600 kilometers long along the coast of Chile.

People ran out of their houses during the first shock, and when the second came waves were visible in the streets and ground. Trees and telephone poles swayed back and forth, loud noises were heard coming from the ground, and cracks formed in the ground. Cars were tossed back and forth across the street and some fell into fissures. Almost all man-made structures in this region were damaged and many were totally destroyed. Landslides caused by the quake buried parts of a number of cities.

The strongest shocks were felt at Isla Chiloe where trees were snapped off, the ground cracked open and highways were split, road fills which had been constructed gave out, and soils became liquid and flowed.

After the main shocks the sea began to retreat well below low tide and came back 20 minutes later as tidal waves between 4 and 11 meters high. The waves destroyed parts of many towns. In one alone five hundred people were drowned. These tidal waves were set up by subsidence of parts of the coast. In places the subsidence amounted to 2 meters. The wave motion caused in Chile by this subsidence crossed the Pacific and destroyed towns in Hawaii and in Japan.

On May 24 an explosion occurred on the side of one of the large active volcanos in Chile. Ash, steam, and finally lava poured from a fissure about a hundred meters long. There was no loss of life and relatively little property damage as a result of this side effect of the earthquake. However, quakes continued, in Chile for several months following the first

shock in May, and these have been responsible for billions of dollars in property damage and the loss of more than 5000 lives in what may have been the most severe earthquake of this century.

Mercalli made studies of the intensity and regional effects of earthquakes between 1890 and 1901. He found that some regions suffered much more intense shocks than others and that the most intense earthquakes for a region tended to occur during a certain period of years. His work called for an accurate scale of the intensity of the quakes, and he devised such a scale. At that time few seismographs were in existence; thus the scale had to be based on readily obtainable information. His scale is still in use today. (Nicholas H. Heck, *Earthquakes,* Princeton University Press, 1936).

MODIFIED MERCALLI INTENSITY SCALE

1. Not felt except by a few under especially favorable conditions.
2. Felt only by a few persons at rest. Delicately suspended objects may swing.
3. Felt quite noticeably under favorable circumstances. Standing automobiles may rock slightly.
4. Felt by many or most persons. Some awakened. Dishes, windows, doors disturbed, walls crack. Sensation like heavy truck striking building.
5. Some dishes, windows, etc., broken; a few instances of cracked plaster, unstable objects moved.
6. Felt by all; many frightened and run outdoors. Some heavy furniture moved; a few instances of fallen plaster or damaged chimneys.
7. Everyone runs outdoors. Damage negligible in buildings of good design and construction; slight to moderate in well-built ordinary structures; some chimneys broken. Noticed by persons driving cars.
8. Panel walls thrown out of frame structures. Fall of chimneys, factory stacks, columns, monuments, walls. Heavy furniture overturned. Sand and mud ejected in small amounts.
9. Buildings shifted off foundations,

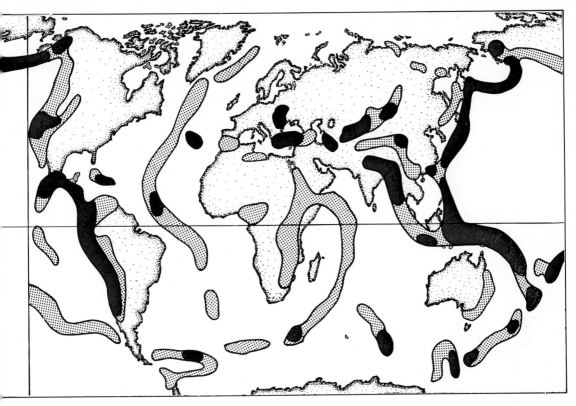

Fig. 11-11. Distribution of earthquakes. Belts of moderately intensive activity are lightly stippled. The darker portions are the zones of most intensive earthquake activity. These belts coincide with the folded mountain belts and the mid-ocean ridges. (After Yu. A. Meshcheryakov, American Geological Institute, International Geology Review, v. 1, No. 8, August, 1959, pp. 48-49.)

ground cracked conspicuously. Underground pipes broken.

10. Ground badly cracked, rails bent, landslides considerable from river banks and steep slopes. Water splashed over banks.

11. Few masonry structures remain standing. Bridges destroyed. Broad fissures in ground. Earth slumps and land slips in soft ground.

12. Damage total. Waves seen on ground surfaces. Lines of sight and level distorted. Objects thrown into the air.

DISTRIBUTION OF EARTHQUAKES

It might appear that the distribution of earthquakes on the face of the earth is a simple matter. However, the picture one gets of the seismicity of the world depends on what factors were taken into consideration when the data were compiled. Different patterns are obtained if each of the following is plotted:

a. Distribution of the number of earthquakes that were felt or recorded.

b. Distribution of deep or shallow earthquakes.

c. Distribution of quakes of different intensities.

Seismograph stations are most abundant in heavily populated areas, and records have been made in some areas for a much longer period than in others. Thus, if a summary of all available data is used, a false idea of the activity of different parts of the earth results. Detailed studies of the distribution of earthquakes have been made by the late Professor Gutenberg and Professor Richter at the California Institute of Technology. The results of their work are shown in Fig. 11-11. Professor Richter summarizes the major features of the seismicity of the earth as follows (Richter, 1958):

Epicenters occur chiefly in a few narrow belts or zones. Certain wider areas show fairly general moderate activity. Seismologically speaking, the most important subdivisions of the earth's surface are:

1. The circum-Pacific belt, with many branches and complexities.
2. The Alpide belt of Europe and Asia; this may be considered an extension of one of the main branches of the circum-Pacific belt.
3. The Pamir-Baikal zone of central Asia.
4. The Atlantic-Arctic belt.
5. The belt of the central Indian Ocean, with branches.
6. Rift zones, notably those of East Africa.
7. A wide triangular active area in eastern Asia, between the Alpide belt and the Pamir-Baikal zone.
8. Minor seismic areas, usually in regions of older mountain building.
9. The central basin of the northern Pacific Ocean; almost nonseismic except for the Hawaiian Islands.
10. The stable central shields of the continents, also nearly nonseismic.

The stable areas (10) are generally known as shields. They include: the Canadian Shield (Greenland being considered a detached part); the Brazilian Shield; the Baltic Shield; the Angara Shield located in northern Asia; the African Shield (Arabia and Madagascar being detached portions); the Australian Shield; the Antarctic Shield; and Peninsular India.

The circum-Pacific belt contains most of the shallow and intermediate-depth earthquakes and almost all deep-focus earthquakes. The belt running through the mountain system which contains the Alps and Himalayas (2, 3) contains most of the remaining shallow and intermediate quakes, and two deep quakes have been recorded in it in Spain and Italy.

NATURE OF SHOCK WAVES IN THE EARTH

Before considering the paths followed by shock waves in the earth, and the recording and interpretation of them, we must gain at least an elementary understanding of the properties of rocks that make it possible for seismic waves started by an earthquake in Japan to be transmitted through the earth with sufficient magnitude to be recorded in New York or London.

Elastic properties of rocks

Rocks possess certain elastic properties which enable them to transmit shock waves or seismic waves. A perfectly elastic material is one which returns exactly to its original form when a deforming force is removed. A rock behaves elastically within a certain limit of deformation. If the strain or change in shape of the rock exceeds that limit, the rock cannot fully recover after the deforming force is removed. If the strain greatly exceeds the elastic limit, the rock may rupture. Strains (changes in shape) in rocks are caused by stresses, forces applied over a certain area of the rock. Several types of stress situations are recognized. An elevator cable tends to pull apart. It is under what is called tensile stress. The elongation of the cable resulting from the stress is a tensile strain. A different type of stress is found in a bar such as the drive shaft of an automobile which is twisted and said to be in torque. This stress is called shearing stress. If, on the other hand, a nail is driven into a board with a hammer, the nail is shortened under a compressive stress with each blow. Still another type of stress is found in bodies submerged in a liquid or in rocks buried under great thickness of rock. The name "hydrostatic pressure" is applied in cases where objects are submerged in water, and "rock pressure" is the corresponding term designating pressure deep in the crust or in the interior of the earth. In the case of rock pressure, the same uniform inward pressure is exerted over the entire surface of the object.

Experimental tests may be run on rocks as on engineering materials, to determine the amount of strain produced by various types of stresses. The expression of these reactions is given by three elastic moduli (a modulus is a antity that expresses the measure of some fect). These three are Young's modulus, hich is a ratio of tensile stress to tensile rain; shear modulus, which is the ratio of earing stress to shearing strain; and bulk modulus, which is the ratio of the pressure rock pressure) to the resulting change in olume due to that pressure, divided by the riginal volume. The bulk modulus is a measre of the compressibility of the rock. The mpressibility of a substance is the fractional hange in volume per unit increase in pressure hydrostatic or rock) on it.

Shock waves

When an earthquake occurs, a sudden ovement of rocks in the crust takes place. his sudden movement may be either the lastic rebound resulting from release of tresses on either side of a fault when the rupure occurs, or the compression on the sides of volcano created by a sudden explosion. This mpetus given to the rocks in the immediate icinity of the quake is transmitted from one art of the crust to the next. If the rocks are omogeneous, then identical reactions to the nitial shock move outward from the point of rigin in spherical shells. Because rocks are igid, the strain produced in one part of the ock is transmitted to the other parts very apidly, and the shock wave travels great disances before its energy is expended.

Two types of waves, dilational and shear, re set up by quakes. The dilational waves are lso known as P waves, compressional, and ongitudinal waves. They involve changes in he volume of the rock through which they are ransmitted. Sound waves are examples of this ype of wave motion. Sound travels through ny compressible medium such as water or ocks. A vibration is set up in the air by moion of the object sending the sound, as in the notion of the surface of a drum after it is hit. s the face of the drum moves out on each vibration it forces the air away from it. The ir is compressed. The layer of compressed air n turn compresses the layer of air next to it, nd so the wave is transmitted. Each time the drum face moves in, the air next to it is pulled as if it were under tension. This pull is transmitted to the next layer of air and follows the compressed layer outward as an expanding spherical shell. The vibration is along the path of travel of the wave front—hence the name "longitudinal." Shear waves are known as S waves, or transverse waves. They vibrate perpendicular to the direction in which the wave front is moving, and they are caused by the transmission of shearing stresses like the twist in a bar. No volume changes are associated with them, but other distortions of shape are.

In addition to the P and S waves, more complicated wave motion is produced and propagated along the surface of the earth. Lord Rayleigh was the first to recognize this special wave type on the surfaces of bounded elastic solids. In the propagation of a Rayleigh wave, motion is vertical and in the direction of motion of the wave front. Each particle involved in this motion follows an elliptical orbit in retrograde motion (along the bottom of the ellipse the motion is in the direction of propagation and at the top in the opposite direc-

Fig. 11-12. Wave fronts and rays. When a shock wave is generated along a fault or from an explosion it travels outward from the focus in a spherical shell-like form. It is customary to represent the position of the wave fronts by lines drawn perpendicular to successive wave fronts. These lines are called rays.

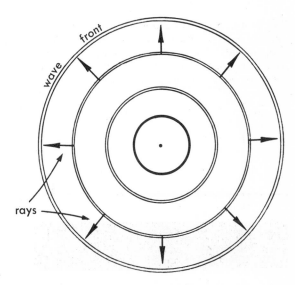

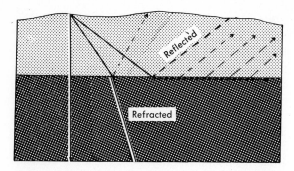

Fig. 11-13. Schematic illustration of the reflection and refraction of a shock wave along a contact between two rock units of different materials. The wave represented by the vertical ray passes through the boundary without reflection or refraction. The second ray is bent into the lower unit at the contact. Part of the energy is reflected back up into the top unit. The third ray is shown approaching the boundary at what is known as the critical angle. Part of the energy is reflected back into the top unit, and the remainder is refracted along the contact. All along the contact energy continues to be refracted back into the top unit. The wave energy which is reflected and refracted into the top unit from the boundary may be picked up by geophones placed on the ground surface.

tion). A. E. H. Love later demonstrated the probable existence of another type of wave, the Love wave, which travels at the surface, with displacements being transverse to the direction of motion of the wave front. These two wave motions move along the ground surface.

Fig. 11-14. A simple seismograph. The mass suspended on the wire tends to stand still while the support and the drum move during an earthquake. This instrument would measure the motion in the direction perpendicular to the page.

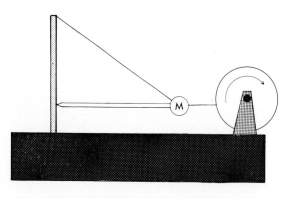

Velocity of the shock waves

The velocity of propagation of seismic waves through a rock is determined by the elastic properties and the density of the rock. The equations for the velocity of the P and S waves are:

P (compressional, waves)
$$V_p = \frac{(x + 2u)^{\frac{1}{2}}}{\rho}$$

S (Shear waves)
$$V_s = \frac{(u)^{\frac{1}{2}}}{\rho}$$

where ρ is the density of the rock.

   u is the modulus of rigidity, the resistance of the elastic solid to shearing deformation, which can be determined experimentally.

   x is a value calculated from the modulus of rigidity and one of the other moduli which can be determined experimentally as:

$$x = B - 2/3\ u.$$
where B is the bulk modulus.

These formulae indicate that the velocity of P waves is increased as the rocks become more rigid and more nearly incompressible, and that the velocity is decreased as the rocks become more dense.

The velocity of the shear wave increases with increased rigidity and decreases with increased density. The shear wave cannot travel through media which cannot be sheared, such as liquids, whereas the P wave does continue through liquids because it depends on the compressibility of the medium. These effects of density should be especially noted since density and seismic velocity increase with depth in the earth. This must mean that rigidity of the rocks increases faster than density.

Bending, reflection, and refraction

Seismic waves are bent as they pass through layers that gradually increase in rigidity with depth. The waves are reflected and refracted when they come to boundaries between layers with different elastic properties or densities. When a shock wave reaches a discontinuity (a change in elastic properties), part of the energy of the wave is reflected back toward the surface. The velocity of the reflected wave remains unchanged, but the remainder of the energy passes through the boundary and continues as a wave with increased or decreased velocity. Because the velocity is changed, the path of the wave is changed according to Snell's Law. (See any introductory physics text.) When the wave passes from one layer to another of lower rigidity (lower velocity), the wave front (as shown by a ray) is bent down (toward a line perpendicular to the contact between the two layers). The reverse occurs when the waves pass from a less rigid to a more rigid layer. Thus the gradual increase in the rigidity of rocks with depth causes the paths of the shock waves to be curved upward.

DETECTION OF SEISMIC WAVES

Motion of the ground surface resulting from an earthquake depends on how deep and how far away the focus of the quake is located. Near the epicenter in zones of high intensity, ground motion may turn buildings on their foundation or throw objects into the air, but at great distances from the quake center the motion will most likely consist of very small displacements. You have probably felt a slight jar resulting from blasting in a quarry or building

site. The seismograph is an instrument designed to detect the magnitude and direction of these minute displacements. Any quantity that has magnitude and direction can be resolved into three mutually perpendicular components. For this reason most seismograph stations employ three instruments to record the components of ground motion along three mutually perpendicular lines. These are horizontal motion along north-south and east-west lines and motion perpendicular to the earth's surface. The principle on which most seismographs operate is very simple. In an earthquake you might see any delicately suspended object such as a chandelier begin to swing. The motion begins after the first shock is felt. Initially the chandelier stood still while the building and ground shook. It did so because like all matter it possesses inertia (that property of matter which causes it to tend to resist a change in its state of motion). The perfect seismograph is one in which it is possible to isolate a mass (as a point of reference) from the motion and measure the motion of the ground in relation to that mass. In essence this is how a seismograph works. A mass is delicately suspended by springs so it is relatively unmoved during the quake. In order to measure the relative movement between the ground and the suspended mass a magnet is used for the mass, and a coil of wire is fixed in position so it is anchored to the ground and moves past the magnet when the ground is in motion. The two are isolated so that they do not touch one

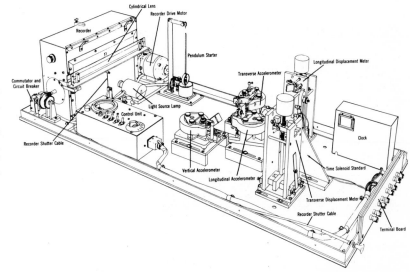

Fig. 11-15. A schematic view of an accelerograph. This instrument is used to measure the acceleration of the ground motion during an earthquake. Note the three components marked vertical, longitudinal, and transverse. (By courtesy of the U.S. Coast and Geodetic Survey.)

Fig. 11-16. Receiving component of a Wilson-Lamison seismometer. (Photo by courtesy of the U.S. Coast and Geodetic Survey.)

another at any time. During a quake the coils move through the magnetic field set up by the magnet. This induces an electrical current in the coils. The magnitude of the current is a function of how fast the coils move and thus of the amount of ground motion. The current is amplified and fed into a mirror galvanometer, causing a deflection of the small mirror mounted in the galvanometer. Again the amount of deflection of the mirror is a measure of the ground motion. A beam of light is directed through a slit onto the mirror in such a

Fig. 11-17. View of a Benioff vertical seismometer. (Photo by courtesy of the U.S. Coast and Geodetic Survey.)

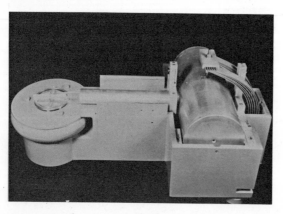

way that it is reflected to hit the surface of rotating drum. A piece of photographic pap covers the surface of the drum. The drum mounted in such a way that it moves along i axis as it rotates. It is set to rotate at a ver constant rate. Thus if the beam of light whic hits the drum were perfectly still it would de scribe a spiral path on the drum with no tw lines crossing or overlapping. A radio at th station receives time signals from the Nav Observatory or other stations broadcastin Greenwich Standard Time (this is used at sei mograph stations throughout the world to avoi confusion in timing the occurrence of an earth quake). This time signal is converted into small impulse of current sent to the galvanc meter each minute, causing a deflection of th beam and thus marking the exact time on th seismogram. The only difference in the thre components is the manner of suspension of th mass and the orientation of the instrument Fig. 11-18 is a schematic diagram of this typ of seismograph.

INTERPRETATION OF SEISMIC WAVES

While the seismograph is in operation, th trace indicating the earth's motion on the seis mogram is rarely at rest. Movements of trees i the wind, waves breaking along the sea shore and even trucks passing on nearby highway are picked up by the more sensitive instru ments. These minor movements are called mi croseisms. With the arrival of the first shock wave from an earthquake the trace is suddenly displaced from the rather sinuous path it wa following. This break is indicated by a sudder change in the direction of the movement and increased amplitude of the swing of the trace The key for the identification of the arrival o subsequent waves is also change in direction and amplitude of the movement of this trace The time of arrival of each wave at the station varies according to the path traveled by the wave in coming to the station and the velocity of the wave motion. The first wave to arrive is the one which travels the most direct path with the highest velocity. That wave is usually the P (compressional) wave which travels through

he mantle with a velocity of 8.1 km/sec. It is
ollowed by the S (shear) wave traveling the
ame path but with a velocity of 4.5 km/sec.
These velocities apply to the waves received
rom quakes not more than 10 degrees (1100
m) away. (Distances between points on a
phere may be given in miles, kilometers, or
egrees.) An earthquake 180 degrees away is
irectly on the opposite side of the earth. The
ime required for a wave to travel from the
uake to the station is called the travel time
or that wave. The travel time for the P and S
vaves is not known at the seismograph station
ecause neither the location nor the distance
o the epicenter is initially known. These can
e calculated, however, because P and S travel
he same path and with known velocities. The
roblem is almost identical to the algebra prob-
em: Given two cars starting from the same
oint traveling with different speeds, after a
;iven interval of time how much farther will
he faster car have traveled than the slower
ne? The longer the path the two have traveled
he farther P will be ahead of S. Thus the time
nterval between their first arrivals is a func-
ion of the distance they have traveled. Three
seismograph stations pool their calculated disances to the epicenter of the quake. The dis-
ance from each station to the quake is laid
out on a globe as an arc or great circle, and the

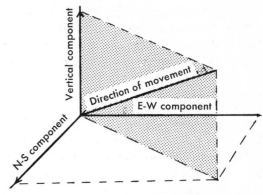

**Fig. 11-18. The movement of the ground being re-
corded by three seismographs at each station.** Each
of the three records the component of movement
along one of three mutually perpendicular directions.

point of intersection of the three arcs is the
epicenter of the quake.

Most interpretations of the structure of
the interior of the earth from seismograms are
based on changes in the travel times and ampli-
tudes of waves reaching stations located at
various distances from an earthquake. Evidence for the first discontinuity below the
Moho is found on records of stations located
between 15 and 22 degrees from the epicenter.
At these distances the velocities of P and S increase considerably—P goes up to 9.1 km/sec,

Fig. 11-19. A seismogram. The minor fluctuations in the trace are called microseisms. They are received
almost continuously. The first break in the trace marks the arrival of the wave which traveled the most
direct path with the greatest velocity. This is the P, or compressional, wave. The shear wave which arrives
some time later started at the same instant as the P wave and travels the same path but at a lower
velocity. The spread beween the arrival of these two waves is a measure of the distance to the focus.

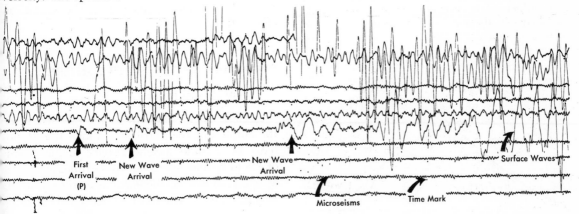

and S up to 5.3 km/sec. Sir Harold Jeffreys interprets this as a change brought about by passage of the waves through a zone in which the rate of change of velocity with depth increases. He postulates that the depth of this zone is about 400 km.

Beyond 22 degrees the velocity of P and S waves increases continually, and apparently the waves do not pass through discontinuities in this zone. This observation holds for all stations located up to a distance of 103 degrees from the epicenter. Beyond 103 degrees the amplitude of P and S waves decreases, or they are not recorded at all. This decreased amplitude is observed by stations between 103 and 143 degrees distant. Then beyond 143 degrees the amplitude increases again for the compressional waves, but shear waves have disappeared altogether. These observations lead to the identification of the second major discontinuity, the outer boundary of the core of the earth. No records or at best only poor records are obtained between 103 and 143 degrees be-

cause waves coming to the boundary of the core along a line tangent to the core are refracted into the core and come out and are recorded at stations between 143 and 180 degrees distant. Thus the zone between 103 and 143 degrees is known as the shadow zone.

Some P waves have been identified in the shadow zone. Lehmann (1936) suggested that they might be due to a small inner core with a higher velocity than the outer core. This has now been confirmed by other observations of the travel times for waves passing through the core and is generally accepted. This inner core has a radius of 1300 km and is more rigid than the outer core. The core as a whole has a radius of 2900 km.

So far no mention has been made of the waves that are reflected and refracted from each of the above discontinuities. They are observed and serve to confirm the interpretations made from the first arrivals of P and S waves. Some paths and the travel-time curves are illustrated, Fig. 11-20. After the arrival of the shear wave the motion of the ground often becomes so complex that the correct identification of many of these phases is impossible. None of them can be identified after the surface waves arrive. Usually a state of resonance is set up in the ground with the arrival of the surface wave. These produce long-period waves on the record that are easily identified by their amplitude.

Seismic evidence suggests that the interior of the earth below but not including the Moho consists of smooth concentric shells of materials that have different properties. The physical properties of these materials appear to be a function of their distance from the center of the earth.

Fig. 11-20. Ray diagram showing some paths followed by waves through the earth's interior. Note that rays are not straight. This is because the rigidity of the rocks increases with the depth in the mantle. The path of P and S waves which passes tangent to the outer boundary of the core has the last waves which do not get refracted at this boundary. Stations located more than 103 degrees away from the epicenter do not receive shear waves, and stations located between 103 and 143 degrees away do not receive either type of wave. For this reason this zone is called the shadow zone. Waves arriving in the shadow zone have been refracted and reflected from the inner core, or have been reflected in the mantle. (After Gutenberg and Richter, 1939. From *Elementary Seismology*, by Charles F. Richter. San Francisco: W. H. Freeman and Company, 1958.)

PROPERTIES OF THE EARTH'S INTERIOR

Density distribution

Those rocks that are found exposed near the surface of the earth and above the Moho have an average specific gravity in the range of 2.8 to 3; they are about three times as dense as water. However, the earth as a whole has an average specific gravity of about 5.5. This indi-

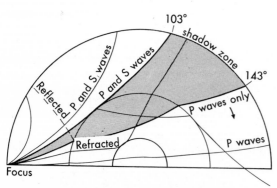

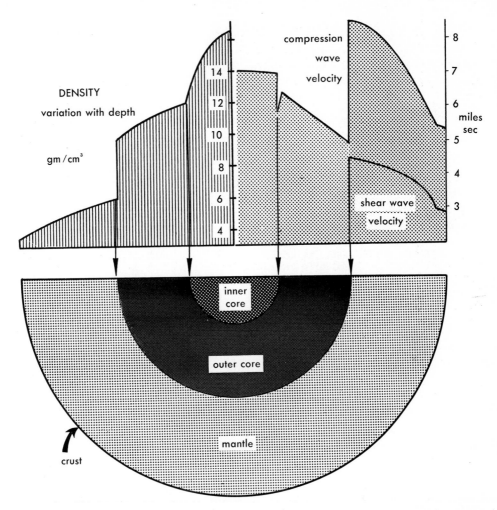

Fig. 11-21. A cross section through the earth. The major divisions of the earth's interior are shown, and the type of data on which these discontinuities are based. The graph at top left shows the distribution of density within the earth. Note the sudden changes which correspond to discontinuities in the interior. To the right is a graph showing the seismic velocities for P and S waves at various depths. No S waves are transmitted through the core. (Based on data from Edward Bullard.)

cates that the center of the earth must be more dense than the surface. This is confirmed by observations made through seismology. The velocity at which shock waves are propagated through rock depends on the elastic properties of the rock and on the density of the rock. Since it is possible to make observations on the velocity of propagation of various waves and to determine their paths, we have a means of estimating the density distribution. Unfortunately both elastic properties and density affect the velocity, so we must make assumptions about elastic properties in order to calculate

the density changes. This gives the results an element of uncertainty. Other limitations on the density distribution are imposed by the moment of inertia of the earth; however, the details of this calculation are beyond the scope of this book. The results are of interest. These are cited in Fig. 11-21.

COMPOSITION OF THE INTERIOR

Indications of the composition of the layer immediately below the Moho all point to the

Fig. 11-22. A seismic shot. Artificially produced shock waves are produced to study the structure of crust. (Photo by courtesy of the Seismic Service Corp.)

composition of olivine basalt or peridotite, two very similar rocks. We have seen that the diamond pipes and similar deep-seated intrusions, the Cortland complex, are peridotites, and this rock type is brought up to the surface from depth and extruded as lavas where the crust is thin. Studies of the seismic velocities of compressional and shear waves through the mantle

Fig. 11-23. Seismic methods. Techniques such as these of studying subsurface structure are one of the most important tools used in the exploration for oil and gas. The time of arrival of the reflected waves at the surface is an indication of the depth to the reflecting horizon. (By courtesy of the Seismic Service Corp.)

provide an indication of the density and elastic properties in the subcrust. These confirm the prediction that the subcrust is rich in olivine or peridotite. The material in the subcrust is either olivine, or like olivine, in that it has a relatively low density and a high velocity for the compressional waves. The completion of the Mohole will finally solve this problem for us, but it seems relatively safe to predict that a peridotitic or olivine basalt will be found.

The next major discontinuity below the Moho occurs about 400 km down. This indicates a change in the properties of the rocks at that depth, but we cannot be sure what sort of change it is. It might be a change in composition, but most of the students of this problem believe that it is a change in the crystal structure or form of the minerals at that depth. It is difficult for us to imagine the magnitude of the confining pressure at a depth of 400 km. We have not yet succeeded in creating pressures in the laboratory that are equivalent to more than 300 km depth. It has been suggested that olivine at a depth of about 400 km would change to a cubic form. This possibility has been substantiated by thermodynamic studies from which Dr. Francis Birch concludes that there is a transition layer in the crust between the depths of 300 to 900 km. In this respect that part of the interior seems to be different from the relatively homogeneous lower mantle, and the inner and outer core. A change in the crystal structure of olivine from a less to a more dense packing of the atoms seems very probable in this zone.

It is often assumed that the outer part of the core of the earth is a liquid because no shear waves are propagated through it. Iron in a molten state is chosen as the composition for this layer. Iron and oxides are the only common minerals that are heavier than silicates. The density of the core is very great, so silicates are excluded. Oxides are excluded because they would dissolve the silicates (olivine) in the mantle since they are mutually soluble. A great many meteorites are composed of iron. This lends support to this idea of the composition of the core because the meteorites and the earth probably formed at the same time or came from the same source. One argument against iron is that its calculated density at the depth of the core exceeds that postulated (Fig. 11-22). Another possibility is that the discontinuity that marks the outer part of the core results from the conversion of olivine from the cubic form to a more dense liquid metallic state. This same conversion is thought to take place in white dwarf stars. There are few data about this conversion for olivine, but there is no definite proof of the widely accepted explanation that the core of the earth is a ball of nickel-iron.

The composition of the inner core is in even greater doubt. It may be a solid, as indicated by the increased velocity of P waves passing through it, but until we have a better understanding of the nature of the changes that can take place in materials under extreme pressures some doubt will persist.

REFERENCES

AHRENS, L. H., RANKAMA, K., and RUNCORN, S. K., Editors, 1956, *Physics and Chemistry of the Earth*, v. 1: New York, McGraw-Hill Book Co., 317 p.

BULLEN, K. E., 1954, Seismology: London, Methuen & Co., Ltd.–New York, John Wiley & Sons, 132 p.

BYERLY, PERRY, 1942, *Seismology:* New York, Prentice-Hall, 256 p.

DALY, R. A., 1940, *Strength and Structure of the Earth:* New York, Prentice-Hall, 434 p.

GUTENBERG, BENO, and RICHTER, C. F., 1954, *Seismicity of the Earth*, 2nd ed.: Princeton, Princeton University Press, 201 p.

JACOBS, J. A., RUSSELL, R. D., and WILSON, J. T., 1959, *Physics and Geology:* New York, McGraw-Hill Book Co., 424 p.

JEFFREYS, HAROLD, 1952, *The Earth, Its Origin, History, and Physical Constitution*, 3rd ed.: Cambridge, Cambridge University Press, 392 p.

KUIPER, G. P., Editor, 1953–, *The Solar System:* 6 vols., Chicago, Univ. of Chicago Press (v. 1, 1953, v. 2, 1954, v. 3-6 in press)

MASON, BRIAN, 1958, *Principles of Geochemistry*, 2nd ed.: New York, John Wiley & Sons, 310 p.

POLDERVAART, ARIE, Editor, 1955, *The Crust of the Earth:* Geol. Soc. America, Spec. Paper 62, 762 p.

12   The Gravitational Field of the Earth

The concept of universal gravitational attraction formulated by Sir Isaac Newton should be familiar to most readers. Newton deduced that every particle of matter exerts a force of attraction on every other particle. The force of that attraction is proportional to the product of the masses of the two particles and inversely proportional to the square of the distance between them.

$$F = k \frac{m_1 m_2}{d^2}$$

(k is a constant first measured by Cavendish in 1797.)

Studies of the gravitational field of the earth have provided the basis for much of our understanding of mass distribution within the crust, from which structure and composition can be inferred. It has also provided the basis for one of the most far-reaching concepts about the strength of the interior of the earth and how this affects deformation of the crust. Detailed studies of the gravitational field of the crust have provided a very important means of exploring for concentrations of mineral resources that have higher or lower densities than the rocks in which they are enclosed. Such methods are possible only because the earth's gravitational field is not uniform. There exist within the field anomalies in which the force of attraction of the earth for objects on the surface is either greater or less than it would be if the earth were an isolated, homogeneous, perfectly spherical body.

Causes of variations in the gravitational field

As might be inferred from the above, the earth is neither isolated, homogeneous, nor perfectly spherical. It is possible, however, to calculate what the force of gravitational attraction would be if the earth were isolated from the pull of other planets, the sun and the moon, and if the mass of the earth were incorporated in a homogeneous, spherical body without irregularities on the surface such as mountains or ocean basins. The following factors bring about variation in the gravity field:

1. Deviation of the earth's shape from that of a sphere. The earth's form closely approximates a sphere in shape, but its radius is 21 km longer at the equator than it is at the poles, and it is slightly pear-shaped. The earth behaves as a perfect fluid balanced between gravitational forces, tending to make it spherical, and centrifugal forces of rotation, tending to flatten it. The force of attraction at the equator is less than at the poles for two reasons:

a. The surface is farther away from the center of mass of the earth at the equator.
b. Centrifugal acceleration of the earth at the equator is outward and opposite in direction to gravitational acceleration. Thus gravitational acceleration varies with latitude.

2. Attraction of extra-terrestrial bodies. In a sense every body in the universe exerts some attraction on the earth, but since the force of attraction varies as the square of the distance between the bodies it is unnecessary to consider those outside the solar system. The effects of the sun and the moon are the most notable. The attraction is exerted along a line connecting the sun or moon with the particular mass on the earth under consideration. The effect of this pull produces such familiar phenomena as the tides in the oceans. It also distorts the shape of the "solid" earth. Likewise it exerts a pull on the instrument being used to measure the earth's field. If the lines of attraction pass through the earth, a high value for the field will be obtained; if the pull is oppositely directed, it will tend to reduce the observed value of the force of gravity. This variation changes from hour to hour and with the seasons as the positions of the moon and the sun with reference to the earth change.

3. Variation with elevation. Because a point on the top of a high mountain is farther away from the center of the earth than one at sea level, it will have a lower gravitational acceleration if the effect of increased elevation alone is considered.

4. Variation due to attraction of surface material. In considering the effect of elevation we neglected to take into account the attraction that the mass of material between sea level and the top of the mountain is going to exert. This is known as the Bouguer effect. Not only that surface material which is directly below the point at which we want a measurement will affect the reading, but every unit of mass in the topography will exert an attraction on the instrument. The force acts along a line connecting the mass and the instrument. If two equal masses are exerting forces from directly opposite positions equidistant from the instrument, the effect of the two will cancel one another, and they will have no effect on the measured value of gravity. But, if an unbalanced force exists, it will tend to lower or raise the observed value, depending on its location.

5. Effect of heterogeneity of the earth's crust. If there is a local concentration of high-density minerals of rocks near the surface, the gravitational attraction near them will be greater than over areas overlain by average-density materials. This makes it possible to outline salt plugs in the Gulf Coast because the salt has a lower density than the sediments. Likewise, concentrations of dense metallic minerals may be located for this reason.

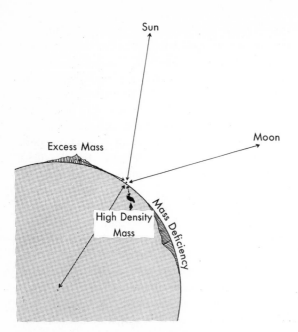

Fig. 12-1. Gravity reading. A reading of the force of gravitational attraction at the point indicated on the surface of the earth will be a net resultant force. The reading is influenced by the attraction of the earth along a line from the point to the center of the earth, the sun, moon, a high-density mass buried close to the surface, the mass of the mountain range, and by the deficiency of mass represented by the ocean.

Fig. 12-2. The gravimeter. This instrument is used to measure the force of gravitational attraction. In a sense it is used to weigh the earth. These instruments are so sensitive that they are capable of detecting a change in the force of gravity amounting to 1 part in 10 million. (Photo by courtesy of the Standard Oil Co. of New Jersey.)

Reduction of gravity observations to reveal anomalies. The insight we gain into the structure of the earth's crust and interior comes mostly from interpretation of the places where the acceleration of gravity deviates from the normal. These anomalies may be obtained by making corrections in the observed value for the effect of latitude, terrain, Bouguer effect, free-air (elevation above sea level), and the attraction of the sun and moon. In effect, the observed value is thus reduced to what it would be at sea level at that position if all the terrain above sea level were removed. If the resulting corrected value still deviates from the theoretically calculated value for a homogeneous earth, the difference in the two values is the amount of the anomaly. Anomalies may be either positive or negative.

Instruments

A number of different types of instruments are used to measure the earth's gravitational field. They are among the most sensitive instruments designed by man. Some are capable of measuring a change in the force of gravity amounting to as little as 1 part in 10 million. In principle, the gravimeters are sensitive weighing devices. The weight of a constant mass varies with any variation in the gravitational field. Thus, if the change in weight can be measured, differences in the force of gravity are obtained. In essence, a mass of metal is delicately suspended from a spring, and the elongation of the spring is measured. This elongation is a measure of the weight. The problem is that the changes in the length of the spring are so small that an enormous magnification of the elongation is needed. A number of different methods are used to obtain these magnifications. The instruments are calibrated to read in terms of units of force. One of the standard procedures for checking the calibration is to take the instrument on an elevator and take readings at various floors. The readings can then be checked against the theoretical changes arising from differences in elevation.

ISOSTASY

The theory of isostasy may at first seem unimportant to the student beginning a study of geology, but it should be mastered, because it will open many doors to your understanding of the deformation and warpings of the surface of the earth and the meaning of features formed as a result of this change in shape. The theory of isostasy postulates a system for the distribution of material in the earth's crust which conforms to and explains the observed gravity values.

The theory was developed from gravity surveys in the mountains of India about 1850. A series of measurements were made at different elevations across the mountain range. These observed values were then reduced to what they would have been if the mountains were leveled off and the observation made at sea level. These values were then compared with the theoretical value for gravity at that latitude. The results show that the actual force of gravity over the mountain range is considerably less than it should be theoretically. In fact the difference is so great in some cases that the two values are more nearly the same if the Bouguer correction (which removes the attraction of the rock material between sea level and the point of observation) is not made. This discrepancy between the observed and theoretical values can be explained only in terms of the distribution of rock densities below sea level.

Two systems of density distribution were set forth by Airy and Pratt in 1855. These two theories have been modified very little since their presentation, and their relative merits are still debated.

Airy theory

Airy postulated that there is a change in the density of rocks at depth in the earth's interior and that the upper lighter material floats on the more dense part, which behaves like a fluid. The depth of this change varies from place to place. Under mountains the depth is greater than under oceans or plains. In other words the mountains have roots of light-weight materials which extend down into the lower,

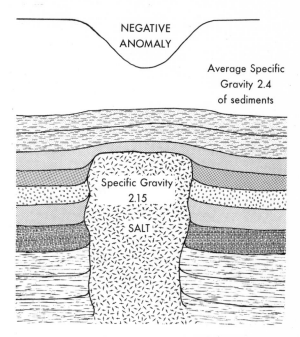

Fig. 12-3. A profile of the force of gravity over a salt dome. Note the marked decrease in the force of attraction over the salt. Salt has a specific gravity of 2.15 as compared with an average value for the unconsolidated sediments of 2.4. A negative anomaly is seen over the salt. A positive anomaly would appear if the profile had been run over a body of high-density rock.

more dense mantle rocks. The lower density (mass) of the roots causes the observed gravity values measured in the mountain ranges to be lower than predicted theoretically.

Pratt theory

Pratt's theory differs from Airy's in that Pratt assumed that the boundary between the upper light material and the lower dense rocks is at a uniform depth, called the depth of compensation. He further postulated that there are variations in the density of the lighter layer which are related to the elevation of the surface. Lighter material lies under mountains, and heavier material under oceans. The weight of columns of rock extending from the surface to the depth of compensation in different parts of the earth is thus the same.

Gravitational studies offer no means of determining which of these theories is more nearly

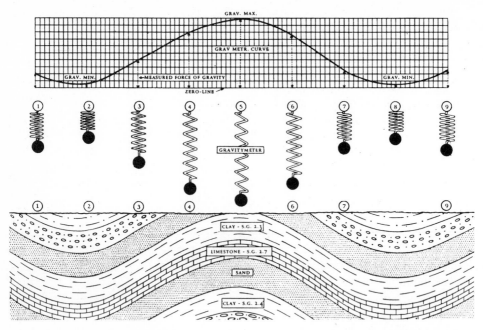

Fig. 12-4. A gravity maximum appears here over the crest of an anticline because a high-density limestone is brought close to the surface in the anticlinal structure. The extension of the springs represents the force of attraction on a mass at the surface. (By courtesy of *The Oil and Gas Journal*, Tulsa, Oklahoma.)

correct. It is possible that neither is absolutely correct, but evidence from other geological studies suggest that Pratt's theory comes closer to fitting all the facts we have. Bucher (1933) observed that, when large parts of the earth's surface are considered, the average density of exposed igneous rocks varies inversely as the average altitude. Seismic studies indicate that more dense material underlies ocean basins than continents. These observations support Pratt's assumption of a connection between density and elevation.

Depth of compensation in Pratt's theory. The Coast and Geodetic Survey uses as the depth

Fig. 12-5. The deflection of the plumb bob is caused by the attraction of the mass of the mountains for the mass of the bob. However, the amount of the deflection is not as great as would be predicted. This suggests that there must be low-density roots to the mountains.

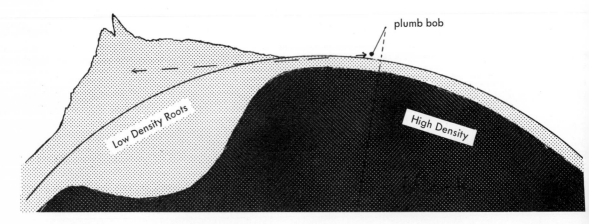

of compensation 113.7 km. This figure is obtained by calculating the isostatic anomalies for stations at a large number of different elevations, using different depths of compensation. The depth that gives the smallest average anomaly is considered the most probable actual depth of compensation.

Heiskanen's theory

Airy postulated that columns of rock are nearly the same in density, floating like blocks in a fluid. Pratt suggested that different segments of the earth are of different densities, but that the differences are compensated at a certain depth. A third hypothesis has been formulated by Heiskanen (1933). He combines the assumptions of both Airy and Pratt. It has been observed that rocks at sea level are more dense on the average than those at higher elevations (2.76 grams per cm³ at sea level down to 2.70 gm/cm³ at elevations in high mountains). He assumes that this change continues downward, tending to make deeper rocks more dense than shallower ones in all sections of the earth's crust. In addition, different sections are thought to have different densities and different lengths. Heiskanen's theory has the advantages of being based on actual knowledge of density variations that can be obtained by direct measurement, and when it is applied to the observa-

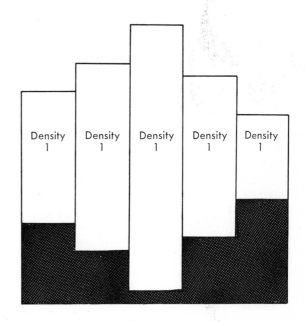

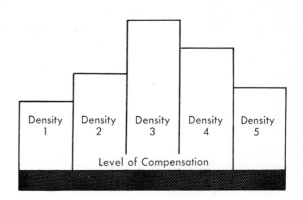

Fig. 12-6. Airy's theory of isostasy. This illustrates one way in which isostatic equilibrium might be obtained if the crust of the earth consisted of an essentially uniform density unit of different heights. Airy would account for the mountains by the presence of deep roots of crustal material extending down into the high-density mantle. This actually represents a case of flotational equilibrium. The mantle rock is plastic and can flow.

Fig. 12-7. Pratt's theory of isostasy. Pratt recognized that the crust of the earth is not made up of materials of uniform density. He visualized isostatic equilibrium as being the result of density. The low-density materials would represent the continents and the high-density materials, the ocean. He postulated a depth or level of compensation at which the effects of different densities above were balanced.

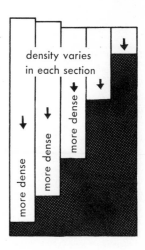

Fig. 12-8. Heiskanen's theory of isostasy. He combines the assumptions of both Pratt and Airy. According to this theory density varies both between columns and within each. The higher densities are represented by the shorter columns and toward the bottom of each column. This theory accounts for the roots of mountains, and for the variations in density in different parts of the crust.

tions we now have on the gravitational field it yields very low anomalies.

The meaning of isostasy

According to all three of these theories the earth's crust is approximately in a state of equilibrium, meaning that there are few large imbalances in the distribution of mass. Most geologists and geophysicists support either Pratt's or Heiskanen's theories or some slight modification of them. If either is correct then we have an extremely valuable tool which may be used to explain large-scale crustal features and to predict the behavior of the earth's crust in response to changes in mass distribution brought about by such processes as volcanism,

Fig. 12-9. Rate of uplift in Scandinavia. During the ice ages this part of Scandinavia was covered by great thicknesses of ice. The weight of the ice caused the crust to be depressed as the additional weight was compensated for by subcrustal movement of materials. When the ice melted away readjustment started and is still going on. This map shows the present rates of uplift in centimeters per 100 years. (After Beno Gutenberg.)

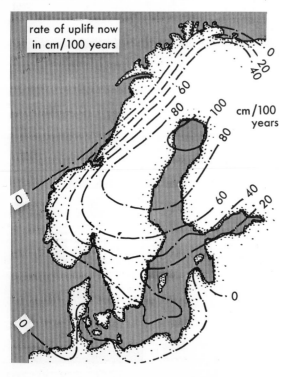

diastrophism, and erosion. Undoubtedly the crust and interior of the earth down to the depth of compensation have some strength and rigidity which enable them to support loads of rock for at least short periods of time. But gravity studies indicate that the crust is about 97 per cent compensated. Thus we may expect that over long periods of time a state near compensation is normal.

The theory of isostasy holds meaning both for the interior and for the crust of the earth. If a zone of compensation does exist, then the rock below that zone must be in a plastic or pseudo-viscous state in order to maintain the compensation as loads on the crust are shifted from one place to another. The tops of mountains are eroded rapidly, and this debris is transported away by mass wasting, running water, and glaciers. As more and more mass is moved, the column of rock through the crust under the mountain is lightened in relation to other columns in the crust. Since the pressure at the zone of compensation is due to the weight of the column of rock over it, the pressure at the zone of compensation under the mountain would be lessened. This would cause material below the zone of compensation to move toward that position and raise the column of rocks under the mountains again. Thus mountains tend to rise as they are eroded away.

Many parts of the earth's crust are still undergoing adjustment as a result of the melting of the thick sheets of ice which covered them during the ice ages. In such areas as the Canadian Shield and the Fennoscandinavian Shield the surface is rising at measurable rates. Negative gravity anomalies have been found in these regions, indicating that the weight of the column of rock down to the zone of compensation is not yet balanced (in hydrostatic equilibrium) with other parts of the crust. The ice melted faster than compensation could take place. Another interesting application of the theory concerns the delta of the Mississippi River where deposition of sediment is going on at a very rapid rate. The addition of large quantities of sediment on the delta should locally increase the mass on that segment of the crust. If addition of sediment is taking place more rapidly than the crust is being warped down-

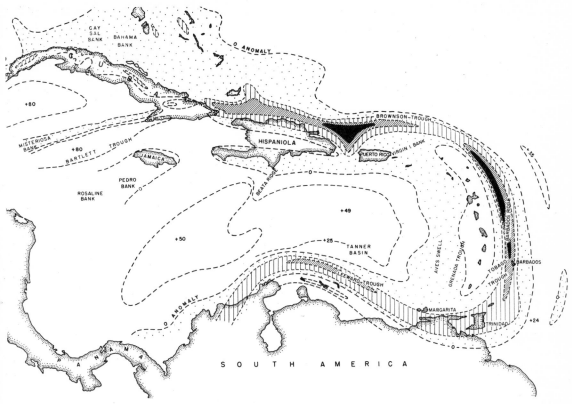

Fig. 12-10. Gravity anomalies in the Caribbean. The black and diagonally lined areas are negative anomalies where there is a mass deficiency. Such negative anomalies are associated with deep sea trenches in the island arc systems of the Pacific also. (From A. J. Eardley, 1957.)

ward and being compensated, then there should be an excess of mass in the delta. This extra mass should make the force of gravity over the delta higher than its theoretical value and reveal a positive anomaly. Measurements of the force of gravity in this region show no such positive anomaly. Thus adjustment and downwarping must be accompanying the formation of the delta.

REFERENCES

HEISKANEN, W. A., and VENING MEINESZ, F. A., 1958, *The Earth and Its Gravity Field*: New York, McGraw-Hill Book Co., 470 p.

HOWELL, B. F., JR., 1959, *Introduction to Geophysics*: New York, McGraw-Hill Book Co., 399 p.

JACOBS, J. A., RUSSELL, R. D., and WILSON, J. T., 1959, *Physics and Geology*: New York, McGraw-Hill Book Co., 424 p.

IV GRADATION OF THE EARTH'S CRUST

13   Gradation of the Crust

We marvel at the achievements of man. He has mastered techniques for building skyscrapers, bridges, tunnels, and harbors. To be sure he is one of the main agents tending to bring about change on the surface of the earth today. Yet all around us there is evidence of changes in the surface of the earth of a sort man could never hope to duplicate. In August of 1959 an earthquake in central Montana set up waves in the crust which triggered a gigantic landslide. In less than 5 minutes about 35 million cubic yards of rock was moved over a distance of about half a mile. In 1960 violent earthquakes in Chile set off landslides that caused the loss of many lives and extensive property damage over thousands of square miles. Tidal waves caused by these earthquakes washed the shores around the Pacific Ocean causing millions of

Fig. 13-1. The Grand Canyon. Running water and mass-wasting processes have cut this canyon about a mile deep through horizontally stratified rock units. (Photo by courtesy of the Union Pacific Railroad.)

dollars in damage as far away as Japan. Rapid changes of this sort are relatively rare. Most sculpture of the crust takes place through processes acting so gradually that man rarely even thinks of them as significant. It is the slow downhill movement of soil, the bits of dislodged rock that fall downslope, the slow solution of limestone by rain water percolating through it, the grains of sand blown by the wind that over long periods of time account for the removal of most material. We are conscious of the muddy water in streams after heavy rainfalls. We take note of the shifts in sand bars along the coast. We see glaciers covered by rock fragments slowly pushing their way down mountain valleys. But we do not always perceive that this is part of a large-scale pattern by which the land forms so familiar to us were brought into existence, and by which they will one day vanish from the face of the earth.

The pattern is one of degradation of the surface of the earth, the shifting of materials, and their redeposition elsewhere. The movement is accomplished by wind, water, glacier ice, and downslope movement of surficial materials. It is always directed from higher elevations to lower elevations. Thus the long-range tendency of these processes is toward leveling of the face of the earth. It is estimated that the rate of removal of materials from the continents today is such that about 21 million years would be required to level the continents. The earth is more than 3 billion years old. Enough time has elapsed for the surface to have become flat many times over. Thus it is obvious that some forces are tending to combat the tendency toward degradation. These are constructive forces; they are diastrophism, the upheaval of the earth, and volcanism and igneous activity. In these phenomena, material is moved from lower to higher positions. Thus the particular configuration of the surface of the crust at any given time, the present, for instance, represents a sort of balance between the forces of up-

heaval in the crust and the forces of erosion and degradation. Throughout most of geologic time we may say that the forces of upheaval have slightly more than counter-balanced the forces of degradation. The shapes and sizes of continents have varied, but the rock record indicates that continents have persisted above sea level.

Gradation is a three-fold process. First, the surface is decayed and eroded. Secondly, the products of this decay and erosion are transported. Finally they are deposited usually at lower levels. Erosion is facilitated by chemical and mechanical disintegration of rocks where they are brought into contact with the atmos-

Fig. 13-2. Talus cones. Mass wasting is most apparent in the mountains. Here you can see talus cones, piles of rock fragments, which have broken from the cliffs. (Photo by E. W. Spencer.)

phere, waters of the surface, and plant and animal life. Once rocks are decomposed or have partially disintegrated they are easily moved. If they are on sloping surfaces they tend to move down those slopes under the constant pull of gravity. Eventually they may come in contact with running water or with a moving body of ice, and they are carried along until the ice melts or the velocity of the water becomes too low to move them. Then they are dropped out and may become consolidated into sedimentary rocks. Thus it is clear that the processes of gradation are divisible into two major categories:

Degradation: weathering, mass wasting, and erosion including removal and transportation.
Aggradation: deposition of sediments.

Geomorphic agents

Certain agents function to bring about gradation and the resulting changes in land forms.

These may be called geomorphic agents. The are:

On Land:
Running water: driven by the pull of gravit
Ground water: driven by the pull of gravit
Glaciers: driven by the pull of gravit
Wind: driven by the rotation of th earth and thermal activit within the atmosphere.

In Oceans:
Waves: driven by the rotation of th earth.
Currents: driven by the rotation of th earth and temperature an density distribution.
Tides: driven by gravitational a traction of the moon an sun.
Tsunami: caused by earthquakes an (tidal volcanic explosions unde waves) water.

Fig. 13-3. Sand dunes. Sand dune are formed from wind-blown sand The sand is derived from the disintegration and decomposition of solid rock units. (Photo by courtesy of Chuck Abbott Photos, Tucson, Arizona.)

Fig. 13-4. The Big Room of Carlsbad Caverns, New Mexico. This photo shows evidence of two stages in the history of the cave. First the cavern was formed through solution of the limestone by underground waters. Then began deposition of massive columns and pointed stalactites of calcium carbonate. (Photo by courtesy of the New Mexico State Tourist Bureau.)

These agents should not be thought of solely as agents of erosion because each serves three functions: they make erosion possible; they provide a means of transportation; and under certain circumstances they promote deposition. The chart of the following pages is designed to illustrate the broad functions of each of these agents. For each of the most important geomorphic agents the following information is given: how it brings about erosion, the features produced as a direct result of the erosion, the means by which the erosion products are removed or transported away, what promotes deposition, and the type of deposits formed. Because gradation of the continents and oceans

differs in the fundamental nature of the media in which each takes place, they are treated separately. It should be apparent that the two have some things in common, including the constant pull of gravity downward on all loose material. This effectively produces mass wasting under water as well as on land. But in the case of other types of erosion and transportation there are great differences. Running water and ground water are driven downward by gravitational pull until they reach the level of the oceans. The effectiveness of these then becomes negligible. Wind is obviously of no consequence in gradation of the ocean floors except in that it drives surficial currents.

Fig. 13-5. Glaciation. These mountains in Alaska are being eroded and lowered by the tongues of ice which are flowing through the valleys. Glaciation has been an important agent of gradation in the high mountains and particularly in the high latitudes. (Photo by courtesy of the U.S. Air Force.)

Basic concepts

The basic concepts that deal with gradation are based either on direct observations, which have been substantiated by repeated proof, or on logical deductions from direct observations. They may serve as guides to understanding where small details fit into the larger picture of gradation.

Base level. If the surface of the earth were not affected by diastrophism and volcanism it would be slowly reduced to a uniform level. That level is called ultimate base level. It is easy to see that most of the processes tending to lower the continents cease to be effective when the area approaches the level of the oceans, so sea level may be taken as the ultimate base level. It should, however, be remembered that, if reduction of the entire earth to sea level did occur sea level would be substantially above its present position. All the volume now above water would be under the sea just before ultimate base level was reached.

The term "temporary base level" is used to describe a transient condition for a region or small area. It is a level below which the dominant forces of erosion will not reduce the area. If a region is being eroded mainly by running water it will not reduce the level of the region below the level of a lake into which the river drains so long as the lake stands. Why? Because the lake acts for the local area just as the ocean does for the earth.

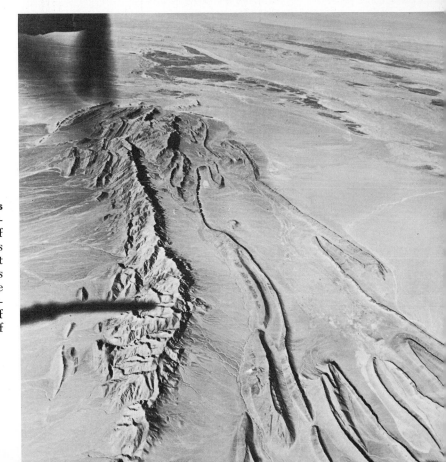

Fig. 13-6. High mountains in China eroded by running water. Mass wasting and running water combine to dissect mountains as shown here. (Photo by courtesy of the U.S. Air Force.)

Fig. 13-7. Belt of folded mountains in Africa (Atlas Mountains). Deformation and uplift of the crust of the earth is one of the main factors in maintaining parts of the crust high. Already these mountains have been deeply dissected. Note the erosion products of the mountains which lie on the flanks of the ridges. (Photo by courtesy of the U.S. Air Force.)

| | EROSION | | TRANSPORTATION | DEPOSITION | |
	Method of Erosion	Features of Erosion	Method	Cause of Deposition	Nature of Deposits
Mass Movement	slump sliding rolling dislodgement falling	slide scars surface subsidence	slump sliding rolling falling plastic flow creep	decrease in slope obstruction to movement loss of water	talus cones talus sheets rock glaciers mud flows felsenmeer
Running Water	corrasion corrosion hydraulicking	river valleys pediments peneplains river terraces wadies (in deserts) pot holes	suspension solution saltation (bouncing) rolling pushing & dragging	decrease in velocity decrease in slope decrease in volume change in channel barriers to flow	alluvial fans bars channel fill alluvial terraces deltas levees flood plain deposits
Wind	deflation corrasion abrasion impact	undercut hills cave rocks table, mushroom rocks ventifacts desert pavement lag gravels	saltation suspension rolling	loss of velocity settling of heavy particles rain	loess volcanic ash & dust dunes (Barchan, longi- tudinal, trans- verse, seif, parabolic)
Glaciation	quarrying (plucking) abrasion	striations & grooves drumlins polished surfaces crescentic marks U-shaped valleys truncated spurs hanging valleys cirques fiords cols arêtes horns	suspension dragging carrying on top pushing	melting of ice breaking up of ice in ocean	moraines (lateral, terminal, recessional, medial, ground) eskers kames kame terraces outwash varved lake clays erratics
Ground Water	solution	caves sinkholes karst topography	in solution (same as surface run- ning water)	precipitation due to 1) evaporation 2) loss of acidity 3) chemical reactions loss of velocity	spring terraces stalactites & stalagmites cementation of sediments (pore fillings) vein & cavity filling replacement (petrified wood)

Fig. 13-8. Geomorphic agents acting on the continents—a summary.

Fig. 13-9. Mt. Fuji in Japan. Mt. Fuji is representative of volcanic and igneous activity which help maintain parts of the earth's crust high. Igneous activity and diastrophism are the two main factors which uplift the continents, while running water, glaciation, wind erosion, ground water, and mass wasting tend to lower the land surface toward sea level. (Photo by courtesy of the Japan Travel Bureau.)

Geomorphic processes leave their imprint upon land forms. This fundamental idea is that each of the geomorphic agents functions in a way peculiar to it, and as a result produces erosional and depositional land forms which are characteristic of that agent. In other words, it is possible to recognize the origin of land forms although the processes by which they were formed may have ceased to operate.

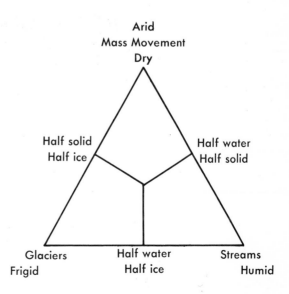

Fig. 13-10. Process of degradation. Degradation is accomplished through breakdown and transportation of the rocky crust of the earth. These decay products move downhill under the pull of gravity. They are transported dry, in water, in ice, and in combinations of these three.

The structure of the crust acts as a control in the formation of land forms. Folds, faults, unconformities, differences in the hardness and susceptibility of rock units to decomposition, and disintegration provide a framework within which the geomorphic agents function. The resulting physiographic forms are always influenced by the structure of the underlying rock. Thus the combination of a particular structure being eroded primarily by one geomorphic agent will result in a predictable land form.

One of the most important of all geologic concepts is that of Uniformitarianism. The idea is that the same laws and processes governing the formation of present-day features have remained constant through time.

Evolution of land forms. If a particular structure is subjected to the effects of certain geomorphic agents acting over a long period of time a particular sequence of land forms will develop. The land forms will slowly undergo systematic change or evolution unless some external conditions bring about a change in the dominant structure or geomorphic agents.

REFERENCES

GILBERT, G. K., 1877, Report on the *Geology of the Henry Mountains* [Utah]: U.S. Geog. Geol. Survey of the Rocky Mountain Region (Powell), 160 p.

HOLMES, ARTHUR, 1945 (revised 1949), *Principles of Physical Geology*: New York, The Ronald Press Co., 532 p.

LOBECK, A. K., 1939, *Geomorphology, an Introduction to the Study of Landscapes*: New York, McGraw-Hill Book Co., 731 p.

SHIMER, J. A., 1959, *This Sculptured Earth: The Landscape of America*: New York, Columbia University Press, 255 p.

THORNBURY, W. D., 1954, *Principles of Geomorphology*: New York, John Wiley & Sons, 618 p.

14   Climates and Weathering

Weathering, like metamorphism, is a response of the materials of the crust to changes in the total energy environment. In particular, weathering changes occur where rocks and minerals come in contact with the atmosphere, surficial waters, and organic life under conditions that are normal to the surface of the earth.

In the sixteenth century many philosophers thought that rocks and minerals were living substances, that they were simply lower forms of life than the plants and much lower than animals. This belief was founded mainly on the observation that rocks appear to be in various stages of life—youth, maturity, and old age. The same rock seen in one outcrop to be a solid, strong, fresh and youthful substance might be recognized elsewhere as a decaying mass obviously dead and starting to disinte-

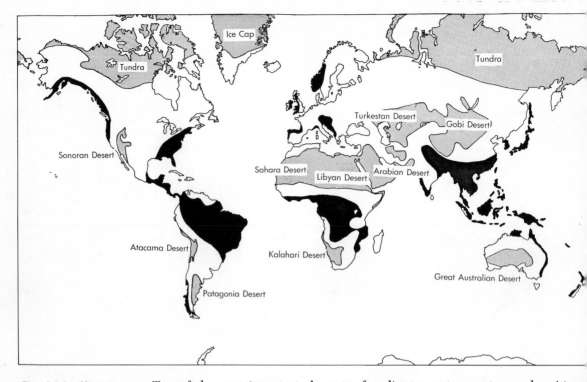

Fig. 14-1. Climate map. Two of the most important elements of a climate are temperature and moisture. This map indicates the location of some of the extreme conditions. Dotted areas are deserts. The black areas have 40 or more inches of rainfall per year.

grate. They were observing what we would call today the effects of weathering. The mechanical breakdown and alteration by chemical changes are directed toward producing new minerals which are stable at the surface of the earth, from minerals formed under other than normal surface conditions.

One of the basic concepts of geology is the idea that the surface of the earth undergoes gradation. Shifting of material is necessary to accomplish gradation. Weathering of rocks is not a direct process of gradation, but it is related to gradation in that it brings about decay and distintegration of rocks and facilitates their

Fig. 14-2. Zones in the bauxite deposits of Arkansas. A feldspar-rich rock, syenite, has been weathered and altered to form these important deposits of bauxite. (After Gordon, Tracey, and Ellis, U.S.G.S. Prof. Paper 299.)

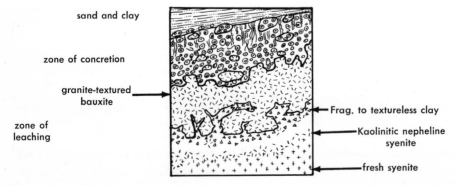

removal by the geomorphic agents. It is usually a very important but not always necessary initial step in degradation.

Evidences of weathering are all about us. Sidewalks and concrete highways are built in separated sections to prevent them from cracking when temperatures fall and the volume of the solid concrete contracts. Houses in moist climates must be painted frequently to prevent the decay and disintegration of wood. A knife left outside in the rain will be acted on by oxygen and water to form rust. The surface of the crust of the earth is constantly exposed to attack by these and other weathering agents. The effects are not confined to the surface; they penetrate into the crust along fractures and faults, between crystals, and along grain boundaries in rocks. Gradually they bring about the loosening, decay, and disintegration of even the hardest and most resistant rocks. One of the most important results of weathering is the production of soils. These become especially important when we realize that soils are eroded away and that they would never be restored if there were no weathering. Because soils form very slowly they are a valuable natural resource which must be conserved.

CLIMATE AND WEATHERING

Climatic conditions more than any other single factor control weathering. Climate is defined as follows: "The sum total of the meteorological elements that characterize the average and extreme condition of the atmosphere over a long period of time at any one region." The elements are temperature, moisture including both humidity and precipitation, wind, air pressure, and evaporation.

The study of climates belongs to a specialized branch of geology, meteorology. This field has become so important and highly specialized that it is frequently considered as a separate science. We can no more than touch on a few aspects of the atmosphere here.

Climates of the various parts of the world may be classified according to the amount of rainfall, the temperature, or the type of vegetation that dominates in each. These and other elements of climate are complexly interrelated.

We cannot fully discuss these interrelationships, but two factors should be considered. They are the principal determinants of rainfall and temperature. These are the amount of solar radiation coming to the earth and the wind currents. Wind currents are driven by the rotation of the earth. The amount of solar radiation coming to the earth is primarily a function of the position of the sun relative to the surface. As the earth moves in its orbit about the sun this position shifts. The shift is such that the northern hemisphere receives more radiation in the months between March and Sep-

Fig. 14-3. Arkansas bauxite region. The bauxite in Arkansas is formed from the leaching of aluminum-rich clays. The clays are weathering products of syenite. The association of the bauxite with lignite coal suggests the types of climatic conditions which prevailed when the bauxite was formed. (After Gordon, Tracey, and Ellis, U.S.G.S. Prof. Paper 299.)

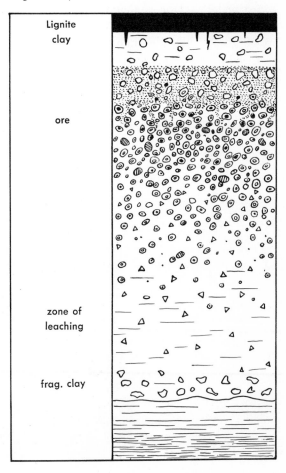

tember (summer in the northern hemisphere). The southern hemisphere receives more radiation during the months between September and March (summer in the southern hemisphere). The effects of these shifts are most prominent within the zone over which the sun shifts. In the zone on either side the effects are much less. Thus there are three major climatic groups if temperature alone is considered. They are:

1. Tropical (temperature is uniformly warm—no winter)
2. Temperate (temperature is highly variable—winters and summers)
3. Polar (temperatures are low all year—no summer)

Rainfall is primarily dependent on the amount of moisture in the air, but many factors determine where that moisture is released. Most of the moisture comes from evaporation of sea water, a process that is greatly accelerated by strong wind currents blowing over bodies of water. Once this moisture is in the air as a vapor it remains there until conditions are right for it to condense and fall back to the surface. The most important of these conditions are the amount of water vapor in the air and the temperature. Warm air can contain more

moisture than cool air. There is a general decrease in temperature with altitude. So, a warm air mass carrying moisture may bypass lower lands, be blown inland until the air mass is forced upward by the topography. At the proper temperature (altitude) precipitation occurs and the remaining dry air is blown inland. For this reason one side of a mountain may be very wet, while the other side is in an arid climate.

Using precipitation as a basis for classification we recognize the following types of climates:

	Annual Rainfall (inches)
Arid (note that dry hot deserts and dry cold ice caps are both arid)	0-10
Semiarid	10-20
Semihumid	20-40
Humid	40-80
Very wet	80 +

Neither the amount of temperature nor rainfall is a perfect means of describing climates, because variations of both of these as well as other factors occur in many areas (i.e., high rainfall, low temperature; high rainfall, high temperature, etc.). The most frequent

Fig. 14-4. Bryce Canyon, Utah. Differential weathering is responsible for the unusual shape of these pinnacles. Some of the units of rock are more resistant to the weathering processes acting in this region than others are. (Photo by courtesy of the Union Pacific Railroad.)

Fig. 14-5. Shells of rock being split up into joint blocks by frost action. Note the tendency to develop joints in parallel sets in a rock which not long ago was essentially structureless and exfoliated freely in any direction parallel to an exposed surface. (Photo by courtesy of the U.S. Geological Survey.)

combinations of factors are given in the following classifications.

A. CLIMATES CONTROLLED BY EQUATORIAL AND TROPICAL AIR MASSES

1. Wet climates of the tropics having uniform high temperatures and large amounts of rainfall all year.
2. Dry climates of the tropics having high temperatures but small amounts of rainfall.

3. Alternately wet and dry tropical climates. Temperatures are always high, but the amount of precipitation is highly variable from season to season.

B. CLIMATES CONTROLLED BY BOTH TROPICAL AND POLAR AIR MASSES

1. Subtropical eastern continental margins having heavy rainfall and high temperatures during the summer, and cool dry winters.

Fig. 14-6. Half Dome in Yosemite National Park, California. Note the disintegration of the rock. Exfoliation and frost action are the dominant processes promoting the disintegration. (Photo by courtesy of the U.S. Geological Survey.)

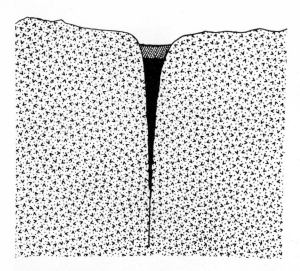

Fig. 14-7. Freezing water may break solid granite blocks. The water seeps down into fractures during the day. At night the top of the water freezes over, forming a partially closed system. As the water below the surface layer freezes it expands and exerts great pressure on the walls of the fracture extending the fracture deeper.

2. Those with abundant precipitation, cool summers, and mild winters.
3. Those with wet winters and dry summers.
4. Those that are highly variable as a result of invasions of polar air masses. Precipitation is increased in warm summer seasons. Annual temperature range is great.

C. CLIMATES CONTROLLED BY POLAR AND ARCTIC AIR MASSES

1. Cold climates of the continental-polar air-mass sources, characterized by low precipitation, long cold winters, and short warm summers.
2. Cold climates of the arctic front zone along the northern continental fringes, severely cold and humid.
3. Cold climates of the arctic and antarctic air-mass source regions having annual temperature averages far below all other climates and showing no above-freezing monthly averages.

In climates dominated by little rainfall and either extremes of temperature or great variations in temperature, mechanical disintegration

of rock reaches its maximum effectiveness. Chemical decomposition is more rapid in hot humid climates than it is in cold humid climates, because high temperatures facilitate most chemical reactions. However, chemical decomposition appears to be an important part of weathering in all climates.

PRACTICAL VALUE OF A FAMILIARITY WITH WEATHERING PROCESSES

Weathering processes are basic to our understanding of the gradation of the surface of the earth, but there are more immediate practical uses that can be made of their study. Ores of two of the most important metals, steel and aluminum, are among those concentrated by weathering processes. Bauxite deposits, the ore of aluminum, are formed by the weathering and chemical alteration of rocks that contain the element Al as a constituent of some of its minerals. The largest deposit of bauxite in America is located in Arkansas. This deposit was formed millions of years ago when an igneous intrusion of syenite, composed of feldspars and hornblende, was exposed to a tropical climate characterized by alternate periods of heavy rainfall and dry spells. The syenite weathered chemically, and the feldspars were altered to clay minerals. The silica was removed from the clay by the warm surface waters containing humic acid from decaying

Fig. 14-8. Frost heaving. When water freezes in the ground, the ice tends to form layers in the soil. Water is pulled into the freezing layer by capillary action, forcing the soil up.

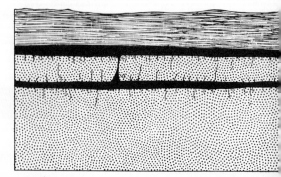

Fig. 14-9. Felsenmeer. Frost action on mountain tops results in the formation of felsenmeer, an area, usually fairly level or on a gentle slope, which is covered with blocks of rock of moderate to large size. Many of the rocks here were forced up through the soil by frost action. This is the Beartooth Plateau, Montana. (Photo by E. W. Spencer.)

plants, and the bauxite, an aluminum oxide, was formed.

A knowledge of weathering effects by contractors has meant the difference between success and failure in many large construction projects. Weathering affects the strength of rocks. Several large dams have failed because they were anchored in weathered rocks that were not strong enough to hold the pressure of the water backed up in the reservoir. Similarly, weathering may affect the strength of a foundation for a highway, an airport, or a large building.

Because the effects of weathering are largely determined by climate, study of weathering effects on buried soils may provide us with information about paleoclimates. This information may in turn prove a valuable lead in present efforts to learn how to control climates.

PHYSICAL DISINTEGRATION — MECHANICAL WEATHERING PROCESSES

Thermal expansion and contraction

Most materials will expand when they are heated and in turn contract with cooling. The changes that take place in a rock as a re-

sult of this daily process are so small that we cannot be sure how effective they are in bringing about weathering, but it is one process that almost certainly plays some part in the imperceptible changes that occur in rocks near the surface. Geologists working in deserts have often heard cracking noises during the night. Looking around the next day for the cause of these noises they found boulders of igneous rocks with scale-like sheets peeling off them. These are called exfoliation surfaces. One of the first ideas advanced to explain the cause of this was that it resulted from isolation, heat ab-

Fig. 14-10. Chemical reactions take place over the entire exposed surface area of a rock. Thus finer-grained materials tend to weather chemically much more rapidly than coarser material of the same composition. By splitting a cube the surface area is increased by a third. The surface area is doubled by splitting it three times as shown.

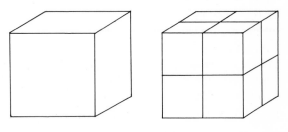

Fig. 14-11. **Mechanical disintegration dominates the weathering of the surface of the moon.** Because it lacks an atmosphere chemical weathering is negligible. These craters are thought to be many millions of years old. They continue to stand out because weathering and erosion are extremely slow. (Photo by courtesy of the Mount Wilson and Palomar Observatories.)

sorption. The outer shell of the rock is subjected to the daily changes in temperature, which in a desert may amount to 70°-80°F. It was theorized that stresses build up and finally cause the outer shell to break away from the interior, which is relatively insulated from temperature changes by the outside part of the rock. Finally the hypothesis was subjected to a laboratory test. It turned out that the stresses developed through isolation were much less than the elastic limit of granite. To test the hypothesis further, boulders of granite were placed in an oven, and the temperature was lowered and raised far beyond the range normally encountered in a desert. The results were negative. There appeared to be no effect of the changes in temperature on the rock.

It seems likely that thermal expansion is competent to do very little more than develop planes of weakness already in the rock. This comes through differences in the thermal expansion of different minerals. Some expand and contract much more than others, so the inter-

granular boundaries may be opened through this process.

Unloading

In quarrying granite for building stones it is sometimes possible to take advantage of natural forces to split the granite. A set of joints or fractures, called sheeting, may develop parallel to the surface of the ground. They represent a response of the rock to release of confining pressure when the weight of the overlying rock is removed. The process is not confined to quarries but may occur wherever erosion is removing material from the underlying rocks.

Crystal growth

After a light rain in the plains or on a desert, the water rapidly soaks into the ground. That water may dissolve limestone or other soluble constituents of the rocks or soils directly eneath the surface. When the sun comes out nd evaporation begins the water present near he surface may be drawn back up to the surace as though it were in a very fine capillary ube. The connected pore spaces in the rock are bout the same size as capillary tubes and act 1 the same way. At the surface the water vaporates, and whatever material is in the olution is precipitated to form crystals or rystalline aggregates in the soil. As crystals row they can exert large expansive stresses, reaking up soil and even some rocks. This is he mode of formation of layers of calcium arbonate, caliche, which is a commonly found ayer or nodular mass in soil profiles underlain y limestone in semiarid plains or deserts. Other crystals that grow in this manner include alts, sulfates, phosphates, nitrates, gypsum, alcite, alum, epsom salts, and saltpeter.

Freezing of water

In climates where there is repeated freezng and thawing this is the dominant mechancal process of weathering. Water expands by bout 9.05 per cent in volume when it freezes. The pressure exerted in the process is great. If he water is enclosed in a solid container and s cooled to $-22°C$. it will exert up to 2113 g/cm² pressure on the container. This is far n excess of the strength of granite. Thus, freezng water is capable of breaking the strongest ocks in the crust. It does this most effectively vhen the rock is fractured. The water seeps lown into the fracture and begins to freeze at he top of the fracture first. This provides a artially effective closed system. As freezing ontinues the fracture is opened and extended leeper, or perhaps new fractures form. The nore frequently the freezing and thawing ocurs the more effective this process will be. It s particularly effective in high mountains vhere temperatures rise high enough to melt ome ice and snow every day and where water efreezes at night when the temperatures drop.

Frost action

In high latitudes and on some high mounains the ground becomes deeply frozen. The

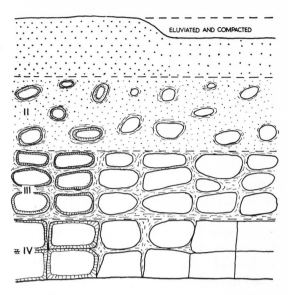

Fig. 14-12. Zones in a profile of a granite which is being weathered chemically. Note that the alteration of the granite is concentrated in the fracture zones within the massive rock. Nearly spherical masses may form as successively deeper shells of the rock are attacked and decayed. The soil profile grades upward from fresh unaltered rock into zones of more and more complete decay until near the surface none of the original structure remains. (From Ruxton and Berry, 1957.)

Fig. 14-13. A soil profile. (Photo by E. W. Spencer.)

ground is permanently frozen below certain depths in some regions. Where the ground does freeze, soils may be heaved upward and completely broken up by the expansion of the freezing water in the ground. Water in the ground is held in the pore spaces between grains of rock and mineral matter. As freezing occurs, layers of ice tend to form particularly at any sort of natural boundaries in the soil such as at the contact between a clay and sand layer. More water is drawn to the freezing layer of ice by capillary action, and the layer grows thicker, forcing the soil above it upward. The soil is further disrupted when the ice thaws and the soil slumps back down. (Water coming to the layer of ice is kept fluid by the heat produced through crystallization of ice.)

CHEMICAL WEATHERING

The atmosphere contains a number of constituents that can react with minerals. Most important of these are water, carbon dioxide and oxygen. The effectiveness of these chemical constituents depends on the composition of the rocks and the size of the particles that make them up. The smaller the particles, the greater the surface areas which may come in contact with the atmosphere and therefore the greater the possibility of and the rapidity of reactions. Compositional effects are very important and usually rather obvious. Quartz, for example, is a very stable substance. It is almost insoluble in rain water and it is unaffected by carbon dioxide and other of the principal con-

Fig. 14-14. Weathered granite in the Black Hills of South Dakota. The rounded pinnacles are characteristic of the weathering of this massive rock. (Photo by courtesy of the South Dakota Highway Comm.)

stituents of the atmosphere; so rocks composed primarily of quartz decompose very slowly. Other minerals are highly susceptible to water and show marked signs of reaction within a few months of exposure to the atmosphere. In a general way we can say that the resistance of a mineral to chemical weathering is approximately the reverse of Bowen's reaction series. The most susceptible minerals are augite and olivine; the least soluble are quartz and biotite.

Three processes are notably responsible for chemical weathering. They are:

1. Oxidation.
2. Hydration.
3. Carbonation.

Oxidation

Oxidation is the process by which oxygen combines with elements or compounds. The combination is aided by the presence of water and high temperatures. Oxygen has a particular affinity for iron compounds, and these are among the most commonly oxidized materials. The pyroxenes, hornblende, and olivine all contain iron. As the minerals are broken down they become oxidized, and the iron is converted to ferric oxide (the mineral hematite) or to the hydroxide, the mineral limonite. These processes are accompanied by color changes in the minerals and in the soils. The green and black soils are changed to red, yellow, or brown colors as limonite is formed. Soils of these colors are most common in warm, moist climates. Reduction, the process by which oxygen is freed from its compounds, is not common in weathering.

Hydration

The term "hydration" refers to the absorption of water and the combination of water with other compounds. It is sometimes confused with hydrolysis, the reaction between water and a compound. These processes, especially as combined with carbonation, are extremely

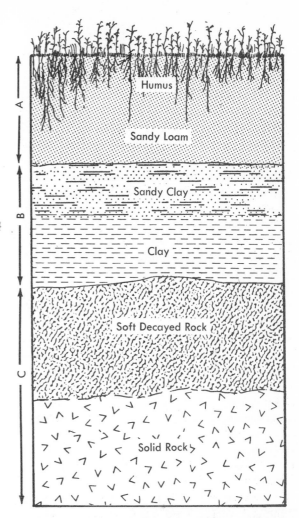

Fig. 14-15. A soil profile of residual soil. The A horizon is characterized by decayed organic matter and sandy loam. The B horizon contains clay, and the C horizon is composed of the rock from which B and A are derived.

effective in the weathering of common rocks and minerals.

Carbonation

This is the process by which carbon dioxide is added to oxides of calcium, magnesium, sodium, and potassium to form carbonates of these metals. Carbon dioxide is a gas and is a common constituent of the earth's atmosphere. It combines with water to form a weak acid called carbonic acid, H_2CO_3. Thus rain water is a weak acid and is the most common solvent acting on the crust.

Weathering of particular minerals and rocks

Feldspar. Since feldspars are by far the most common minerals in rocks, the way they are affected by chemical weathering is very important. Orthoclase and microcline feldspars are composed of $KAlSi_3O_8$. When these feldspars come in contact with rain water the feldspar combines with carbonic acid and water to form a clay mineral, kaolinite, plus a soluble compound, potassium carbonate, plus free silica which is in solution and may later be deposited as one of the amorphous or cryptocrystalline forms of quartz.

$$2KAlSi_3O_8 \quad + \quad H_2CO_3 \quad + \quad H_2O \quad \rightarrow$$
feldspar   carbonic   water
                      acid

$$K_2CO_3 \quad + \quad Al_2(OH)_2\,Si_4O_{10} \quad + \quad 2SiO_2$$
potassium   clay   silica
carbonate   (in solution)

Quartz. This mineral is virtually unaffected by chemical weathering.

Biotite mica. This common rock-forming mineral reacts with water, oxygen, and carbonic acid to form clay, limonite, potassium bicarbonate, magnesium bicarbonate, silica, and water.

$$2KMg_2Fe(OH)_2AlSi_3O_{10} \quad + \quad O \quad +$$
biotite   oxygen

$$10H_2CO_3 \quad + \quad H_2O \quad \rightarrow$$
carbonic acid   water

goes to form:

$$2KHCO_3 + 4Mg(HCO_3)_2 + Fe_2O_3 \cdot H_2O +$$
potassium   magnesium   limonite
bicarbonate   bicarbonate

$$Al_2(OH)_2Si_4O_{10} \quad + \quad 2SiO_2 \quad + \quad H_2O$$
clay   silica   water
            (in solution)

Calcite (and limestone). Calcite is slightly soluble in water. It dissolves to form a solution composed of ions of calcium and carbonate. It has already been pointed out that water and carbon dioxide combine to form carbonic acid. This weak acid in solution forms ions of hydrogen and bicarbonate. The hydrogen ion from the carbonic acid will combine with the carbonate ion from the calcium carbonate to form more bicarbonate. This process will continue as long as the two ions H^+ and CO_3^{--} are present; so, as long as a fresh supply of rain water is percolating through the limestone it will continue to be dissolved.

$$CaCO_3 \rightleftarrows Ca^{++} + CO_3^{--}$$

$$H_2O + CO_2 \rightleftarrows H_2CO_3 \rightleftarrows H^+ + HCO_3^-$$

$$H^+ + CO_3^{--} \rightleftarrows HCO_3 -$$

Soils

One of the most immediate results of the weathering processes is the formation of soils. The soils in any given place may either have developed in place as residual soils or they may have been weathering and erosion products transported from some other locality. The two types of soil differ greatly in their relation to the underlying rock. A residual soil is characterized by the gradual transition from top soil

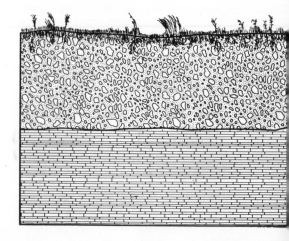

Fig. 14-16. A transported soil. Note the sharp discontinuity between the bedrock and the soil.

Fig. 14-17. The Pinnacles, in Oregon's Crater Lake. Some of these needles are 200 feet high, carved out of soft volcanic material by weathering and erosion by running water. (Photo by courtesy of the Oregon State Highway Dept.)

to the partially decayed rock and finally to solid unaltered rock. A transported soil will not grade down into the solid rock. Instead there is usually a rather sharp contact between the soil and the solid rock. What other criteria might be used to make the distinction? Since the soil is a product of decay it should contain the constituents of the solid rock beneath it. While solution and leaching may remove some elements, only those present in the atmosphere will be added. So, in spite of the possible alterations and recombination of elements, it is possible to test by identification of minerals in the soils or by quantitative and qualitative chemical analyses to find if the soil could have been derived from the underlying rock.

REFERENCES

BENNETT, H. H., 1947, *Soil Conservation*: New York and London, McGraw-Hill Book Co., 406 p.

BLACKWELDER, ELIOT, 1927, *Desert Weathering* (Abstract): Geol. Soc. America Bull., v. 38, p. 127-128

GOLDICH, S. S., 1938, *A Study in Rock Weathering*: Jour. Geology, v. 46, p. 17-58

JENNY, HANS, 1941, *Factors of Soil Formation*: New York, McGraw-Hill Book Co., 281 p.

KELLER, W. D., 1955, *The Principles of Chemical Weathering*: Columbia, Mo., Lucas Bros., 88 p.

REICHE, PARRY, 1950, *A Survey of Weathering Processes and Products*: N. Mex. University Pub. Geology, No. 3, 95 p.

15   Mass Movement

VARIETY OF FORMS OF MASS MOVEMENT

Evidence of the down-slope movement of rock and soil is found almost universally. The greatest variety of forms appears in high mountains where the slopes are steep and the rate of erosion by mass movement is most rapid. A trip into the upper parts of any high mountain range would provide opportunities to see these processes vividly displayed at every turn.

The trees begin to thin out or disappear altogether between 10,000 and 11,000 feet elevation. Past the timber line effects of mass wasting become increasingly prominent. The ground is strewn with rock and large quantities of jointed blocks and fragments in the process of being moved down slope.

To those unfamiliar with such areas it is usually surprising to discover that the summits of many ranges are not peaks at all but broad plateau surfaces. If there is a sufficient amount of precipitation these surfaces will be covered with thick grass through which irregular blocks of rock protrude. Quite common among the strange assortment of rock shapes are the elongate masses standing on end, giving the appearnce of having been picked up and stuck into the ground on a pointed end. In certain places these are so numerous that they almost completely cover the plateaus; in others they form polygonal-shaped rings, called stone polygons. Both situations are the result of frost heaving. As water in the soil freezes and expands, the rocks are forced upward. Then, as thawing begins, soil slumps down into the spaces under and around the lifted blocks before they can move back into their former positions. As this process continues, with every freezing the rocks are pushed up farther and farther out of the soil. In the higher mountains this freezing and thawing may take place daily throughout the summer. With nightfall, the ground, warmed by the hot sun during the day, is rapidly returned to the frigid, high-altitude temperatures.

When frost heaving moves the soil on a slope it is usually pushing the soil or rocks straight out, perpendicular to the ground surface. When thawing occurs, the material settles back, but not along the same path. It is pulled down by the force of gravity toward the center of the earth. Thus, there is a component of down-slope movement with each cycle. This same principle may be applied to any mechanism which tends to lift material up from the ground surface and then allows it to fall back freely.

Rock fall

Dropping down from the plateau surfaces and high peaks of the mountains are broad, deep amphitheater-shaped bowls, called cirques,

Fig. 15-1. Mt. Aso, Kyushu, in spring. Sheet wash is one of the most important types of mass movement. When it rains the surface of this volcano is covered by a thin sheet of water which in moving down-slope carries particles of ash, cinders, and dust. As this type of erosion and mass wasting continues lines of drainage become more clearly defined and the water concentrates along these lines. (Photo by courtesy of Japan Tourist Association.)

Rock Glacier

Cirque

Talus

Fig. 15-2. High oblique view of the Beartooth Mountains, Montana. Note the plateau surface, 11,000 feet high. This ancient, nearly flat erosion surface has been dissected by glaciers, but now mass movement is one of the main processes tending to change its appearance. High piles of talus may be seen on the sides of the valleys. These converge at the bottom of the valleys to form rock glaciers which slowly move downhill under the pull of gravity. The tops of the plateaus are strewn with frost-heaved boulders. (Photo by courtesy of the U.S. Air Force.)

which once formed the heads of glaciers. Their walls are nearly vertical and in places as high as 1000 feet. With crashing noises, huge blocks of rock break loose from these oversteepened sides. As they bounce and hit the wall they dislodge other rocks, sometimes starting landslides and leaving a cloud of dust along their path. As this rock debris, called talus, hits the bottom of the cirque, it generally piles up to form what is known as a talus cone. This in turn becomes a talus sheet as it spreads out with the continual addition of broken blocks. The talus cones or sheets are naturally composed of whatever rocks make up the face of e source cliffs. They may be of any rock type. Mechanical weathering on such steep slopes, particularly freezing and thawing, is so much more rapid than chemical decay that the talus rocks on top of the piles usually appear freshly broken. These broken blocks are of all sizes, but seldom smaller than the size of a hand specimen (3 by 4 inches). The sheet-like masses of talus covering the lower slopes of the valley walls continue to become larger and spread as the bare, exposed cliffs are gradually disintegrated by the never-ending process of weathering.

Rock glaciers

Snow and ice cover the floors of some of the basin-shaped bottoms of these valleys, particularly those at the higher elevations. In the Northern Rockies this ice may be an active glacier, but in the United States it is more often a remnant of one active during the last few thousand years. Rock fragments, landing on the ice and snow cover, roll and slide rapidly down hill. They may become incorporated in a talus pile or they may rest on the surface of the ice. Frequently the ice in the bottom of the valley

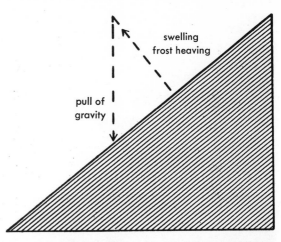

Fig. 15-3. The mechanics of down-slope movement through swelling or frost heaving. The rock is uplifted perpendicular to the ground surface; then it is pulled straight down by the force of gravity and gradually moves down-slope when disturbed.

is completely covered by converging talus cones or sheets.

If the floor of the valley is flat, the talus may lie there, moving at very slow rates and then only because it is disturbed by freezing and thawing, by animals, or by the impact of new rocks falling on it. But if the valley floor,

Fig. 15-4. Talus cones. These cones line the side of this high mountain cliff in the Madison Mountains of Montana. (Photo by E. W. Spencer.)

Fig. 15-5. A rock glacier seen from the trail pass near the head of Horseshoe Basin, Silverton quadrangle, Colorado. (Photo by courtesy of the U.S. Geological Survey.)

Fig. 15-6. A rock glacier in Silver Basin near Ouray County, Colorado. (Photo by courtesy of the U.S. Geological Survey.)

Fig. 15-7. Madison River Canyon slide. This giant slide filled the Madison River Canyon to a depth of two hundred feet with weathered rock debris from the valley side. This slide is more than 400 feet high on the right-hand side of the valley. A lake is seen as it began to form on the upstream side of the natural dam. This landslide was triggered by an earthquake. The dark covering on the side is a mass of trees which were uprooted by the slide. (Photo by courtesy of the Montana Highway Commission.)

whether covered with ice or dry, is inclined, then the converging piles of talus may form a tongue-shaped projection down the valley. These lobes of talus move so slowly that their motion can be detected only by checking the position of the end of the lobe over a period of years. Such is the movement of the rock glacier. As the rock glacier advances it assumes garland-shaped loops, giving the appearance of being a very viscous liquid. Of course, some of these sheets have considerable amounts of ice mixed in with the rock, making the movement of the glacier more rapid than sheets at lower elevations and lower latitudes which are completely dry.

Creep

Besides the mass movement on steep slopes, there are many other forms of a still slower nature. These become apparent on close inspection of almost every hillside. Residual soil is being gradually pulled down slope. In some places clay remnants of rocks and boulders are drawn out into long, lens-shaped masses. Small, parallel rows, circling many hillsides, which were originally paths used by grazing animals, remain to give indication of this creeping down-slope movement. Frequently fences and telephone poles set on slopes may give an indication of these surface movements, as their positions slowly become inclined down hill away from their initial vertical attitude.

Of course a trip to the Rockies is not necessary to see many of the forms of mass wasting. On every hillside and valley in the world some of them are going on continuously. Mass wasting ceases only when the surface of the ground becomes flat. Its speed increases as the angle of the slope increases.

Mass wasting takes still other forms than those already described. The following examples will illustrate the variety of forms and the effects produced. Although the slower types of mass wasting, which usually pass unnoticed, have the most important effects because of their widespread occurrence, there are other movements which are occasionally quite spectacular.

Madison Canyon landslide

About midnight on August 17, 1959, a severe earthquake shook the region west of Yellowstone Park in Montana. The ground was set in motion, and surface waves were set up that rocked water in nearby lakes, threw the soil up in waves, and cracked the highways and ground surface over a large area. The movement was caused by a displacement along a fault in the solid crust. This fault extends near the Madison River Canyon, a narrow and very steep canyon that is cut some 1300 feet down through a mountain mass composed of Precambrian rocks.

The earthquake triggered a movement in the decayed soils and rock debris on the side of the Madison River Canyon, and in the chaos that followed some 35 million cubic yards of rock, soil, and trees slid off of one side of the canyon leaving a scar from the top of the mountains almost to the river. The debris engulfed the valley, a campground, and the high-

Fig. 15-8. Land slump caused by the Montana earthquake of 1959. At a number of places along the edge of this lake, Hebgen Lake, the loosely consolidated talus and weathering products from the sides of the mountains slumped into the lake. (Photo by E. W. Spencer.)

way through the canyon, burying about 135 acres of land with an average thickness of 150 feet of rock. The movement of this great quantity of material was extremely fast—estimates run as high as 60 miles per hour. As the movement occurred, the mass of debris forced the air at the bottom of the valley aside, setting up a wind of gale force. When the slide hit the river, water was splashed out leaving mud splashes in trees high up on the sides of the valley. Material broken loose from the south side of the valley moved downward with such impetus that it continued up the north side of the valley until the debris was piled up more than 400 feet. As the slide filled the valley, a wave of water was forced up the river for almost a mile. The slide consisted of material ranging in size from blocks 30 feet across to fine soil particles.

The disaster was triggered by the earthquake, but the potential for mass movement had been there for many years. Even before the slide occurred the slopes were oversteepened. They were between 40- and 60-degree slopes on which deeply weathering Precambrian gneisses and schists were exposed. These deep soils were held on the slope by the presence of a massive layer of dolostone exposed near the bottom of the valley. Dolomite or dolostone tends to be resistant in the semiarid climates of the west. Another important factor in the slide was the presence of many lines and planes of weakness in the rocks that were inclined toward the river. The rock units of gneiss, schists, and dolostone are inclined—that is, dip—toward the river on the south side of the valley, and they are fractured. Thus there were many potential planes of slippage such as fractures, bedding planes, and foliation surfaces. When the earthquake movements began, blocks of the dolostone became dislodged, and the main mass movement was started.

Solifluction

This term, which literally means soil flowage, is applied to the downslope movement of soils, rock debris, and fragments in frigid climates where the ground is solidly frozen in the winter and only partially thaws out in the summer months. When thawing occurs, the upper layers of the soil, which have been forced up and deranged by frost heaving, are bathed in meltwater. The lower layers of the soil remain solidly frozen. This facilitates flowage and slow movement of the upper layers over the lower frozen layers even on very low slopes. The moving soil and debris takes sheet, lobate, or tongue-like forms as it moves. Where valleys are present, the material will move into the valleys and down valleys as slowly flowing tongues. The nature of the debris depends on what makes up the soil. On Bear Island of the North Atlantic the surface becomes covered with a thick flowing mud, while in places on the Falkland Islands the debris is made up of quartzite fragments.

Mudflow

As the name suggests, this is a flowage of the finer sizes of debris and soil mixed with water. One of the most spectacular of these occurred in the San Gabriel Range of southern California. The San Gabriels are high mountains with steep slopes. A few years before the flow there was an extensive forest fire on the western slopes of the range. The flow started on a warm day when the heat caused melting of the snow cover in the high mountains. The meltwaters percolated into the very thick weathered cover of decaying schists. Finally the weathered material became saturated, and the mass broke loose. It left a scar extending 1000 feet up the mountain side with 150-foot-high cliffs around the edge of the scar. The mudflow continued for 5 days, and at its height it splashed mud 20 feet into the air, leaving a mud coating on tree tops. The mixture was about 25 per cent water.

Mudflows occur commonly in deserts also. Here the fine weathering products may be dry most of the year. When rain does fall it comes in large quantities with perhaps all or a large part of the annual rainfall coming in a single rain. The water seeps into the weathering products, and the mixture moves rapidly down steep slopes, more slowly on lower slopes. The flows slip into channels and gullies. They are

Fig. 15-9. This view of the Slumgullion mudflow shows its source. The flow is seen here to extend to Lake San Cristobal. (Photo by courtesy of the U.S. Geological Survey.)

Fig. 15-10. The Gros Ventre slide, Wyoming. (Photo by E. W. Spencer.)

not dry but the mass does not contain much free water. Sometimes large boulders will float in the mud. Mudflows are favored by intermediate water supply, little vegetation, and unconsolidated rock debris.

Gros Ventre slide (earthflow)

Where the Gros Ventre River cuts through the mountains east of the town of Kelly, Wyoming (just east of the Teton Mountains), the earth began to flow slowly from one side of the river valley into the valley during 1909–1911. The movements there were facilitated by the structure of the sedimentary strata exposed on the mountain side. The strata exposed there are clays and shales interbedded with thin sandstones. They dip at about 20° toward the river. The stream cut through the sandstones overlying the muds and shales before movement began. Then slow flowage and slipping occurred in the layers of plastic clay. The flowage was most rapid in the spring after thaws when meltwater from ice and snow seeped into the top of the flow scars and saturated the underlying clays. The slide occurred on this slippery clay base. The mass left a large scar extending up the mountain, and a lobe-like mass of earth filled the river valley and moved up the opposite side of the valley during the most rapid movements. It formed a dam across the river and backed up a large lake. The river topped the dam and in 1925 rapidly cut through the weak clays and sand in the dam causing a flood downstream which destroyed most of the town of Kelly.

The Panama Canal (slides, slumps, and plastic flowage)

The construction of the Panama Canal was plagued by many costly earth movements. At

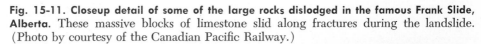

Fig. 15-11. Closeup detail of some of the large rocks dislodged in the famous Frank Slide, Alberta. These massive blocks of limestone slid along fractures during the landslide. (Photo by courtesy of the Canadian Pacific Railway.)

times they were so bad that some question arose as to the feasibility of completing the canal. The slides and slumping of the sides of the canal became worse where the canal was cut through the Cucuracha formation. This unit is partially composed of a highly plastic clay. At first the slides were a result of cutting the sides of the canal too steeply so that the material slid because the sides exceeded the angle of repose for the material. The conditions were aggravated when the sides were cut down to lower slopes because the debris was dumped just above the top of the cut. The weight of the debris piled up led to the development of slumps. A slump is bounded underneath by a curved surface along which movement occurs. As the top cracks and moves down, the toe or

bottom moves up and out. The first sign is the development of a crack at the top of the slumping mass. After the crack forms, the slumping mass may move rapidly if it is on a steep slope or it may creep slowly downward.

Other mass movements plagued the construction. In places plastic clays underlie the bottom of the canal. When the canals were dredged to deepen the channel, the mixture of water and clay was pumped up on the sides. The weight of this mass further compressed the layers of clay, and the plastic clay was squeezed along within the clay zone until it came to a point where the pressure was less— that, of course, was where the canal had been cut. So lumps of clay continued to rise in the canal. This process continued until the clay

Fig. 15-12. Air view of landslide on steep mountain slopes. Note the slide scar and the lobate form of the toe of the slide where the loose material spread out. (Photo by courtesy of the Royal Canadian Air Force.)

Fig. 15-13. Topographic forms due to landslides in Dolores County, Colorado. (Photo by courtesy of the U.S. Geological Survey.)

Fig. 15-14. Details of landslide topography near Ouray, Colorado. (Photo by courtesy of the U.S. Geological Survey.)

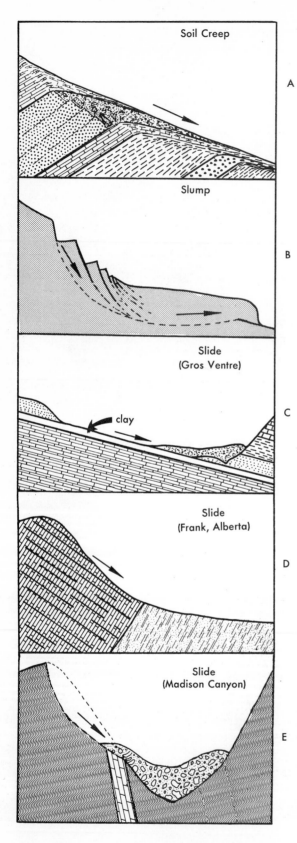

Soil Creep

A

Slump

B

Slide
(Gros Ventre)

clay

C

Slide
(Frank, Alberta)

D

Slide
(Madison Canyon)

E

layer was squeezed off and this method of dredging was given up.

Turtle Mountain slide (Alberta)

The landslide that occurred on Turtle Mountain in 1903 is of particular interest because of the high velocity of the slide. An estimated 40 million cubic yards of rock moved from the mountainside a distance of about 2 1/2 miles within a period of under 2 minutes. The slide occurred in a jointed limestone unit. The bedding in the limestone and underlying shales and sandstones is inclined toward the mountain, but a system of joints in the limestone is inclined almost parallel to the side of the mountain. The clays at the bottom of the slide gave plastically, allowing the limestone to slip along the fractures, which were loosened by the action of freezing and thawing waters. Once the slope gave way, the debris rolled, slid, and flowed out into the valley.

Principles governing mass movements

From the above specific cases of mass movement it is not difficult to see that few generalities can be made about the nature of this degradational process. At least one generality holds true in all cases. That is that the driving force behind all these movements is the pull of gravity. It is most effective when the material is loose, saturated with water, and on steep slopes.

Fig. 15-15. Types of mass movement. A: the effects of soil creep where rock units outcropping at the surface have become partially disintegrated and decomposed by weathering processes. **B:** in a slump the steepened slope breaks away at the top where a prominent fracture or break in the ground surface appears. The slump mass rotates with the toe rising and moving forward. **C:** the conditions that existed at the site of the Gros Ventre slide. The sandstone slid down the wet clay units filling the valley below. **D:** the approximate conditions at the Turtle Mountain slide in Alberta. The limestone is jointed. Note the orientation of the joints so that slippage along them was possible. **E:** hypothetical section through the Madison Canyon, Montana, showing the location of the dolostone strata and the attitude of the foliation in the schists.

Many classifications of mass movements have been attempted, although none has yet proved entirely satisfactory. Among the bases for these various classifications are:

1. Kind of material moved.
2. Size of the material.
3. Rate of movement.
4. Water content.
5. Organization of the material in the moving mass.
6. Relation of the moving material to the solid surface.

One of the most frequently used classifications uses several of these—type of material, rate, and nature of the movement. The types of material moved are classed in the following groups:

1. *Rock* (Solid, fragmental rocks). It is implied that the material moved was predominantly rock without quantities of soil, mud, or other material.
2. *Earth.* The term is used loosely and is applied to disintegrated particles of solid matter.
3. *Soil.* The disintegration and decomposition products of rocks and minerals.
4. *Debris.* A term applied to the loose material arising from the disintegration of rocks. A mixture of rocks, soil, and plant matter.
5. *Mud.* A mixture of water with the finer particles of earth and soil.

Needless to say, the terms earth, soil, and debris are very similar in meaning and frequently are used almost interchangeably.

Movement. Two types of movements may be recognized. First there are those in which there is some discrete surface along which slippage occurs, such as in the case of slides or rock falls. These surfaces of slippage include such features as bedding planes, fractures, and fault surfaces. The second type of movement is that of flowage. Flowage may be either a slow rotation, slippage, and sliding, as in the case of creep, or it may be very rapid, as in flows where large quantities of water act as a lubricant for the mass. A satisfactory classification of mass movement based on these two factors is given:

I. SLOW FLOWAGE
Rock creep.
Talus creep.
Soil creep.
Rock-glacier creep.
Solifluction.

II. RAPID FLOWAGE
Earth flow.
Mud flow.
Debris avalanche.

III. SLIDING
Slump.
Debris slide.
Debris fall.
Rock slide.
Rock fall.

IV. SUBSIDENCE (the sinking in of the ground over underground caverns).

Significance of mass wasting

Mass wasting by itself and particularly in combination with running water is the most important process of degradation. Running water and glaciers move material faster and farther, but initially, at least, mass-wasting processes provide the bulk of the supply to the streams and glaciers from the slopes of valleys. It is perhaps a mistake to emphasize the differences between gradation by mass wasting, running water, and glaciation. Like all classifications it is an artificial one imposed to help us clarify our thinking about these natural processes. It is most helpful to think of them as being closely interrelated and as processes which by their very nature grade from one to the other. We may think of this gradation as being from freely moving solid materials in air to solids in solution at one extreme, and to solids frozen into ice at the other extreme. Naturally there are many borderline cases. With a little more water some mudflows would be called streams, and with a little more ice some rock glaciers would be glaciers.

REFERENCES

ALDEN, W. C., 1928, Landslide and Flood at Gros Ventre, Wyoming: Am. Inst. Mining Metall. Engineers Trans., v. 76, p. 347-361

SHARPE, C. F. S., 1938, *Landslides and Related Phenomena:* New York, Columbia University Press, 136 p.

SHARPE, C. F. S., and DOSCH, E. F., 1942, Relation of Soil Creep to Earthflow in the Appalachian Plateaus: Jour. Geomorphology, v. 5, p. 312-324

TERZAGHI, KARL, 1950, Mechanism of Landslides, p. 83-124 in Paige, Sidney, Editor, Application of Geology to Engineering Practice (Berkey Volume): Geol. Soc. Am., 328 p.

THORNBURY, W. D., 1954, *Principles of Geomorphology:* New York, John Wiley & Sons, 618 p.

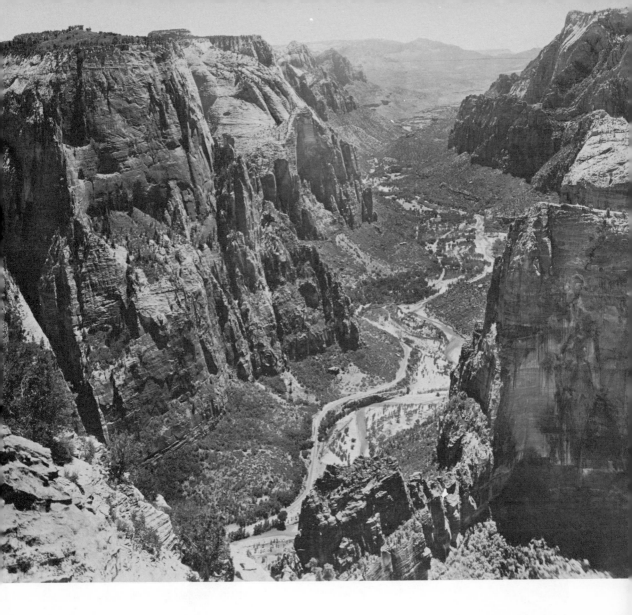

16 Running Water

Nature of stream flow

It is the pull of gravity on surface waters that causes them to run downslope, to coalesce, forming streams, and to continue toward sea level. Although the pull of gravity is a constant, the nature of the flow undergoes many changes in the course of the journey. The journey may start in the mountains where the water literally jumps, boils, and foams as it rushes down the steep slopes, confined to narrow channels filled with boulders and rock debris. At the foot of the mountains the stream is more likely to follow a sinuous course through rolling landscapes. The water seems quieter except for

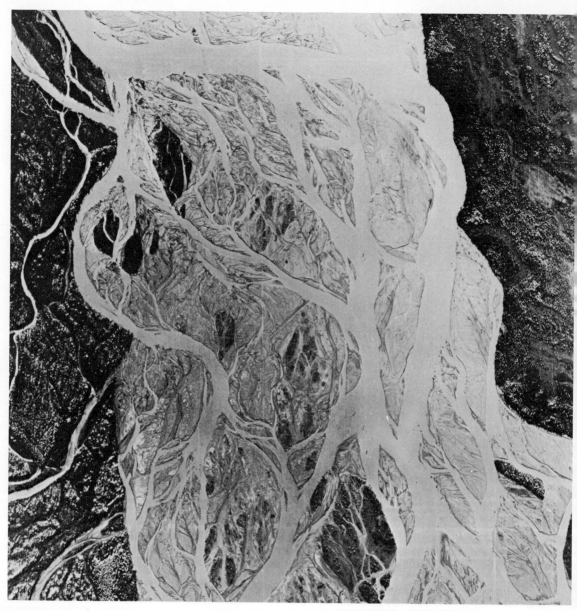

Fig. 16-1. Vertical photograph of the braids in the Tanana River, Alaska. Braided streams are characterized by shallow channels, great width, and they are most common where debris is supplied in great quantity such as near the margin of a melting glacier. Most braided streams are found on very low slopes. (Photo by courtesy of the U.S. Air Force.)

occasional floods and rapids as it moves toward lower elevations. Finally as the stream approaches sea level it may follow a broad meandering path across a flat countryside. The water flows gently with only mild surficial disturbances.

Along the course of almost any river ob-

vious changes in the nature of the movement of the waters can be seen. These range from the extreme turbulence of the water where it cascades down a rough stream channel, or where it hits at the foot of a waterfall, to the very smooth even flow which may be seen at the lip of a waterfall or wherever the slope of a smooth stream channel suddenly steepens. Turbulence is brought about by obstructions, which tend to deflect the movement of the water from a straight or streamlined path. At the obstruction the smooth flow pattern is disrupted, and eddy currents, whirlpools, and boiling are set up. The flow of most streams on medium to low slopes is slightly turbulent. It is called streaming flow. The surface is smooth in some places, slightly undulating in others. A mild slow eddying and boiling near the surface may be visible. The turbulence in streaming flow arises from irregularities in the bottom and sides of the stream channel and at the surface. At these places there is frictional drag on the water. Even the air offers some frictional drag to the movement of the water, as is shown by waves formed on the surface of a pond over which a strong wind is moving.

At the opposite extreme of complete turbulence is laminar flow. In laminar flow water moves as though it is made up of very fine layers that are free to slip over one another. The path of a particle in any one layer is smooth or streamlined, not the irregular or whirled path of a particle in turbulent motion. Laminar flow is most closely approached in natural streams when the water is moving very slowly through a channel with smooth sides, or when the velocity increases very rapidly in what is called shooting flow. The second condition is obtained at the top of a waterfall. A lip forms where the water, dropping over the suddenly steepened slope, runs ahead of that upstream. The surface of the water drops and becomes smooth, showing no signs of turbulence or eddying. The velocity has become so great that the paths of the water particles are straightened out.

Turbulence is promoted by high stream velocity and rough channels. Laminar flow is promoted by either high or low velocity in smooth channels. Thus the type of flow is closely related to the shape and nature of the stream channel. The amount of frictional drag and the opportunity for more obstructions increase as the area of contact between water and the ground increases. For this reason a more streamlined flow pattern may be expected in streams that are semicircular or parabolic in cross section than in those that are very wide and shallow.

Methods of transportation

Muddy waters usually characterize streams of all sizes after a heavy rainfall. The increased surface runoff sweeps large quantities of dirt and weathering products into the streams. The water appears muddy because part of its load is being transported in suspension. The lightest particles may float on the surface, and all the materials are buoyed up by a force equal to the weight of the water they displace. Thus the effective weight of a sand grain in water is less than the weight of the grain measured in air. This is an important fact to remember about all the transported load of a stream. The suspended load is usually made up largely of silt and clay sizes. Colloids make up an important part of the suspended load, but much larger particles may be suspended if the water is turbulent. An estimate of the sizes may be obtained by taking a sample of the water from a nearby stream and allowing it to stand. The true colloidal-sized particles will stay suspended in the still water; the silt and sand sizes will soon settle out.

Fig. 16-2. Imaginary flow lines are drawn in the stream to indicate the type of motion. Laminar flow is found where the water breaks away at the lip of the falls, and maximum turbulence is found at the foot.

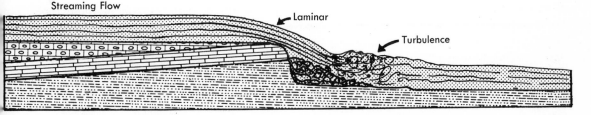

Fig. 16-3. Profile of a long river. Note the variations in the stream pattern from the mountains through the rolling countryside and the flat coastal plain to the coast. The greatest part of the load carried by the stream is obtained in the mountains where the slopes are very steep. Once out of the high country the

Solution

Some weathering products of chemical decomposition of soil and rocks are carried in solution in the waters of most streams. The load in solution actually becomes a part of the liquid in the stream. A very large part of the soluble load in streams in humid climates comes from ground water that finds its way into surface streams. Streams flowing out of deserts where large quantities of soluble minerals may exist at the surface of the ground also have large loads in solution. In most streams the load in solution is a small part of the total load, but in the slow sluggish streams it may make up a considerable portion of the load. Limestone, dolostone, and salts are notably soluble. These make up much of the load carried in solution. An estimated 270 million tons is removed from the United States in solution each year.

Traction

The remainder of the load of the stream is carried along the bottom of the stream in traction. Sand, pebbles, and small cobbles may bounce along the bottom, hitting irregularities and traveling as suspended material for a short distance until the pull of gravity brings them back to the bottom again. The larger cobbles and the boulders are rolled along the bottom,

or they may slip and slide downstream. The main factor determining the largest boulder that a stream will be capable of moving is the velocity of the water. Experimental evidence indicates that the largest size that will roll along a gently sloping stream bottom varies as the sixth power of the velocity. Thus a slight increase in velocity will bring about a great increase in the sizes that the stream can move.

Competence and capacity

The largest particle that a stream can move is defined as the competence of the stream. The total load that a stream is capable of transporting at any given time is called the capacity of the stream. Unlike competence, capacity depends on the amount of water in the stream and the rate at which the water is being discharged. We may think of the stream at any given time as having a certain amount of energy, which is available for use in transporting debris. This energy may be expended in moving material in suspension, in traction, or in solution. The load of most streams is made up in part of each of these three, but most of the load may be moved in any one of the three ways, depending on conditions at that particular time. Along the lower Mississippi River most of the load is carried in suspension and solution, and only a small part in traction. On the other hand, the load of the

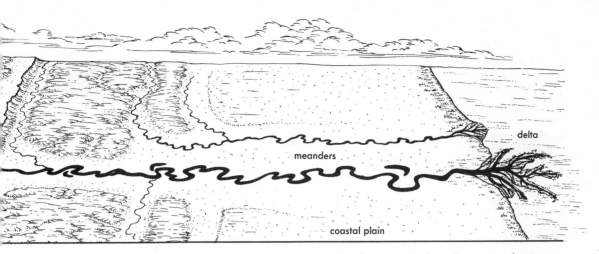

coastal plain

meanders

delta

stream follows a sinuous course across rolling countryside. In the flat coastal plain the stream begins to meander across its valley, and when the stream reaches the ocean the load it carries along is dropped to form a delta.

Arkansas River in the Colorado Rockies is largely carried along the stream bed. Of course the amount of load in transport is also dependent in part on the availability of debris. Streams do not always have enough debris coming into them to fill them to capacity. The effects are the same if the sizes available cannot be entrained, picked up, by the stream. This applies both to the larger boulders, which are not moved because of their mass, and to the smallest particles, clay colloids, which are held together so tightly by cohesive bonds that they are not readily dislodged. Fine sand and coarse silt are the most easily entrained sizes.

Sources of load

Most material transported by streams ultimately is derived from the weathering of rocks. These products of rock disintegration are moved downhill by the processes of mass wasting. This downslope movement is accelerated and facilitated by surface wash. After a heavy rain the surface of the ground on steep slopes is covered by small rills or trickles of water carrying dirt and soil along in them. Second in importance as a source are the bottom and sides of the stream. A stream channel is ordinarily partially filled with bed load which cannot be transported. This condition prevails except during periods of unusually high water.

Thus the bottom of the channel is a source of debris which has already gotten into the stream. Even the bottom of the channel below this channel fill may become a source during floods. The banks of the stream and the sides of the channel are also sources. The stream may slightly undercut the sides of the channel on curves, bringing about slumping or sliding of the sides into the river. Melting glaciers, wind-blown materials, and volcanic dust are important sources of the load of streams locally.

Distribution of velocity and turbulence

Turbulence is greatest where the most irregularities are present in a stream. That is near the outside perimeter, the water-channel contact. In turbulent flow the motion of par-

Fig. 16-4. A stream obtains its load from the valley sides. Sheet wash, creep, and other types of mass wasting cause soil and rock to be dumped in the stream. Slumping of the steepened bank is often responsible for the lateral erosion accomplished by streams. The black area in the stream channel represents the zone of maximum turbulence. The maximum velocity zone is directly above it.

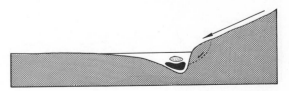

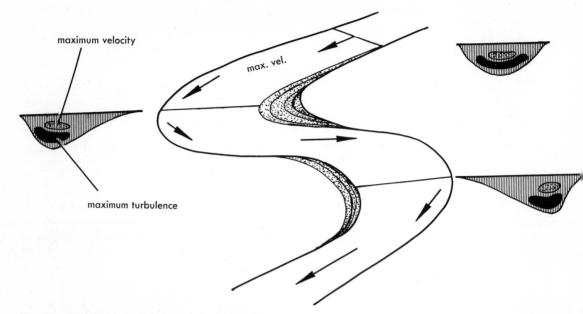

maximum velocity

max. vel.

maximum turbulence

Fig. 16-5. Distribution of velocity in a sinuous stream. The maximum surface velocity is indicated by arrows. In the three cross sections the black zone is the position of the maximum turbulence and the stippled area is the zone of maximum velocity.

ticles is irregular. They are carried up, down, and sideways as well as downstream. Thus the net effective forward velocity of the stream is reduced by turbulence and frictional drag along the bottom. In a straight channel the greatest velocity is usually found in the deepest part of the stream channel beneath the surface. This is true of both streaming and laminar flow. If we could trace the path of a number of particles of water all initially in a vertical section through a stream we would see those about one-third of the way down from the surface get ahead of the others very rapidly. Those at the surface would be somewhat retarded, and the ones near the bottom would be much slower. If a stream channel is symmetrical, the greatest velocity is usually toward the middle, but if the channel is asymmetric, as when a stream follows a curve, then the greatest velocity is shifted toward the deeper water. The

Fig. 16-6. A cross section through the Hudson River at the George Washington Bridge in New York City. The channel is largely filled with sediment which has been moved by the river. During floods much of the sediment may be picked up from the channel bottom and the depth of water increased. (After C. P. Berkey, 1948.)

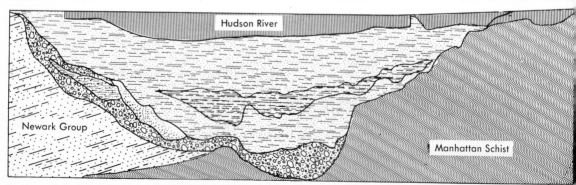

Hudson River

Newark Group

Manhattan Schist

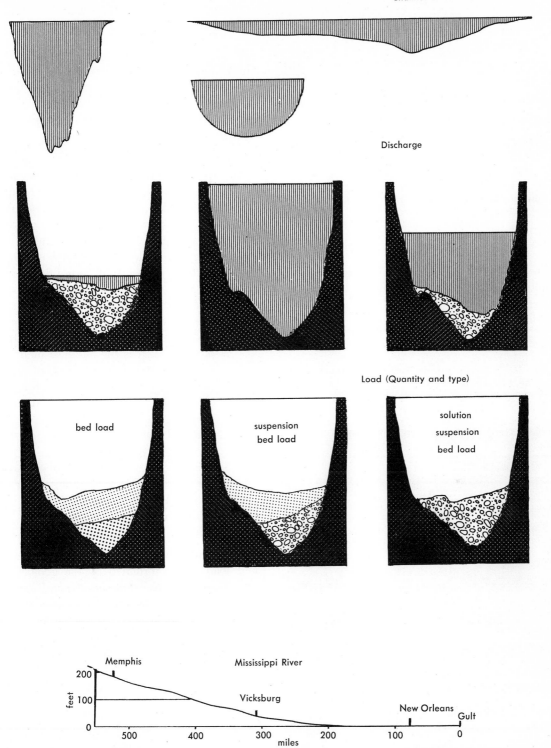

Channel Characteristics

Discharge

Load (Quantity and type)

bed load

suspension
bed load

solution
suspension
bed load

Mississippi River

Memphis

Vicksburg

New Orleans
Gult

feet

200

100

0

500   400   300   200   100   0
miles

Fig. 16-7. Hydraulic factors in stream flow. Stream erosion and deposition are governed by a group of complexly interrelated hydraulic factors. These include the shape and roughness of the channel cross section, the amount of water discharged through a given cross section, the amount and type of load, the slope of the stream channel, and the velocity of the water. (Discharge after L. Leopold and T. Maddox, 1953; gradient after Henry Gannett, 1901.)

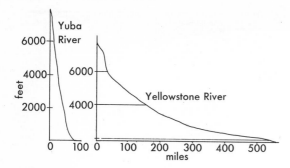

Fig. 16-8. Stream gradients of two steep streams flowing down very steep slopes. (After Henry Gannett, 1901.)

deepest part of the channel is generally on the outside of a curve. Maximum turbulence lies just beneath and to either side of the maximum velocity.

Fig. 16-9. Debris transported by a stream during spring thaw. Note variety of sizes. (Photo by E. W. Spencer.)

Hydraulic factors

The word hydraulic means "of or pertain ing to fluids in motion." Thus hydraulic factor are those that influence the behavior of fluid in motion. They are a closely related and in terrelated group of factors that determine th nature of running water. They are:

1. Discharge: This is the amount of wate passing through a given cross section o the stream at any given time. The quan tity of the discharge may be calculate by multiplying the area of the cross sec tion by the velocity of the water.
2. Amount of load: The total amount o material being transported in solution traction, and suspension.
3. Gradient: The slope of the bottom o the stream channel between two speci fied points. The gradient along a stream is variable. It is the angle of inclination or the difference in elevation of the two points divided by the horizontal distanc along the stream between the two points.
4. Channel roughness: The irregularity o the bottom and sides.
5. Width, depth, and shape of the chan nel.
6. Size and distribution of different size of the sediment in transport.
7. Velocity of the stream.

The first two of these factors, discharge and load, are determined by the geology and physiography of the drainage basin. They can not be controlled by the stream nor are they in any way determined by the other factors They are independent factors. The amount o discharge in a stream is controlled by the amount of rainfall, the amount of surface run off, and the size and shape of the drainage basin. The load supplied is similarly a function of the nature of the source of the load and how readily it can get into the stream.

The gradient or slope of the stream is de pendent on many of the other factors. Adjust ments of the slope of the bottom of the stream channel are constantly taking place. If, for ex ample, the amount of load being brought into

g. 16-10 A and B (upper and middle right). U.S.
my Engineer Waterways Experiment Station model
the Mississippi River. This model has been suc-
ssfully used to predict the arrival of flood stage
vels at various points along the river from data
llected on the amount of rainfall and river levels
rther upstream. (U.S. Army photographs, by C.
. Lefeve, U.S. Army Engineer Waterways Exper-
ent Station.)

ne part of the stream is more than the stream
n carry, then some is left in the channel, and
he slope between this place and one farther
own stream is increased. Processes acting
ithin the stream tend to adjust the slope of
he stream so it can carry its load.

Channel roughness, width, depth, size of
aterial in transport, and velocity of the stream
ater are partially dependent on processes act-
g within the stream. They are complexly in-
rrelated or interdependent. The complexity
f these interrelations is much greater than was
riginally recognized. In recent years much
ore attention has been directed toward un-
erstanding these interrelationships as in-
reased efforts are made to control flooding and
ake the best possible use of our natural water
sources. The results of scale-model experi-
ents have been closely related to actual ob-
rvations along streams. Measuring stations
ave been set up at thousands of points along
ivers and smaller streams to obtain the data
ecessary for the work. The results show that:

1. The width, depth, velocity and suspended sediment load are all functions
   of the amount of water discharged.
2. The shape of the river cross section and
   its roughness determine the distribution
   of the velocity in the cross section.

ig. 16-10 C. (lower right). Interior of one of the au-
omatic control houses used in the operation of the
Mississippi Basin model. Along the center left of
he photo are the stage recorders which plot the
tages obtained on the model rivers. Just below
nd along the lower right are the flow program-
ners which set the amount of discharge to be re-
eased into the model rivers. (U.S. Army photo-
raph, by C. H. Lefeve, U.S. Army Engineer
Waterways Experiment Station.)

Fig. 16-11. The Gros Ventre River in Wyoming. This view is taken just below the famous Gros Ventre slide. The arrow points to a large scar left in the valley alluvium, river deposits, during the flood which followed the slide. (Photo by E. W. Spencer.)

3. The shape of the channel is at least partially determined by the erodibility of the beds and banks.
4. For a given width and discharge, the total load depends on the velocity. Any change in the velocity will be accompanied by a change in depth.

Fig. 16-12. Pot holes formed in a limestone rock.

5. The slope tends to become adjusted t provide the velocity-depth relatio necessary to carry the load. The steepe the slope, the higher the velocity, an thus the greater the transporting powe

STREAM EROSION

Streams are usually considered the mos important of the geomorphic agents in bring ing about the degradation of the land surfac of the continents. Certainly the streams are re sponsible for moving more material than an other agents, but they are effective in accom plishing erosion primarily because mass wastin keeps a constant supply of material movin down valley sides toward the streams. Shee wash plays an important role in this down slope movement. The stream channel and bank are eroded by the moving water and the ma terial carried in it. This erosion is accomplishec by:

1. Abrasion.
2. Solution.
3. Impact.

In regions where humid climates prevai the courses of many streams are determined b the outcrop patterns of soluble rock units. Onc a stream reaches a belt of rock that is eithe soluble or easily eroded, it tends to remain i that unit. Solution is increased where the trans ported material abrades or breaks up the sol uble bedrock. Dissolution takes place mor readily where the surfaces of rocks have beer scratched and fractured by abrasion and im pact, because of the increased surface area Pot holes are striking evidence of the work o solution and abrasion. These smooth roundec holes found in the bottom of many streams where solid rock is exposed to the stream wate are formed by the continued circular motior of eddy currents carrying sand, silt, and grave with them. Most are formed in weak or soluble rocks. The surface of the hole is repeatedly abraded, giving a new surface on which solu tion can take place. The dissolved products are then washed up and out of the hole. Most potoles are relatively small—only 1 or 2 feet cross, but they occasionally become 20 feet r more deep.

Erosion is concentrated on the bottom of he stream channel in streams that are flowing apidly on steep gradients. The debris being ransported is constantly moved by turbulence, ut its motion is usually directed toward the ottom because the materials are always under he downward pull of gravity. Thus these treams tend to concentrate erosion, cutting traight down. Some accomplish just this. The Bighorn River in Wyoming flows through a anyon that is more than 200 feet deep and not much wider at the top than at the bottom. The Arkansas River at the Royal Gorge in Colorado has cut into a very narrow gorge more than 1000 feet deep. The Black Canyon of the Gunnison River in western Colorado is a similar feature. In these places lateral erosion is negligible.

Lateral cutting takes place in streams flowing on low slopes. The channel usually follows a sinuous or meandering course. At each turn he water is shifted toward the outside of the urn. This means that more turbulence and rosion will occur there. The water deepens on he outside of the curve, and the bank is teepened there. This tends to make the outside unstable, and it slumps or slides into the tream. In this fashion the stream brings about ateral erosion of its valley. The impact of the arger materials being transported against the ides and bottom of the channel is also an effective means of stream erosion. Heavier materials may dislodge the loose debris or crack even the hardest and most solid rock.

DEPOSITION

Like Mark Twain, everyone who must pilot a boat through rivers learns to predict where he shifting sand bars are likely to be found. They know, for example, that you are much less likely to go aground on the outside of a curve han on the inside of the curve. Why? The velocity of the water is shifted toward the outside of the curve, and that means more turbulence will pick up debris from the bottom on

Fig. 16-13. View of the Zion Canyon. Downcutting by a stream is evident in this view of the Zion Canyon. Streams along which downcutting is the dominant form of erosion are usually confined to narrow steep-sided valleys. (Photo by courtesy of Union Pacific Railway.)

Fig. 16-14. Stream dissection of flat-lying beds of a plateau. This is an early stage in the dissection of this plateau. Later the divides will be narrowed and the valley will become wider. (Photo by courtesy of the U.S. Air Force.)

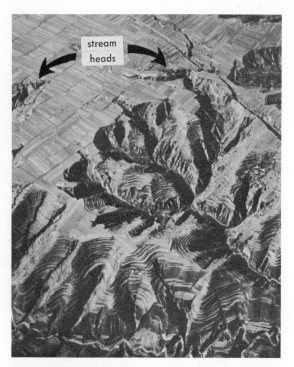

Fig. 16-15. Stream dissection of flat-lying rocks. Note how the stream is eroding into the plateau. This is called headward erosion because the head of the streams is slowly migrating farther on into the plateau as erosion proceeds. (Photo by courtesy of the U.S. Air Force.)

that side of the channel until it becomes deeper. If the amount of water in the river hasn't changed, the inside of the curve must be shallow. Where the water is shallow there will be more frictional drag on it, it will be slowed down, and deposits of sand will accumulate.

So one of the most important factors that brings about deposition is a decrease in velocity. We have already seen that the competence (largest size that can be moved) depends on the velocity of the water. Decreases in velocity will occur where:

1. The slope of the stream channel is reduced.
2. There is a loss of water or a spreading out of water. Streams in arid climates lose their water by evaporation; in addition, when the water table is lowered below the level of the stream bed, water moves out of the stream toward the

water table. Spreading out of the water may occur where a change in the shape of the channel occurs or where the channel splits into several distributaries as it does near the mouth of the Mississippi River.
3. There is a situation in which streams encounter obstructions in their paths. These obstructions include such features as natural dams, timber rafts, or fans of debris piled into a stream by one of its tributaries.
4. Local stagnant pools form or the stream enters a standing body of water such as a lake or the ocean. Flow may stop altogether. A similar condition exists where a stream enters the standing backwaters of a flooded area.

In addition, streams deposit part of their load if there is more load than the stream is capable of transporting. The causes of this condition are:

1. Excessive loads produced by rapid weathering and surface wash.
2. Loads made available by the loss of soil cover such as timber or plants.
3. Volcanic ash falls or glacial sediments.

The work of man is sometimes a major factor in the creation of the first two of the above conditions. We carelessly burn our forest or allow the soil covers to be removed without thought of the added erosive effects made possible by these actions. As a result we pay for it by loss of valuable topsoil and increased flood hazards.

THE CONCEPT OF THE GRADED STREAM

Definition. "A graded stream is one in which, over a period of years, slope is delicately adjusted to provide, with available discharge and with prevailing channel characteristics, just the velocity required for the transportation of the load supplied from the drainage basin. It is a stream in equilibrium; its diagnostic characteristic is that any change in any of the

Fig. 16-16. Lateral erosion by this braided stream is apparent. Notice how the stream is confined on either side by cliffs. The streams have shifted back and forth across the alluvial plain, undercutting and defining the valley. Erosion of this terrace has proceeded much farther than that in Fig. 16-15. Compare the general pattern of the erosion. Notice how the divides between adjacent basins are narrower in this region. (Photo by courtesy of the Royal Canadian Air Force.)

edge of
alluvial
plain

Fig. 16-17. A dendritic, tree-like, stream pattern.
The black dashes outline a single drainage basin which is a part of a larger basin drained by the main stream in the center of the photograph. This picture was taken near Del Rio, Texas. (Photo by courtesy of the U.S. Air Force.)

controlling factors will cause a displacement of the equilibrium in a direction that will tend to absorb the effect of the change" (J. H. Mackin). We should not consider any river as being perfectly graded all the time. The graded stream is not a perfectly stable stream; it is one in which the various hydraulic factors are constantly changing, shifting, and compensating

to bring about a state of equilibrium. Grade is reached when the stream is just able to remove all the debris supplied to the stream from its drainage basin.

Factors controlling the slope (gradient)

The longitudinal profile of a stream is a picture of the configuration of the channel bottom along the length of the stream's path. In general the longitudinal profile of streams shows a marked change from steep slopes near the drainage divides to slight slopes that approach zero at or near sea level. It is not absolutely necessary that a graded stream have a systematic down-valley decrease in slope. The slope may even be highly variable with water falls and lakes along the path. In fact, irregularities rather than smooth slopes characterize all streams including graded streams. Although there is no systematic change in slope downstream it is obvious that the various segments of a graded stream are not completely independent. The condition of perfect grade is reached when each segment along the entire path is able to move its load. This condition is rarely realized even along the oldest graded

Fig. 16-18. Longitudinal stream profiles showing the migration of a nick point upstream. In the top profile the stream has a water fall at the point where a resistant stratum of rock outcrops. In the weaker units downstream the channel is lower. A nick point will be formed which will migrate upstream after the resistant stratum is cut as the stream continues to adjust its gradient.

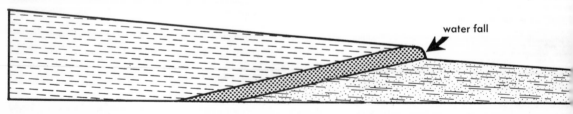

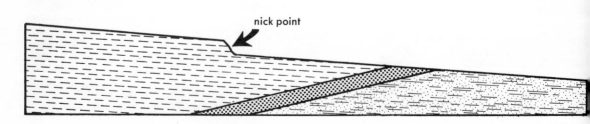

treams. Many changes take place in a stream along its longitudinal profile. Some of the more important of these are:

1. A down-valley increase in discharge. Small and large tributaries enter the main stream channel along its course, increasing the total amount of water in the main channel and therefore the amount of discharge. Where a large graded tributary enters the main channel of a graded stream we may expect a graded stream with a lower slope below the confluence. Why? The increased quantity of water makes a larger channel necessary. The channel becomes deeper, making the increase in cross-sectional area of the channel greater than the increase in the wetted perimeter (where water touches the ground). This means there is a net reduction in the frictional drag on the water, and consequently a greater velocity is possible. The greater velocity makes a reduction in the slope or gradient of the stream possible.

2. A down-valley decrease in the amount of load relative to the amount of discharge. The greatest supply of debris to a stream comes at the head of the stream. Farther downstream only a small amount of material is eroded from the banks and channel by comparison. The wetted perimeter of the main channel of a major stream near its mouth doesn't begin to compare with the total water-ground contact of all of its tributaries—thus there is more erosion and more load near the head of the stream.

3. A down-valley decrease in size of load. At the head of a stream in the mountains large boulders may start the long journey toward the sea. They are knocked against one another, chipped, cracked, and broken with a resulting decrease in size. Slowly and systematically the quantity of the small fraction, in sand-size range, increases relative to larger sizes. This is accompanied by a rounding of the particles. Because of this attrition there is a very definite down-valley decrease in the size of the material moved. This is a major factor leading to lower slopes down valley. The slope and therefore velocity required to transport fragments decreases as the size of the load decreases, making steep slopes down stream unnecessary.

The concept of the graded stream is particularly useful because it helps us to predict the behavior of a stream if any of the conditions affecting it change. The response of the graded stream to changes in some controlling factors are:

1. Increase in load: A steepening in the slope below the point of influx of the load takes place. This is accomplished by deposition of a part of the load. The effect is a down-valley movement of a wave of deposition until the slope is everywhere adjusted to provide the velocity necessary to transport all the increase of load.

2. Decrease in load: The stream below this point makes up for deficiency in load supplied from above by picking up additional load from its channel floor. Downcutting continues until the slope is such as to give just the velocity needed to transport the supplied load.

3. Change in discharge: A decrease in discharge tends to lead to deposition of load and therefore an increase in slope. An increase in discharge leads to erosion from the bottom of the channel along the upper parts of the stream and therefore reduction in gradient and velocity.

Fig. 16-19. Waterfalls in Yellowstone Park. These falls will gradually migrate upstream as the channel is cut deeper. The steepened slope at the falls causes erosion here to be accelerated. Falls are characteristic of streams which are not perfectly graded. (Photo by E. W. Spencer.)

Fig. 16-20. A braided stream flowing out of the mountains near Mt. McKinley, Alaska. Note the debris piled up as an alluvial fan where the tributary at right enters the main stream valley. (Photo by courtesy of the U.S. Air Force.)

Fig. 16-21. A straight stream flowing out of glaciated mountains. Notice that the main stream is flowing parallel to the outcroppings of rock ridges formed where the units are folded. It appears that this part of the stream has become adjusted to the structure of the rock, a subsequent stream. Near the head of the stream the tributaries flow directly downslope, consequent streams. (Photo by courtesy of the Royal Canadian Air Force.)

note attitude of strata

4. Rise of a barrier across the path of the stream: The stream has effectively a lower slope above this point. It is unable to transport its load, and deposition occurs. This leads to the silting in of dams and natural obstructions such as lakes. So, these are transient features.

5. Sudden lowering of the stream channel: Where it tops a waterfall or where as a result of faulting the lower reaches of the stream have been lowered, there is a sudden increase in gradient. This increases the velocity of the stream at and just below that point, which increases the transporting power. A nick is formed in the channel. This nick point will then migrate upstream by undercutting of the falls or cascades until the gradient becomes adjusted.

FEATURES OF STREAMS ON LOW AND MODERATE SLOPES

Streams form many types of patterns, and they flow in a great variety of valleys, but it is possible to select four examples to represent those most commonly found. These are streams with a braided stream pattern, those that follow sinuous courses, those flowing in broadly meandering patterns, and finally those confined to nearly straight channels. Each of these is characterized by features which are peculiar to it. Other features may be found in the valleys occupied by any of them. Three features which may be found in any of the valleys are flood plains, deltas, and alluvial fans.

Alluvial fans are usually formed where streams flow out of an area of high relief into one of low relief — that is, where a stream channel passes from a steep to a low gradient. At such a place the velocity is reduced, and deposition takes place. The stream flowing from a mountainous region may carry great quantities of material which is too coarse to be transported across lower surfaces without large increases in velocity. The result is the formation of a broad low cone-shaped deposit called an alluvial fan. Such fans are composed of poorly sorted, stratified stream deposits. Usually the streams on them are not confined to particular channels very long. The stream shifts position back and forth across the cone, or it may form

Fig. 16-22. Meandering stream patterns. Note the old meander scars, oxbow lakes, and typical flat terrain. (Photo by courtesy of the U.S. Air Force.)

many distributaries. These spread the debris evenly across the fan's surface. Alluvial fans may be found along the sides of many valleys which are paralleled by higher land and particularly mountains. The fans are best developed in the semiarid and arid climates where

Fig. 16-23. A hypothetical cross section through a delta. Note the cross bedding. This is found on a great variety of scales. Cross bedding may be seen in specimens of sand and siltstone only inches across, or it may extend over an area several miles across.

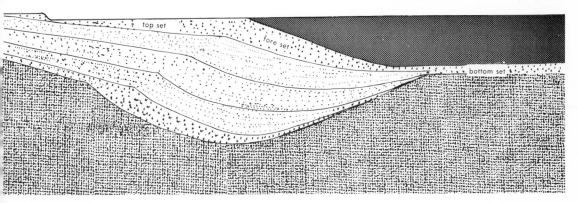

top set

fore set

bottom set

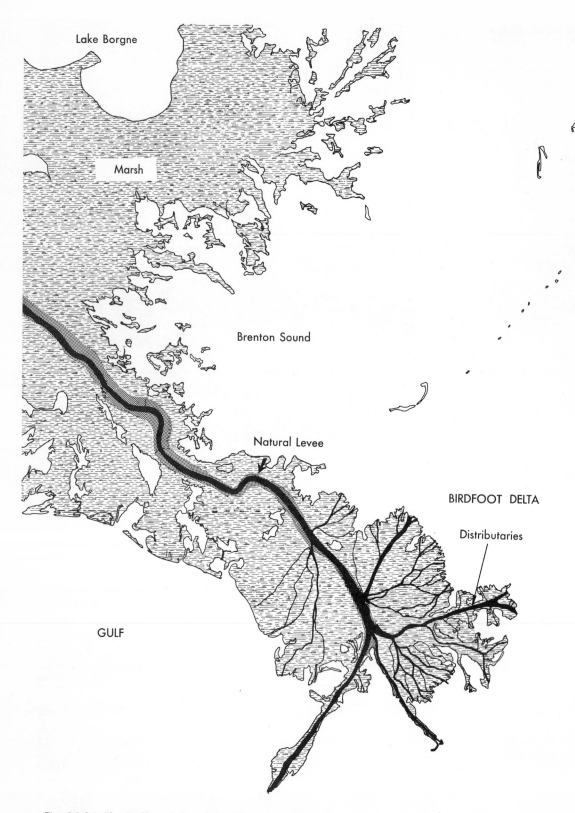

Fig. 16-24. The Birdfoot delta of the Mississippi River.

Fig. 16-25. The flood plain of a river flowing from the mountains of New Zealand. The deposits visible on this flood plain are composed mainly of cobbles and pebbles. The arrows indicate the margins of the plain. (Photo by courtesy of Qantas Airways.)

Fig. 16-26. Features of the meandering stream and its valley. The edge of the flood plain is marked by a cliff. Oxbow lakes, meanders, meander scars, and a neck are clearly shown. The natural levee is not obvious. (Photo by courtesy of the Royal Canadian Air Force.)

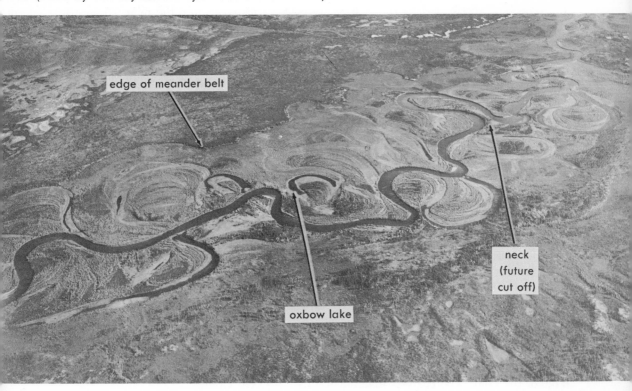

edge of meander belt

oxbow lake

neck
(future
cut off)

Fig. 16-27. Chute cutoff. A chute cutoff has formed at the left, cutting back of the bar deposits laid down on the inside of the meander. The cutoff has shortened the stream considerably. (Photo by courtesy of the Royal Canadian Air Force.)

the process is accelerated by the lack of abundant rainfall, which creates an even greater imbalance in the amount of water relative to the amount of load.

Deltas are the submerged equivalents of alluvial fans. A delta is built where the amount of load entering a body of water is in excess of that which can be moved. Counterparts of the famous deltas of the Nile and the Mississippi may be found in many small lakes and streams. Deltas may be built into a large stream flowing on a low gradient where a heavily loaded tributary flows into it. Of course the chances that such a delta will last very long are remote compared with deltas formed in the ocean. In the Mississippi River's delta a huge area has been flooded with the debris eroded off half the surface area of the United States. This delta is being actively built out into the Gulf of Mexico today. The debris is spread out across the marshes of the lower Mississippi valley through a system of distributaries. At the end of one of these distributaries the load is dropped at the edge of the delta. The coarsest material settles

out first, and the finer silts are carried on out into the deeper water. At the edge of the delta just a few fathoms beneath the surface the slope steepens. At this point the beds are sharply inclined as the debris assumes its angle of repose beneath water. When more material is brought out to the end of the delta the tops of these inclined beds are cut off by the movement of the current across them. This leads to the development of three types of beds in a typical deltaic deposit: the bottomset beds formed of the finest material carried farthest out, the foreset beds which are the steeply inclined units, and the topset beds, which lie on the steeply inclined beds.

Flood plains occur in the following manner: Stream channels on low and moderate slopes are not ordinarily confined in location. They have in the past moved in position by lateral erosion, and the channels of many have shifted back and forth. When the channel shifts in position it leaves behind a channel filled with the transported load. Shifts of this sort become increasingly common in regions of low relief and where unconsolidated sediments underlie the channel. Similar plains are formed where tributaries come into the main stream. Eroded surfaces on either side of the stream are approximately at the same elevation as the main stream, and they are periodically flooded when the water rises. These broad nearly flat areas near the level of the streams are known as the flood plains.

Meandering-stream patterns

The Mississippi River and its valley below Cairo, Illinois, are classic examples of meandering streams and the features associated with them. A map illustrates the most prominent features of a section of a meandering river.

The features include:
a. Broad flood plains.
b. Meander belt.
c. Cutoffs.
d. Oxbow lakes.
e. Natural levees.
f. Yazoo-type rivers.
g. Bayous.
h. Chutes.

The Mississippi's flood plain is as much as 0 miles wide in many places. If there were no rtificial levees the waters would cover large parts of this plain, spreading a thin veneer of the material carried by the river over the plain. This still happens during unusually high floods long the Mississippi and frequently along other rivers. The flood-plain sediments are thickest near the stream channel because the channel is the site of the greatest velocity and of the main part of the load just before and after the flooding starts. Once the waters spread beyond the main channel they become very shallow and extend over a broad area. The frictional drag on these waters is great. As they begin to recede the velocity decreases, and deposition occurs. The thickness of sediment is greatest where most of the load was originally being carried. That position is in and on either side of the main channel. A wedge-shaped layer of sediment is deposited. The thickest part of the wedge is on either side of the channel. Thus the river builds natural levees by the flooding process itself. The effects of this process are most interesting along the Mississippi south of Baton Rouge, Louisiana, where the surface of the river is flowing down a narrow ridge built up above the delta surface by the flood-plain deposits.

The meanders are loop-like channel patterns. Some of these almost double back on themselves. Meanders are common where the gradient of a stream becomes extremely low. The lower part of the Mississippi is flowing down a slope that is approaching horizontal, 2 feet per mile. We have already seen that the velocity is greatest on the outside of a curve. This makes it possible for the outside of the loops to move laterally by undercutting the banks or by bringing about collapse through sliding and slumping of the outside of the bends. This process may continue until a more resistant material is encountered. Since the process is largely one of slumping, it is very

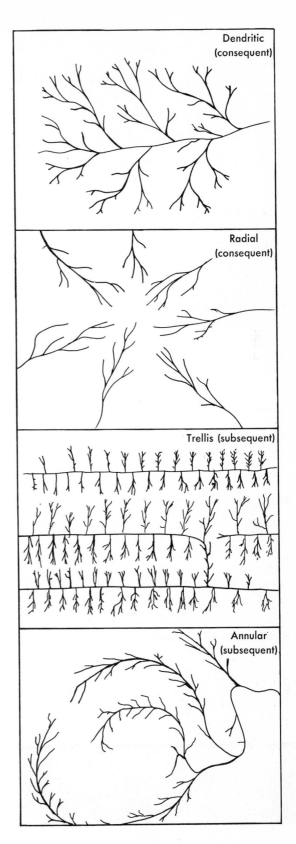

Dendritic (consequent)

Radial (consequent)

Trellis (subsequent)

Annular (subsequent)

Fig. 16-28. Stream patterns. The top two, dendritic and radial, are usually formed where the stream is controlled by the slope. Trellis and annular patterns reflect underlying differences in the structure of the rocks.

slow when the river flows against a rock which is strong. This may cause the direction of lateral movement to be stopped or reversed. Another factor tends to limit the extent to which a meander may grow. That is the presence of other loops on either side of it. If the loops begin to get too large they will cut into each other. A cutoff occurs, the river channel straightens out its path for a short distance, and a meander loop is left cut off from the main stream. Frequently these loops become isolated when clay and silt are deposited by the main stream in the quiet waters at the entrance to the loop. Thus a loop-shaped lake is formed. These are called oxbow lakes.

Some of the sediment removed from the outside of the curves migrates downstream and stops on the quiet waters of the inside of the next meander. Thus curved bars of sand are formed on the inside of the curves. It sometimes happens that part of the river will become diverted and return more or less to an older path flow inside these bar deposits. Such a course is called a chute.

Fig. 16-29. A planed-off dome. Note that the stream follows a pattern which reflects the structure. (Photo by courtesy of the U.S. Air Force.)

Streams entering the flood plain may be unable to enter the main stream channel because of the natural levees, in which case they, like the Yazoo River of Mississippi, follow a nearly parallel course along the edge of the flood plain behind the natural levee until they find a place where they can cut into the main stream. Bayous are the slow sluggish streams flowing on the flood plains which drain these nearly flat surfaces. They almost always follow meandering courses of their own.

Braided streams

These are streams that flow in two or more channels which interfinger or form interwoven patterns giving the appearance of a braid. Some braided streams are commonly formed where the amount of load is excessive and the stream is incapable of transporting all of it. The coarser fractions of the load tend to form islands in the center of the stream, which breaks up into paths around them. These streams almost always are very broad and shallow. In many instances the amount of load held in the stream channel is no more than might be found in the bottom of the channel of a meandering or sinuous stream, but the channel is not cut deeply below the surface of the braided stream, so the load is spread out. In this respect many braided streams are no more heavily loaded than other types.

Drainage patterns

The drainage basin. The drainage basin is the area drained by a particular trunk stream. Basins are divisible into smaller and smaller drainage-basin units until you are down to the area drained by a single small creek or stream. The line of separation between drainage basins is called the drainage divide. The drainage basin of a river like the Mississippi is exceedingly large. It may be subdivided into several very large basins, the basins of the Arkansas River, Missouri River, and the Ohio River, and each of these in turn may be subdivided into its tributaries.

cuesta

← braided stream

water gap →

dendritic pattern →

anticline

Fig. 16-30. Variety of stream patterns seen in relation to the underlying rock structure. Note that the large braided stream is following a sinuous course just to the right of a prominent cuesta. On the back slope of this cuesta the streams undoubtedly follow courses dictated by the slope. A dendritic stream pattern is visible in the center foreground. It is a tributary to the large braided stream. At several points there are water gaps where drainage from the right hand valley flows into the main stream. In the folded belt streams follow courses parallel to the trend of the folds. (Photo by courtesy of the U.S. Air Force.)

Patterns. The pattern of a network of streams reflects the effects of the structure of the underlying rocks. Streams are sensitive to variations in the resistance of rocks to erosion. Usually streams occupy paths of less resistance, and the more resistant units become etched into relief. If a stream's path is governed solely by the slope of the surface of the ground we say the stream is a consequent stream. Its path is a consequence of the slope. Three patterns are commonly developed where this is the case: straight streams flowing down steep slopes, dendritic patterns which resemble the outline of limbs of a tree, and radial patterns which develop on domed surfaces such as structural domes or volcanoes.

If the stream's course has become adjusted to the underlying structure of the rocks and follows a path as a consequence of the underlying structure rather than the original slope of the land then it is called a subsequent stream. Common patterns formed in this manner are rectangular or trellis patterns which develop where the streams have become adjusted to units of varying resistance which are lined up in parallel rows or ridges. An annular, circular, pattern forms where the streams have become adjusted to different resistances around the sides of a domal structure.

REFERENCES

GANNETT, HENRY, 1901, Profiles of Rivers in the United States: U.S. Geological Survey Water-Supply Paper 44, 100 p.

GILBERT, G. K., 1877, *Report on the Geology of the Henry Mountains (Utah)*: U.S. Geog. Geol. Survey of the Rocky Mountain Region (Powell), 160 p.

———1914, The Transportation of Debris by Running Water: U. S. Geological Survey Prof. Paper 86, 263 p.

HIJULSTREM, FILIP, 1939, Transportation of Detritus by Running Water, in Trask, P. D., Editor, *Recent Marine Sediments, A Symposium*: Tulsa, Am. Assoc. Petroleum Geologists, 736 p.

LEOPOLD, L. B., and MADDOCK, THOMAS, 1953, The Hydraulic Geometry of Stream Channels and Some Physiography Implications: U.S. Geological Survey Prof. Paper 252, 57 p.

LEOPOLD, L. B., and MILLER, J. P., 1956, Ephemeral Streams—Hydraulic Factors and Their Relation to the Drainage Net: U.S. Geological Survey Prof. Paper 282-A, 37 p.

LEOPOLD, L. B., and WOL, M. GORDON, 1957, River Channel Patterns: Braided, Meandering and Straight: U.S. Geological Survey Prof. Paper 282-B

MACKIN, J. H., 1948, Concept of the Graded Stream: Geol. Soc. American Bull., v. 59, p. 463-511

THORNBURY, W. D., 1954, Principles of Geomorphology: New York, John Wiley & Sons, 618 p.

17 Glaciation

The present is an age of glaciation. Glaciers occupy the valleys of many mountains in all parts of the world. A huge and thick sheet of ice almost covers one entire continent, Antarctica, and others cover a large part of Greenland, Iceland, and islands in the Arctic Ocean. If we could not actually walk across these glaciers, watch them in action, and see the deposits forming at their margins it is doubtful that we would ever believe that the semi-consolidated sand, silt, and morainal deposits that cover the northern United States and northern Europe had been left there by an advancing sheet of ice. We probably wouldn't consider

the accumulation of such large bodies of ice a condition that might normally be expected on the face of the earth. For many years the glacial deposits that are so prominent in northern Europe were thought to be debris dropped during the flood in the time of Noah.

Glaciation has not played a very important role in the formation of deposits or in shaping the face of the continents of past ages. Only four periods of glaciation are known from the rock record. Thus the present is in this respect, as well as in many others, an unusual time. Although glaciers have not always been prominent factors in shaping the landscape in the ast, they have been extremely important in producing the present configuration. In fact most of the present topography of the world was formed within the past few million years, and for the past million years ice has been present in large quantities at the poles and in mountains all over the world.

The history of the Pleistocene glaciations and other periods recorded in our stratigraphic records are discussed in the study of Historical Geology. Here we will confine our attention to the processes by which glaciers begin to form, how they move, and the nature of the deposits laid down by them. The following outline is intended to serve as a guide to this analysis of glaciation.

I. The accumulation and metamorphism of snow.

II. Gravity—the force driving glacier movement.

III. Types of glaciers:
Valley Glaciers
Continental Ice Caps

IV. How erosion is accomplished:

Valley Glaciers	Continental Ice Caps
1. Plucking (frost wedging).	1. Plucking.
2. Rasping (abrasion).	2. Rasping (abrasion).
3. Avalanching (mass wasting).	

V. How transportation is accomplished:

Valley Glaciers	Continental Ice Caps
1. Suspension of debris in ice.	1. Suspension in ice (especially near the bottom).
2. Debris on surface of ice.	2. Pushed in front.
3. Pushed in front.	

VI. Features produced by erosion:

Valley Glaciers	Continental Ice Caps
A. Small features:	A. Small features:
1. Striations.	1. Striations.
2. Grooves.	2. Grooves.
3. Polished surface.	3. Polished surface.
4. Crescentic marks.	4. Crescentic marks.
B. Large-scale physiographic features:	B. Large-scale physiographic features:
Valley Glaciers	*Continental Ice Caps*
1. U-shaped valleys.	1. A general suppression of whatever topography existed before glaciation.
2. Hanging valleys.	
3. Truncated spurs.	2. If the cap covers mountains, many of the features of valley glaciation may be formed.
4. Cirques, tarns.	
5. Fiords.	
6. Cols.	
7. Arêtes.	
8. Horns.	3. Drumlins.

VII. Deposits: The same types are associated with both types of glaciers.
A. Classified according to type of material:
1. Till (mixed sizes and unstratified).
2. Glaciofluvial deposits (stratified).
   a. varved clay (deposited in lakes).
   b. rock flour.
   c. sand, silt, clay.

B. Physiographic features:

1. Moraines.	1. Moraines.
a. Terminal.	a. Terminal.
b. Recessional.	b. Recessional.
c. Ground.	c. Ground.
d. Medial.	
e. Lateral.	
2. Eskers.	2. Eskers.
3. Kame and kettles. Kame terraces.	3. Kame and kettles. Kame terraces.
4. Outwash plains.	4. Outwash plains.
5. Erratics.	5. Erratics.

THE FORMATION OF GLACIERS

Within the last million years a sheet of ice covered most of Canada. It extended southward into the United States, where the terminus is marked by ridges of debris piled up and pushed along the front margin. In the time since the sheet began to recede, parts of these moraines have been eroded away, but they are well preserved in other places and can be traced for hundreds of miles. One of these moraines forms the ridge that makes up what is known as the backbone of Long Island, crosses Staten Island into New Jersey, and can be traced across Pennsylvania to the Ohio River. The southern margin of the ice cap is marked approximately by the position of the Ohio and Missouri Rivers. Today there is no sign of an ice cap in Canada. This causes us to wonder in what way conditions differed when the ice did cover such extensive areas, and if there is any chance that glaciers might return. We do not have a definite answer to the second question, but it is obvious from observations on present-day glaciers that the only condition necessary for the growth and expansion of glaciation is that the amount of accumulation of snow and ice must exceed the amount of ice wastage through melting and sublimation (the name applied to changes from the solid to gaseous state without going through the liquid state) for an extended period of time. Growth of glaciers is accelerated by increased precipitation in the form of snow and sleet, and temperature low enough for the ice

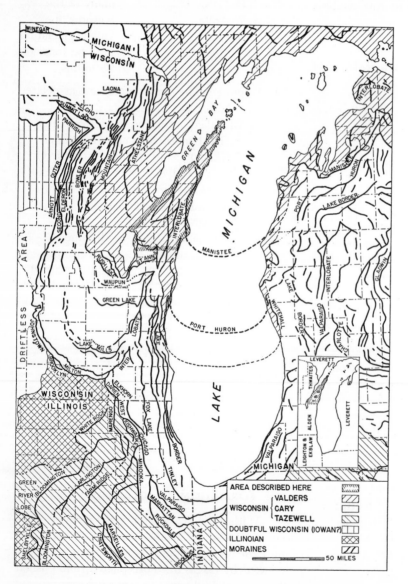

Fig. 17-1. Details of the location of morainal debris left by advancing ice sheets from the north. The Great Lakes were formed as a result of glaciation. (From Thwaites and Bertrand, G. S. A. Bull., v. 68, No. 7, 1957.)

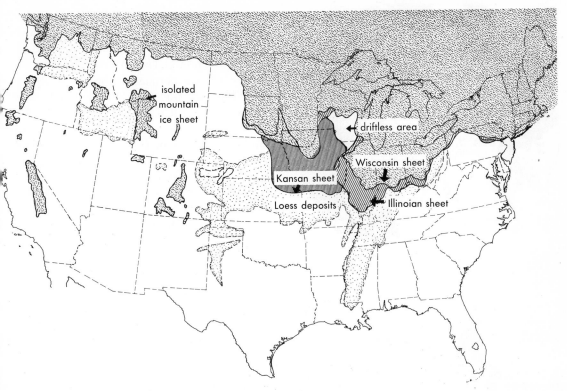

isolated mountain ice sheet

driftless area

Wisconsin sheet

Kansan sheet

Illinoian sheet

Loess deposits

Fig. 17-2. The margins of the ice sheets which have advanced into the United States during the Pleistocene.

Fig. 17-3. Vertical photograph of Arctic ice showing cracks and pressure ridges. The ice sheet covers most of the Arctic Ocean in the winter. (Photo by courtesy of the U.S. Air Force.)

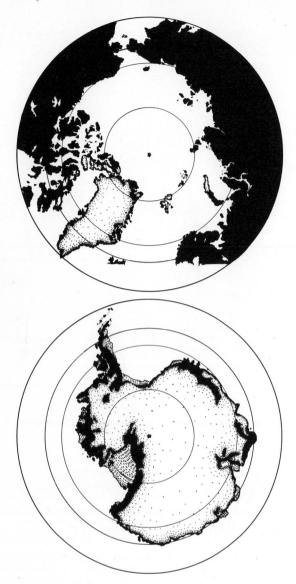

Fig. 17-4. The North and South Polar regions, sites of modern ice sheets of continental extent.

ice on the continents. These would form fir in the high mountains where the temperature are now nearly low enough to promote large scale mountain glaciation. Accumulation occur where snow is permanent throughout the year The limit of this area of perennial snow mountains is called the snow line.

Shortly after a snowfall the snow begins t undergo a metamorphic change (change c form) that eventually turns it into glacier ic Snow is a crystalline form of water, it is a min eral. It crystallizes in the hexagonal system Snow flakes display an almost infinite variet of delicate and beautiful hexagonal patterns. the temperatures remain below freezing afte the snow fall, the individual flakes will begi to recrystallize. The ends of the delicate pat terns dissolve, and the water moves toward th center of the flake until all the ice is crystal lized in a small ball, called firn or névé. Th newly formed firn is usually covered by mor snows. As more snow is added, the pressure o the overlying snow and firn compacts the smal ice grains together at depth. If the snow is ly ing on an uneven surface, and this is usuall the case in mountains, the rounded grains o firn will rotate and tend to move down slop under the weight of the overlying firn and snow Once the thickness of overlying snow and fir reaches about 200 feet, the weight is so grea that the firn becomes compacted into a solic mass of ice. Grains may become part of thi mass of ice when they become so oriented tha one grain may fuse into another, becoming single crystalline mass. In this fashion larg crystals grow. Movement in the layer of glacie ice is quite different from the rotation which characterizes the firn. The movements of the ice layer are largely accomplished by slippage between the layers of atoms making up the ice These slippage surfaces are usually too small t be obvious, although zones of shearing withi the ice are sometimes visible as blue streaks The net effect of these small slippages is lik plastic flowage.

Types of glaciers

Glaciers may be divided into two mair groups: valley glaciers and ice-cap or continen

to be preserved throughout the year. The extreme temperatures of the Antarctic, which average –60° Fahrenheit, are certainly not necessary for the formation and growth of continental glaciers. In fact, glaciers are most likely to grow when temperatures are only slightly below freezing, because the air at that temperature can hold much more moisture than that at extremely low temperatures. If the average annual temperatures over the face of the earth dropped 5° to 10° it would almost certainly bring about the formation of large masses of

l glaciers. The main difference between them
; that valley glaciers are confined to mounains, and the continental glaciers spread out
ver continents, burying whole mountain
anges. The prime mover in both types is the
ull exerted on the ice by the force of gravity.
'he movement is accelerated down slope where
 component of the force of gravity is directed
long the slope, tending to pull the entire mass
f ice and its load along. Like valley glaciers,
ontinental ice sheets move down slope, but
hey also flow over extensive flat regions and
ven over high irregularities. In part this is
ccomplished by the push exerted on the front
f the lobe of ice by the ice moving down
lope behind it, but for a sheet covering an area
he size of Canada this is hardly a sufficient
xplanation, particularly when it is noted that
he ice sheet did not originate in the highest
art of Canada and move out from there over
he rest of the country. The plastic behavior of
ce has already been mentioned. A plastic will
leform continuously once a certain threshold
alue of stress is applied to it. The ice sheets
hat covered Canada accumulated to a very
great thickness, probably comparable to that in
he Antarctic, 5000 feet in places. Once the
hickness became great enough, pressure on the
ower layers from the weight of the overlying
nass caused plastic flowage near the bottom of
he ice sheet. Thus the sheets slowly spread out
ver irregularities.

Rate of movement

Many of the modern-day valley glaciers
re moving at slow but measurable rate. The
notion of a large number of glaciers has been
tudied. One early technique was to drive a
eries of stakes across the surface of the valley
glacier in a straight line and come back periodically to observe the position of these stakes.
The distribution of movement is similar to that
n a stream. Frictional drag at the sides and
along the contact between ice and the earth
retards movement there. The center moves
along much more rapidly. Probably the maximum velocity of a glacier is near the surface
instead of a third of the way down, as in
streams, because the frictional drag of the air

on ice is negligible, whereas that on water is
significant. Some glaciers move so slowly that
trees and other plants grow in the debris on
top of them; others move at rates as high as
tens of feet or in exceptional cases 100 feet per
day. That the margins of continental glaciers
are in motion is shown by the continual spalling off of masses of ice where the sheet extends
into the seas. This process is called calving.
The big blocks of ice broken off in this way
form icebergs.

EROSION BY GLACIERS

The natures of erosion by continental ice
sheets and by valley glaciers are similar, but the
processes are not equally effective in the two
types of glaciations. The two types of glaciers
differ greatly in thickness and extent. Continental glaciers such as we find in the Antarctic
cover major mountain ranges comparable to

Fig. 17-5. The head of a mountain glacier. The
cirque is an amphitheater-shaped feature at the
head of most mountain glaciers. This photograph
shows the cirques and snow fields in which snow
accumulates. Valley glaciers are fed from snow
fields. (Photo by courtesy of the Qantas Empire
Airways, Ltd.)

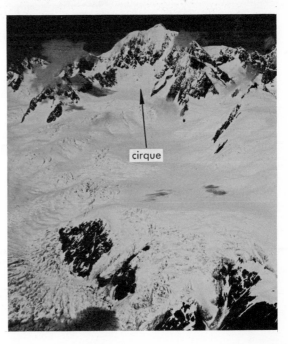

cirque

Fig. 17-6. Glaciers on the flanks of Mt. McKinley, Alaska.   This view is looking up one of the large valleys filled by a modern glacier. Note the sharp ridges, called arêtes, and the crevasses in the glacier where the ice flows over irregularities in the valley floor. (Photo by courtesy of the U.S. Air Force.)

Fig. 17-7. Longitudinal cross section of a glacier.   This section has a schematic representation of the zones of movement, accumulation, wastage, and other features associated with glaciers.

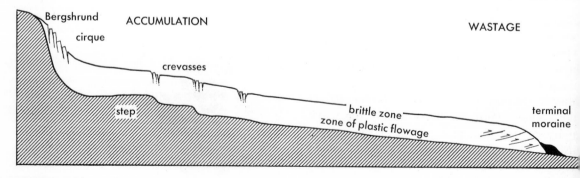

those in the Rockies. It is probable that the mountains began to be glaciated before the ice sheet covered the entire continent as it now does.

Scraping and pushing. The front edge of glaciers functions somewhat like a bulldozer pushing and scraping the ground in front of the ice. This is particularly effective in removing soil and semiconsolidated sediments. It is a truly abrasive action. The term "rasping" is often used to describe the scraping or abrasion on the sides and valley floor accomplished by rocks frozen in the bottom of the ice sheet. The results are much like that produced by a rasp; bare rock surfaces are scraped and scoured, leaving long grooves, striations, and polished surfaces as witnesses of the abrasion.

Mass wasting. This process plays an important role in glacial erosion. Along the margins of a valley glacier the valley sides are scraped, and blocks are broken off which become frozen into the ice and are carried away. This leads to undercutting of the sides of the

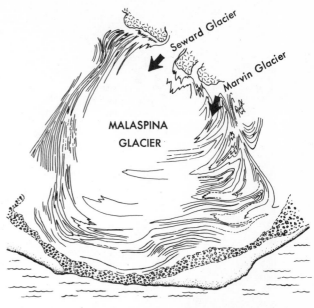

Fig. 17-8. Malaspina Glacier, Alaska. The map view shows folds which have developed in the ice as it flowed. Note the position of Seward and Marvin Glaciers which feed into Malaspina Glacier. (After a diagram by R. P. Sharp, G.S.A. Bull., v. 69, No. 6, 1958.)

Fig. 17-9. Air view of Malaspina Glacier. The dark streaks are debris covering the ice and infolded in it. (Photo by courtesy of the U.S. Air Force.)

Fig. 17-10. Close-up of the rocky cliffs in the cirque of a Swiss mountain glacier near St. Moritz. Frost action and freezing and thawing loosen the rocks which fall onto the glacier or are plucked out of the cliffs by glacial action and become a part of the glacier's load. (Photo by A. Pedrett, St. Moritz, courtesy of the Swiss National Tourist Office.)

valley. Once a side is undercut the probability of mass wasting is greatly increased. Slumping, sliding, and debris avalanches bring great quantities of debris onto the top surface of the glacier.

Plucking (quarrying). During the summer months the surface parts of a glacier may partially melt, or rain instead of snow may occasionally fall on the glacier. This meltwater or rain water seeps down along the sides of the ice mass, finding its way into the cracks and fractures in the rocks along the edges and at the

head of the glacier. At night or when the temperatures drop this water freezes. It breaks up the rock by frost action. The broken blocks may be gradually forced out from the walls as successive wedges of ice form behind them, or the ice in the cracks may become frozen into the glacier ice. When the next movement of the glacier takes place these blocks are pulled along with the ice. They are frozen in suspension in the ice. Open cracks do not usually form at the sides of a glacier, but at the head of the glacier where it breaks away from the snowfield a large crack is frequently formed, refilled with ice and snow, and then pulled open again. This break is called the bergschrund. It forms between the valley walls at the head of the glacier, called the cirque, and the glacier itself. It is within the bergschrund that plucking of rocks from the walls goes on most rapidly. Through this process the glacier tends to erode in a headward direction toward the divide separating its valley from others.

Methods of transportation

A large part of the load of valley glaciers is carried on the surface where it is dumped by landslides produced by undercutting. The mass-wasting processes which normally are effective in mountains are stepped up by the increased amount of frost action during glaciation. Large quantities of talus fall on the margins of the valley glaciers. Much of this load is carried frozen within the ice. Some of the debris may remain frozen within the center of the ice mass all the way from the cirque to the terminus of the glacier where it melts out, but the larger blocks slowly work their way down into the ice toward the bottom. Eventually this leads to accumulation of a heavy load near the bottom of the ice mass. This part of the load is responsible for the rasping and abrasive action of the glacier. The remainder of the load is pushed along in front of the ice mass.

Continental glaciers carry very little of their load on top because once the sheet has become thick enough to flow over flat areas its top surface is usually above all but the highest mountain peaks, so mass wasting is not responsible for supplying much debris to it. The ice caps or sheets carry a much smaller load per unit volume of ice than do valley glaciers. Almost all the load is carried frozen into the bottom of the sheet or pushed along in front.

FEATURES PRODUCED BY EROSION

Many small-scale erosional features are common to continental and valley glaciers. These are scour features. Striations, grooves, and polished surfaces are found both on the bare rock over which the ice moved and on the rocks carried at the bottom of the ice. These striations are very much like the slickensides produced by faulting. You can sometimes determine the direction of motion of the ice by moving your fingers along the striations to see in which direction the surface feels smoother. Crescentic marks may be made on the bare rocks of the valley floor where blocks moving in the ice hit obstructions and eventually chip off pieces of the bedrock.

Large-scale erosional features produced by continental glaciers are not nearly so distinctive as those produced by valley glaciers. In general the continental ice sheet tends to streamline the pre-existing topography, removing irregularities such as peaks and sharp ridges. The effect is to repress any land forms that might stand out. These features inhibit the movement of the ice sheet; therefore, they are removed or smoothed off as rapidly as possible. One of the streamlined features shaped by continental sheets is the drumlin. Drumlins are hills shaped somewhat like the back of a whale, with the steeper slope facing toward the direction from

Fig. 17-11. Close-up of the surface of a glacier broken by many crevasses. These crevasses form in the upper brittle part of the ice where the glacier moves over irregularities in the valley floor. (Photo by courtesy of the U.S. Air Force.)

Fig. 17-12. Sketch of some of the important physiographic features which result from erosion and deposition

which the ice moved. They are composed of glacial till, unconsolidated earth materials in a great variety of sizes and compositions.

Erosional features of valley glaciers

Cirque. The heads of most glaciers occupy hollowed out amphitheater-shaped features called cirques. The cirque is the site of much glacial quarrying or plucking where the bergschrund is formed as the glacier pulls away to start movement down valley. The walls of the cirque produced by this quarrying action become precipitous and may drop almost vertically as much as 1000 feet before they curve out into the floor of the valley. Cirques usually form at the head of the glacier near the former drainage divide of the streams that predate the glaciers, but they can develop on the valley

sides where no stream valleys preceded them. The bottom of the cirque is often so gouged out that it is lower than the bottom of the valley. After the glacier melts, a small lake called a tarn usually occupies this depression. The depression is abraded by the increased load of the glacier within the cirque.

The natural course for a glacier to follow is the old drainage pattern through the mountains. Thus glaciers begin by following the line of least resistance, but the flow and methods of erosion by streams and glaciers are so different that stream valleys are not perfectly suited for optimum movement of glaciers. Ice is essentially a solid in its behavior and cannot turn the sharp curves of rivers. Therefore, the spurs of mountains that extend out toward the major valley between tributaries are rapidly cut back. These features are called truncated

col

chain lakes

kame terrace

recessional moraine

by mountain glaciers.

spurs. The ice tends to streamline the valley, cutting off or smoothing out curves and removing obstacles. Flow is not concentrated in a glacier in the same way it is in a stream, in which the central part of a channel carries most of the water and load. Instead, the ice is distributed evenly across the valley. It cuts out a U-shaped valley instead of the V-shaped valley characteristic of mountain streams.

The valleys of tributary streams also become the sites of glaciers, but like the streams which precede them they are smaller than the major glacier, they accomplish erosion at a slower rate, and they do not cut their valleys as deeply as that of the glacier to which they are tributaries. If the glacier recedes, the valleys of the tributary glaciers are exposed. They open into the larger valleys high up on the valley sides and are called hanging valleys for

this reason. Waterfalls or cataracts develop where the renewed streams flow out of the hanging valley into the larger valley.

Fiords. These features, which characterize the coast of Norway, are formed where a glacier flows from the mountains into the sea. The glacier ice is able to carve its valley slightly below sea level before the ice is melted in the sea water or breaks away to form icebergs. Thus the U-shaped valley may continue right out into the sea. Today these large valleys are partially filled with sea water. This is largely due to rises in sea level since the last major glacial advance.

Arêtes. This name is applied to the sharp ridges produced by glacial erosion. The term is applied to acute and rugged ridges formed along the crest of a mountain range, to ridges between two mountains, and to mountain spurs that separate two cirques. The processes of plucking, quarrying, and rasping cause the cirque to cut into the walls behind them. Eventually they may come so close together that a sharp ridge, the arête, is produced.

Col. A col is a pass formed where two cirques converge, cutting into the same wall, and thus lower the wall below the level of the remainder of the summit area. The col is usually a depression in an arête.

Horn. This is a sharp peak formed by glacial erosion. The Matterhorn is a classic example. The horns are formed during a late stage in glaciation after the summit of the preglacial mountains has been reduced to a few isolated peaks. If there is more than one they are often aligned since they are often remnants of an arête.

DEPOSITION

Materials

The deposits of glaciers are composed of fragments of all types of rocks. Glaciers may carry as great an assortment of rock types as streams. These come from the cirque walls and from the sides and bottom of the valley through which the ice moves. Deposition by a glacier takes place when the ice begins to melt and the glacier slows down and vanishes, losing its transporting power. Thus deposition from ice occurs most rapidly at its terminus. Meltwater carries the smaller parts of the load out beyond the ice. The terminus may slowly move forward as it melts, it may remain in one position with the amount of melting and sublimation just equal to the amount of ice moving to the end of the glacier, or the melting may exceed the rate of movement, in which case the terminus of the glacier recedes.

Glacial deposits may be classified in two groups. The first, called "till," is the unstratified, unsorted debris dropped more or less in a random fashion by glaciers as they melt. The term is also applied to moraines pushed up in front of the ice and those left on the ground after the glacier melts. Till is characterized by its variability. It is probably more variable than any other rock known by a single name.

Fig. 17-13. Sketch of some of the important features, such as moraines, kettles, outwashes, and eskers,

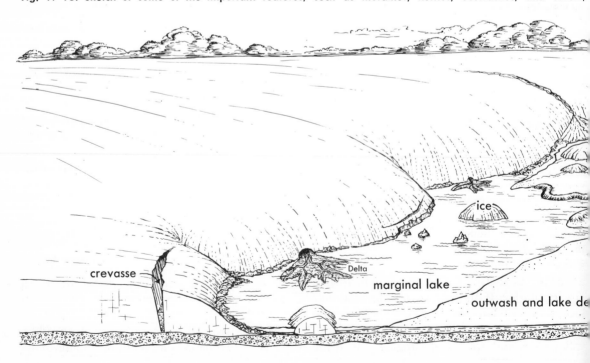

crevasse

Delta

ice

marginal lake

outwash and lake de

The sizes in it range from clay to boulders. Depending on what makes it up it is compact, loose, or firmly cemented into a hard rock. It rarely has any apparent fabric or orientation of particles, although careful study may reveal some alignment of certain sizes and shapes of particles. The larger fragments in till are often striated or polished.

Glaciofluvial deposits (also called stratified drift). These are the deposits laid down under and beyond the glacier by meltwaters. These deposits as well as till differ from most other sediments in that the particles of which they are composed are fresh. They are dominated by fragments and particles of rock that have been broken down by disintegration, not decomposition. Thus such minerals as hornblende, feldspar, and other easily decomposed minerals are present. Except for their composition, glaciofluvial deposits have the same characteristics as other water-deposited sediments. They are stratified, sorted, and may have cross-bedding or other primary sedimentary structures. A milky-colored water often issues from streams flowing out of glaciers. The material in the water is rock flour. It is a product of abrasion, the powdery material resulting from the grinding of rocks against one another. This is deposited in the lowlands beyond the end of the glacier. This is thought to be the source of the surficial deposits that cover the central part of the Mississippi Valley, called "loess."

Form of glacial deposits

Moraines. These are deposits of till. Terminal moraines are formed at the terminus of continental and valley glaciers; they are ridges of debris pushed ahead of the glacier, supplemented by the debris that is continually melting out of the glacier while it remains in one location. Meltwater may flow over the terminal moraine while the glacier is up close to it, but when the glacier begins to retreat the great quantity of meltwater usually forms a lake, tops the dam made by the moraine, and drains out carrying finer debris which is laid down as glaciofluvial deposits out beyond the terminus.

Recessional moraines. These are also characteristic of both continental and valley glaciers.

formed by erosion and deposition by continental glaciers.

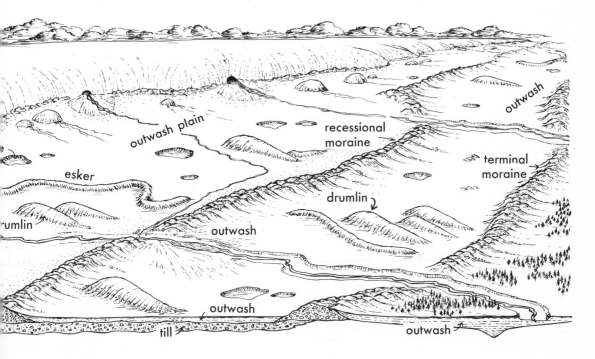

Fig. 17-14. Glaciated valley hanging high above the floor of the main valley. Note the waterfall where the hanging valley enters the larger valley. (Photo by courtesy of the Royal Canadian Air Force.)

As the margins of the glaciers retreat, load is dropped as the ice melts. If the end margin remains in one position for any period of time a ridge-like mass of till accumulates from the debris coming off the top of the glacier and out of the middle of it. Their formation is similar

Fig. 17-15. Tongues of ice descending from an icecap into a large U-shaped valley at the head of a fiord, in the distance. (Photo by courtesy of the U.S. Air Force.)

to that of the terminal moraine—they differ only in position. Moraines may be destroyed if the glacier readvances. They are simply pushed ahead to a new position or to the terminal moraine.

Ground moraines. This is the till scattered and dropped at random from melting continental and valley glaciers over the ground as the glaciers retreat. Ground moraine forms when the glacier does not remain in one position long enough to build a ridge of debris.

Lateral moraines. In valley glaciers a large amount of the load may be carried on the surface of the glacier along the margins where it has been dumped through mass wasting from the valley sides. These deposits sometimes form very noticeable ridges on the surface of the ice. When the ice melts they are laid down as ridges along the edge of the valley. Like other moraines they are composed of till.

Medial moraines. Where a tributary glacier enters a larger glacier the ice from the tributary is squeezed in along the side on which it enters. If the tributary has debris piled on top of the ice near the sides (such as that forming lateral moraines) then after confluence the large glacier has a ridge of debris on either side and a ridge down the middle where the two side loads are brought together and deflected to the center of the glacier. A glacier may have many tributaries and many medial ridges. Once the glacier melts, these are laid down as long ridges of till more or less paralleling the lateral moraines but in the middle of the valley.

Eskers. Both continental and valley glaciers may partially melt during the summer. The water flows on the surface of the ice or seeps down along the margins or even moves through holes in the ice. Some of it accumulates beneath the glacier and forms a stream flowing in a channel beneath the ice. This stream may be quite different from ordinary streams, however, in that its banks are composed of ice. Thus the stream flows on the ground surface and not necessarily in a channel beneath the surface of the ground. All sorts of the transported load of the glacier may get into the stream. The small fractions of the load are carried easily down stream, but the coarser boulders and blocks are not. After the glacier melts a sinuous ridge of this debris may remain marking the former stream channel. This is called an esker. Eskers also form where the stream cuts into weak rock beneath the glacier and leaves deposits of the coarser part of its load. After the glacier melts the weak rock on either side of the stream deposits may be eroded more easily than the materials of the esker, leaving the esker etched out.

Kames. These are glaciofluvial deposits formed on the top surface of a glacier where the surficial meltwaters wash sediment from the top into depressions. As the ice melts, the material that formerly filled depressions on top of the glacier is dropped and makes small hills. Streams also flow along the margins of valley glaciers or along trough-like depressions in continental ice sheets. Here also meltwaters concentrate debris in these channels. If the water cannot carry the entire load, part is dropped. Terraces, called kame terraces, are built in this way.

Outwash plains. Beyond the terminus of most mountain glaciers there are low hills or plains. Likewise there are often flat areas beyond the limits of continental ice sheets. These areas become the sites of deposition for a large part of the glaciofluvial deposits. When a glacier first begins to melt there is a great deal more debris to be carried than the meltwater is capable of transporting. This is deposited as broad flat alluvial fans or, in the case of continental ice sheets, as a series of coalescing alluvial fans called the outwash plain. Here the rock flour is dropped along with most of the silt, sand, and clay carried from the glacier. Because the streams are overloaded, and because they are shifted by often-changing conditions, braided stream patterns characterize the outwash-plain streams. Later, if the rate of melting begins to increase, the streams may establish more permanent channels through which large amounts of the debris are moved on beyond the immediate region of the glacier.

Erratics. The name is applied to any rock that is carried by a glacier and laid down on a different type of rock. The size of some of these is astonishing. One that rests on the north shore of Long Island is as large as a one-story house. It is a Precambrian metamorphic rock such as

Fig. 17-16. The Matterhorn, the classic example of a horn. Isolated peaks such as this give us an idea of how high the surrounding country was before erosion cut it down. (Photo by courtesy of Trans World Airlines, Inc.)

Fig. 17-17. A quiet stream now occupies the valley which had been filled by a large glacier during the Pleistocene. Half Dome in the center background is located on one side of the large U-shaped glacial valley. The glacier cut into the side of the granite, forming the nearly vertical cliffs. (Photo by courtesy of the Santa Fe Railway.)

Fig. 17-18. Snowfields, cirques, valley glaciers, arêtes, cols, lateral and medial debris on the glacier, and horns are all clearly depicted in this photo. (Photo by courtesy of the Royal Canadian Air Force.)

those exposed in New England, yet it rests on top of semiconsolidated deposits of Cenozoic age.

CAUSE OF GLACIATION

Glaciers have not always covered the polar regions. In fact, judging from the scarcity of glacial deposits in the rock record of past times, periods of glaciation are very unusual. The remains of corals and other animals that ordinarily favor warm waters are found in rocks of past ages in the Arctic and Antarctic. What has caused glaciers to form on earth is an intriguing question that has given rise to a great deal of speculation. Scientific literature abounds in hypotheses which try to answer the question. Some of them are based on assumptions that have proven to be fallacious, but the validity of others remains unestablished. No definitive answer can be given to the question, but several of the hypotheses are worthy of consideration to illustrate how theories are formulated to explain natural phenomena, and how these may easily go astray when there are inadequate data.

What must be explained

For any hypotheses to be acceptable it must explain as many of the observed facts about glaciation as possible, or at least it must not contradict these observations.

1. One of the most important of these is the history of periods of glaciation. The occurrence of till containing striated and grooved pebbles assures us that there have been several periods of glaciation besides the one in which we now live. The oldest of these took place in the Precambrian, and it seems probable that there may have been more than one glaciation

during the billions of years that this era covers. The oldest ice sheets occupied an area in the southern part of the Canadian Shield. Glacial sediments are also found in widely separated areas in rocks that lie just beneath the Cambrian system. These tills are more than 500 million years old. They are scattered over the Canadian Shield, in Utah, Norway, Australia, eastern Greenland, and India. One of the most unusual things about these is the distribution of glacial debris in areas that now lie in temperate and even tropical climatic belts. The third major period of glaciation seems to have been during the late part of the Paleozoic Era in the Carboniferous and Permian Periods. At this time, about 230 million years ago, glaciers apparently covered parts of South Africa, Australia, and India. In Australia there are five separate sheets of till of this age, which are interbedded with coal. This relation indicates cold periods of glacial advance separated by warm, moist interglacial periods during which plant life flourished.

2. We live in the Pleistocene, so it is not surprising that we have a relatively complete understanding of the events that have taken place during it. These impose important limitations on the theories of glaciation. This pe-

Fig. 17-19. Air view across a continental ice sheet. The arrows indicate the main directions of ice movement. The dark areas in the foreground are moraines resulting from melting of the ice. Several peaks stand up above the level of the ice. They are called nunataks. (Photo by courtesy of the U.S. Navy.)

Fig. 17-20. The terminus of Columbia Glacier in Alaska is in water. Note the fractured surface of the ice. The ice masses break off and float out into the water forming icebergs. The process is called calving. (Photo by courtesy of the U.S. Air Force.)

Fig. 17-21. The island in the foreground is a drumlin formed during the advance of an ice sheet. Note the topography in the background. The ice sheet moved across it, tending to smooth out large irregularities in the topography. (Photo by courtesy of the Royal Canadian Air Force.)

riod of continental glaciation started about a million years ago. Since it started there have been at least four major intervals of glacial advance and three interglacial ages, not counting the present which may or may not be an interglacial age. The last great resurgence of ice came about 10,000 years ago. During the periods of advance of the ice sheets they have covered most of Canada, the northern United States, Greenland, northern Europe, northern Siberia, Antarctica, and high mountains throughout the world. Each of these advances took place essentially simultaneously throughout the northern hemisphere. Thus whatever caused the glaciation must have affected this huge region at about the same time. Even within each of the glacial advances there were fluctuations in the position of the ice sheet and minor advances and retreats of relatively short duration. There appears to be no periodicity to these advances and retreats, and there are not enough data to demonstrate whether or not the major glacial periods occurred at regular intervals. Consequently, we cannot be sure if the cause of glaciation is one that occurs at fixed intervals.

3. Ice caps grow and decay rapidly. This is borne out by the fact that the last ice sheet to cover the northern United States was over this area only 10,000 years ago, a short time geologically.

4. The position of sea level fluctuates with the amount of ice piled up on land areas as ice caps. There is presently enough water tied up in ice on land to raise sea level 75 to 100 feet or more if it should melt.

5. The accumulation of ice and snow is favored in mountains and on land masses with high elevation.

6. Variations in temperatures on earth of only a few degrees Centigrade and at most 10° should be sufficient to cause glacial advances and retreats. Even today a lowering of only a few degrees in the mean annual temperatures would certainly give rise to a great increase of the land area covered by ice and snow throughout the year, and it might be sufficient to trigger a new resurgence of ice caps across North America.

There are so many possible causes of glaciation that they may be separated into three groups. It seems probable that the final solution of a problem as complicated as this will involve a combination of the various factors. These three groups and some of the ideas that may be classified in each are:

1. *Cosmic* (variation in the heat produced by the sun; the intersection of radiant energy from the sun by cosmic dust clouds).
2. *Planetary* (periodic changes in motions of the earth cause it to reach a point of maximum distance from the sun, thus reducing the amount of solar radiation and cooling of the earth's atmosphere).
3. *Geological* and *geophysical* (variation in internal heat production of the earth; movements of the poles of the earth relative to the crust; changes in oceanic circulation; variations in the amount of volcanic dust in the atmosphere).

Cosmic theories

The temperatures on the surface of the earth might be lowered enough by fluctuations in the amount of solar radiation leaving the sun to bring about a general glaciation. At the present time the average amount of energy reaching the earth's surface is about 2 calories per square centimeter each minute. This value has fluctuated by about 3 per cent since 1918. Thus fluctuations of the amount of energy coming to the earth from the sun actually do occur, but the question of whether the variations are ever sufficient to cause glaciation is still open. Even if this is the cause of glaciation, there is still the question of whether increased or decreased solar radiation would be responsible for glaciation. One of the most popular theories among geologists is that decreases in solar radiation would cool the earth, cause increased snow fall, and cause the accumulation of snow and ice in mountains and in high land areas until ice sheets developed and began to advance. Then, when the amount of radiation began to increase, the ice would melt, and the glaciers would retreat.

However, it is also possible to reason that increased solar radiation would cause glacia-

Fig. 17-22. Icebergs. Most of the ice is beneath the water. In order to float the ice must displace a volume of water equal in weight to that of the ice. (Photo by courtesy of the U.S. Air Force.)

Fig. 17-23. Icebergs frozen in sea ice. (Photo by courtesy of the U.S. Navy.)

tilted iceberg

sea ice

capsized iceberg

lay-over iceberg

1000 feet

Fig. 17-24. Icebergs calving from the margin of a continental glacier. Notice how these are breaking ou along a set of perpendicular fractures. This is in the Antarctic. (Photo by courtesy of the U.S. Navy.)

tion. How? If solar radiation did increase, the increase would be greatest at the equator and least at the poles. Temperatures at the equator would increase, there would be more convection in the atmosphere in this region, and stronger winds. This would give rise to increased evaporation of sea water, more clouds, and consequently more precipitation. This pre-

cipitation would fall as snow in the polar re gions at least in the early stages of the in creased radiation. Thus more snowfall woul account for more snow accumulation and a ice age. If at this point temperatures continued to rise they would eventually bring about melt ing of the ice and retreat and disappearance o the glaciers. This would instigate a warm, we

Fig. 17-25. The margin of a continental ice sheet in the late summer. The arrow indicates the direction of ic movement. The black line across the photograph is a recessional moraine. It is being eroded, as the melt water streams flowing over it show. This is in the Antarctic. (Photo by courtesy of the U.S. Navy.)

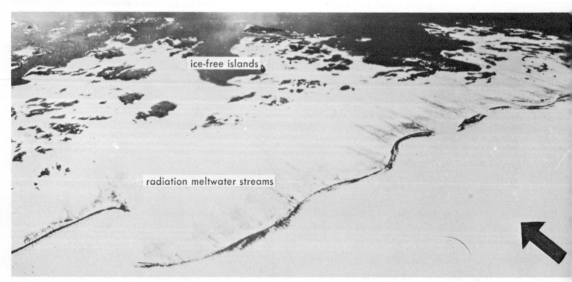

interglacial period such as those that are known between ice advances of the Pleistocene. Now if the amount of radiation began to diminish, then the temperature would fall, and the amount of precipitation would decrease so a dry cold glacial period might follow.

A second type of cosmic theory is that clouds of cosmic dust swept through the solar system. This theory was proposed before we realized that these dust clouds are so rarified that they contain less dust than the best vacuum chambers we can produce on earth. Thus such clouds would be incapable of reducing the solar radiation enough to have any effect even if one did come through the solar system.

Planetary hypothesis

There are a number of movements of the earth and the earth-moon system that cause periodic changes in the position of the earth relative to the sun. The factors include:

1. Eccentricity of the earth's orbit about the sun. Once every 92,000 years the earth's position is at a maximum distance from the sun for this reason.
2. The angle that the earth's axis makes with the plane in which it circles the

sun varies through 3° every 40,000 years.
3. The axis of the earth wobbles because of the gravitational effect of the sun, moon, and planets. The period of this movement is 21,000 years.

It has been suggested that conditions will be most favorable for glaciation of the poles when they are farthest from the sun. This condition is reached once during each of the above periods, and would be a maximum if all the above should coincide in time. The objection to this idea is that there is considerable doubt that the magnitude of the changes in position of the earth relative to the sun would be sufficient. There is also no explanation of the interglacial periods.

Geological and geophysical theories

Volcanism. The idea that there is a connection between volcanism and glaciation seems unfounded on the basis of the association of volcanic and glacial sediments. One of the most active periods in terms of the volcanic activity was the Ordovician; yet no glacial tills are known in rocks of that age.

Oceanic circulation. It may well be that the cause of glaciation is related to oceanic circula-

Fig. 17-26. Pitted outwash plain. The depressions are kettles. (Photo by courtesy of the Royal Canadian Air Force.)

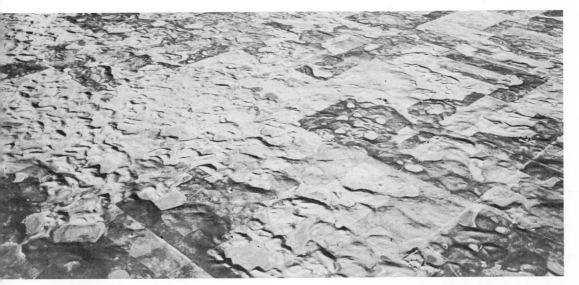

tion as well as to variations in the mean temperatures of the earth. One of the most recent of these (Ewing and Donn, 1956) explains that melting of the present Arctic ice sheet would increase the interchange of water between the North Atlantic and the Arctic Oceans. With a rise in sea level more water could move between these oceans over the relatively shallow waters that cover the northern part of the North Atlantic. This would cool the North Atlantic and warm the Arctic, increasing the amount of moisture in the atmosphere in the Arctic. At that point two factors would favor the growth of glaciers:

a. Increased precipitation.
b. Changes in atmospheric circulation.

As the glaciers grew, sea level would be lowered, and this would greatly decrease the interchange of water between the two oceans. The Arctic waters would become colder, and the amount of moisture in the atmosphere would be reduced, causing less snow to fall. At this point the glaciers would stop growing, and glaciation would begin to wane. With the melting of the ice, sea level would again begin to rise, and interchange of waters between the oceans would increase. The warm waters that would flow into the Arctic would tend to raise the temperatures of the region generally and promote more rapid melting of ice until the cycle started again.

Shifting of the magnetic poles

Grains of the mineral magnetite are freed from igneous rocks during weathering and erosion. Eventually many of these are deposited in water as part of sedimentary rocks. These tiny particles of magnetite are susceptible to the pull of the earth's magnetic field, and they become aligned in the magnetic field. Thus the magnetite particles in sediments may be used to discover the orientation of the earth's mag-

netic field in localities in which they wer formed. As soon as the sediment becomes consolidated rock the position of the magnetit is fixed. Thus by taking oriented specimens o ancient sedimentary rocks that contain this min eral it is possible to determine the position o the poles at the time they were deposited. I order to do this a number of specimens of th same age in widely separated regions must b collected. The interesting aspect of this discov ery is that it appears on the basis of this evi dence that the north and south poles have no always been in the position they now occup in relation to the crust. In the early Precam brian Idaho was at the north pole; in the lat Precambrian Hawaii was near the pole; and i the Silurian Period the sea south of Japan wa close to the pole. The significance of this dis covery is that the crust of the earth and th continents seem to have shifted their position through time relative to the core of the earth which is responsible for the earth's magneti field. Perhaps the cool and solid crust has ro tated relative to the plastic and probably liquid interior. This explanation makes it much easie to understand how glaciation might have take place in India and Africa.

REFERENCES

CHARLESWORTH, J. K., 1957, *The Quaternary Era With Special Reference to Its Glaciation*: vols., London, Edward Arnold & Co., 1700 p

COLEMAN, A. P., 1926, *Ice Ages, Recent and An cient:* New York, The Macmillan Company 296 p.

FLINT, R. F., 1945, Glacial Map of North America Geol. Soc. America Spec. Paper 60 (map an pamphlet)

THORNBURY, W. D., 1954, *Principles of Geomor phology:* New York, John Wiley & Sons, 618 p

ZEUNER, F. E., 1945, *The Pleistocene Period, It Climate, Chronology and Faunal Successions:* London, printed for the Royal Society, sol by B. Quaritch, Ltd., 322 p.

18   Ground Water

Those of us who have spent most of our lives in areas of abundant rainfall rarely think of fresh water as a valuable natural resource. At a time when the industrial demands for water are so great, when populations are increasing, and with more pollution of fresh water than ever before, we should be more aware of the value of this resource and take steps to determine the extent of our holdings as we do with iron or petroleum reserves. A few cities in the United States have already experienced periods of short water supply, and we may expect more widespread shortages in the future.

THE EARTH AS A RESERVOIR

That water is stored in the soil and outer crust of the earth is apparent from the springs that issue from valley sides, from the geysers

Fig. 18-1. Variations in porosity. Water is stored in intergranular pore spaces, in fractures, and in cavities of all sorts in the earth. How much water may be stored and how readily the water may move depends on the nature of the rock in which it is stored. This illustration points out some of the variations in porosity which result from differences in size, shape, and packing of a clastic sediment.

that spout columns of water hundreds of feet into the air, and from the wells that produce most of our drinking water. So common is the experience of seeing water come out of the ground that we are lulled into a feeling that water supplies are inexhaustible.

Sources

The water that is contained in the ground beneath the surface and that is obtained for drinking purposes, for irrigation, and for industrial use has gotten into the earth from one of three sources:

1. Rain water (meteoric water) includes rain, sleet, snow, hail, and other forms of precipitation. A total of about 26,000 cubic miles of water falls on the continents each year. It is this water which fills the soil and upper crust. It is the most important source of water used by man.

2. Connate water is the marine or fresh water trapped in sediments when they are deposited on lake or sea bottoms. Since most sediments originate in marine water it is usually salty. It is this source which supplies water found deeper in sedimentary units in the crust. Connate water is often in rock units with oil. The oil floats on it and rises upward until it is trapped.

3. Juvenile water (magmatic water) is water produced from volcanoes and from magmatic activity within the crust. It is hard to determine how much of this water is coming to the surface of the earth at present. Many volcanoes are located under water, and many more are found around the margins of the oceans. It may be that a large part of the water gets into the volcanic vents from the ground or oceans. More than 90 per cent of all material coming out of volcanoes is steam. We do not know how much of this is water that has been recycled back into the volcano from the surface.

How is the water stored?

Water getting into the crust from any of the above three sources may be stored in a great variety of ways. One place is in old buried river channels. Many people think that in order strike underground water you must find an underground river. There are some underground streams, but they are small in size and number. Most water is stored in the following ways:

    a. Intergranular pore spaces.
    b. Solution pores and cavities.
    c. Fractures and faults.

The amount of pore spaces in a rock is called the porosity of the rock. A measure of porosity is the percentage of the total volume of the rock that is occupied by voids. Some pore spaces are formed at the time of deposition of the rock, particularly in sedimentary rocks. Others are induced at a later date by weathering, solution, or deformation. How much porosity a granular rock has depends on a number of factors:

1. Sorting and size. It might seem likely that a boulder conglomerate would be more porous than a sandstone, but the reverse is usually true. The large particles are more likely to have smaller sediments mixed in, filling up the spaces between larger blocks. Thus a great assortment of sizes in the sediment is unfavorable for the development of maximum porosity.

2. Shape and packing. These two factors play an important role in determining porosity. A mass of cubes may have almost no porosity if the cubes are stacked together in an orderly fashion, but it will be very porous if they are jumbled together. Likewise, rounded particles can differ in porosity according to the way they are packed. If each sphere is directly above the center of another, maximum porosity results. Minimum porosity occurs when the spheres are offset. If the particles in a rock are

Fig. 18-2. Hall of the Giants in Carlsbad Caverns National Park in southern New Mexico. Thirty-seven miles of the caverns have been explored, but no one knows how extensive they may be. These caverns reach more than eight hundred feet beneath the surface of the ground. Caverns are formed by solution and erosion by ground water. (Photo by courtesy of the New Mexico State Tourist Bureau.)

Fig. 18-3. Cross section of a log of petrified wood. Silica carried by ground water has completely replaced the woody matter in this tree. It was buried in sandy clays in the Triassic Period. The cell structure of the tree is faithfully preserved in such replacements. (Photo by courtesy of the U.S. National Museum.)

Fig. 18-4. Cavity fillings are often formed by minerals carried in solution by ground water. Crystal-lined cavities are called geodes. The banded material is agate, a form of silica. (Photo by courtesy of the U.S. National Museum.)

elongate minerals the porosity of one rock in which the particles are all aligned in one direction will be very different from that in one where they are oriented at random.

Storage in solution cavities is much more irregular than that in intergranular pore spaces. Caverns provide some lakes and channels which may be filled with water, but more commonly the solution pores are small. They may be solution cavities located along fractures, or where disseminated soluble minerals have been etched out of a rock.

Fractures are common in all types of rocks. Sometimes they are open, and almost always there is enough space for a film of water to seep down along the fracture surface. Where areas have been subjected to intense deformation, fractures of tectonic origin may be common and may provide adequate storage for water, but over larger areas there are not enough fractures for them to be important reservoirs.

Destruction of porosity. The pore spaces of a rock may be closed or filled in by natural processes. The ground water usually carries elements in solution. These may be deposited in the pore spaces cementing the cavities, pores, or fractures and thereby preventing the future storage of water. Man may also destroy the porosity of some water-bearing sedimentary units by drawing the water out of them too fast or too completely. If the water is removed some sediments will become more consolidated and compacted. The water in a sediment tends to buoy up part of the weight of the grains in it. The removal of this buoyancy allows them to become more compact and less porous.

MOVEMENT OF GROUND WATER

A rock can be very porous and still not allow fluids to move through it. The permeability is a measure of the ability of a stratum or rock units to transmit fluids. It is the ease with which the fluids are moved. Of course for movement of water the pores must be interconnected. Most well-sorted granular rocks have high porosity and high permeability. The partially cemented rocks, those composed of clay

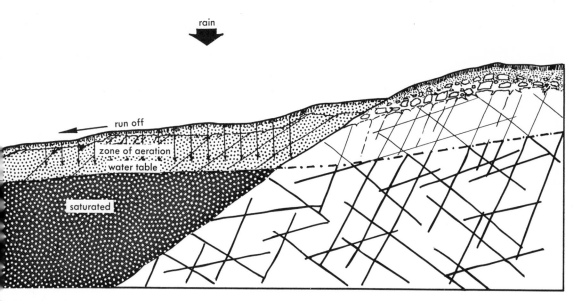

Fig. 18-5. Rain water percolates into the soil, through the decayed bedrock and into the pore spaces and fractures in the bedrock. In massive igneous rock the water moves mainly in fractures but in sediments such as sandstone it can move through the pore spaces.

particles, and massive igneous and metamorphic rocks tend to be less permeable unless they are intensely fractured.

Most ground water in the upper parts of the crust comes from precipitation. This water must find its way from the surface of the ground down into the saturated rocks below. The exact way in which this movement occurs is as varied as the soils are. The water is pulled downward by the force of gravity. It is pushed down by the weight of water above it, and it is retarded by surface tension of the water as it clings to the particles of soil through which it must pass. Gradually it seeps into and through the soil. In this zone it is mixed with air, and together they bring about decay of the soil and rock fragments in the soils. After passing through the soil the water strikes the contact between soil and the unaltered rock. If the rock is porous and permeable the water will continue into the rock; if the rock is impermeable then the water will either accumulate or it will tend to move laterally down slope along this contact. If the rock is a homogeneous porous granular material the water moves through it until it reaches a depth below which the rock is saturated with water. The contact between the zone in which air and water are moving rapidly downward, called the zone of aeration, and the zone of saturation is called the water table. The term may be somewhat misleading because the water table is neither flat generally, nor does it maintain the same level or configuration all the time. Immediately above the water table there is a thin zone in which very small thin tubelets of water extend up into the overlying rock. These behave as capillary tubes, and the zone is called the capillary fringe.

Darcy's law

Movement of water within a porous and permeable unit below the water table is a complex problem. The nature of these motions has been the subject of many experiments, and

Fig. 18-6. Cross section of a homogeneous rock such as sandstone showing the lines of movement of water beneath the water table.

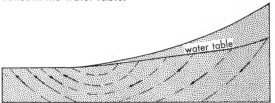

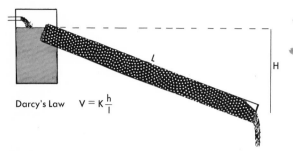

Darcy's Law $V = K\dfrac{h}{l}$

Fig. 18-7. Experimental set-up to test the validity of Darcy's Law. The law states that the velocity of the flow of water through a unit is proportional to the permeability of the rock, K, and the hydrostatic head, h, and inversely proportional to the length of the path of the flow. This law enables us to predict the amount of water which may be pumped from aquifers.

these have yielded theoretical results which can be applied with success to natural conditions. Of notable importance is the work of Henry Darcy, a French hydrologist whose work was carried out in the middle of the nineteenth century. He formulated a law which may be applied to water in porous and permeable rock units confined above and below by impervious beds or to those units which are not so confined. His law states that the velocity of movement of the water in a rock unit between two points is equal to the permeability of the rock through which it must pass multiplied by the difference in elevation of the points and divided by the length of the path between them.

The significance of the difference in elevation is that the weight of the water above the outlet is pushing down on that below it. This distance, or difference in elevation, is called the hydrostatic head. The gravitational pull on thi water is the force driving the water down. Th amount of the hydrostatic head divided by th length of the path is the slope of the path o motion and is called the gradient. In applyin this to ordinary ground-water problems it i possible to measure the length of the path an the hydrostatic head, and to determine the per meability by making tests on the rock type through which the water passes. Thus the veloc ity of movements along particular paths ma be calculated. The value of such a calculatio is immediately apparent if you consider th applications.

Rate. The rates of water movement be neath the water table are very slow. They var considerably from one place to another accord ing to the permeability of the rocks. A typica value for the rate of movement is 50 feet pe year, but it may be as great as several hundre feet per day under exceptional circumstances.

Configuration of the water table

The configuration of the water table an the changes that take place in it depend on th configuration of the ground surface, the per meability of the rocks below, and the suppl of water.

Granular pervious material. This represent the most general case since most of the conti nents are underlain by sedimentary rocks, an these are in large part granular pervious unit As a generalization we may say that the wate table conforms to the shape of the land surfac It is depressed most under hills and it come

Fig. 18-8. Cross section of an effluent stream at left and an influent stream at right. The black parts of the sec tions indicate portions of the ground which are saturated with water. Arrows indicate the general direc tions of water movement.

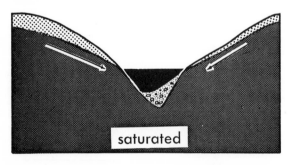

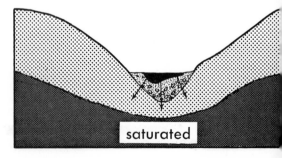

losest to the surface at lakes and along streams. If, as a result of long periods of drought or any other condition causing a lack of water, the table becomes deeply depressed, then the lakes and streams tend to lose water as it migrates toward the water table. Such a stream is said to be in an influent condition. The normal condition is for water to move down into lakes and streams from the water table, an affluent condition. Note the illustrations of various conditions.

Effects of varying permeability. What happens if the porous and permeable granular material is a thin layer over an impervious basement rock? Percolation may become concentrated in filled channels cut in the bedrock; otherwise, the water table will be located at greater depths under steep slopes and at shallow depths under gentler slopes. Of course many other conditions may arise from variations in permeability. There may be vertical changes or lateral gradations in texture, packing, cementation, or some other one of the factors affecting porosity and permeability. Each of these will give rise to local irregularities in the water table.

Perched condition. If there are interbedded strata of varying permeability then a condition known as a perched water table is likely to develop. If water is moving down on an impervious layer faster than it is being transmitted laterally and faster than it is passing through the layer, then a localized water table develops above that unit. When the level of

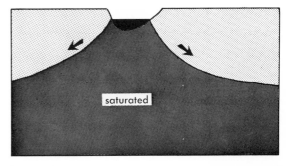

Fig. 18-9. Cross section of an influent stream. Loss of water from the stream has built up a ridge of water under the stream.

the regional water table is below this impervious unit a perched water table is said to exist above it.

Water tables in contact with salt water

Along the coasts where the sediments are largely sandstones it is normal to find that the fresh water is bounded below by a contact with salt water. Because of its lower density fresh water floats on salt water. Consequently a salt-water wedge extends from the ocean under the edge of the fresh water. Along this wedge there will be some salt-water contamination of the fresh water making it unsuitable for drinking purposes. The density differential between salt and fresh water is such that a balance is reached when there is about 38 feet of fresh water beneath sea level for every foot of ele-

Fig. 18-10. Cross section of a region showing one condition which might give rise to a perched water table. The shale unit in the mountain is impervious and prevents the flow of water to the lower regional water table.

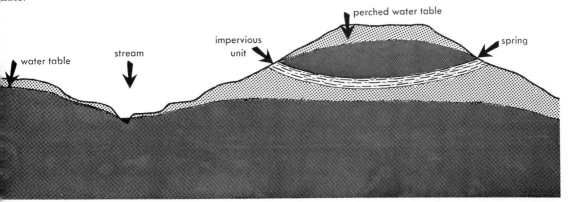

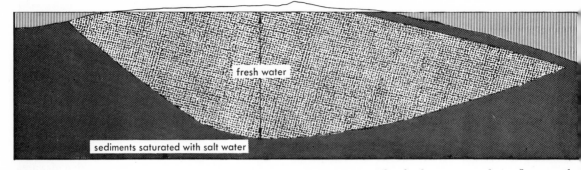

Florida Peninsula   Atlantic Ocean

fresh water

sediments saturated with salt water

Fig. 18-11. Storage of water in sediments in contact with the ocean. The fresh water tends to float on the more dense salt water. For every foot of elevation of the water table above sea level there are 38 feet of fresh water beneath.

vation of the water table above sea level. Thus if a water table is 1 foot above sea level the fresh-water—salt-water contact will be found at a depth of 38 feet below sea level. This condition holds in Florida where the fresh water is stored in the porous limestones and sands that underlay the peninsula. The fresh-water supply is a large dome-shaped mass. Problems arise when the rate at which water is pumped from the ground greatly exceeds the rate at which water is moving toward the area pumped. Excessive pumping brings the salt-water wedge closer to the surface and therefore endangers the fresh-water supply.

Geysers

Since the discovery of Old Faithful in 1870, this geyser in Yellowstone Park has regularly spurted forth about 10,000 to 12,000 gallons of steam and water to an average height of 130 feet about once every hour. Very few geysers are as regular as Old Faithful, but many other geysers are known, and the nature of their activity is similar. Outside of Yellowstone Park other areas of geyser activity are found in New Zealand and in Iceland.

If you carefully observe several eruptions of Old Faithful in sequence you will begin to perceive a very regular cycle of activity:

1. Immediately following an eruption most of the water goes back into the ground at the vent or through nearby holes. A small part runs off in small streams directed away from the cone.
2. This is followed by a period of quiet during which only a few whiffs of steam rise from the vent.
3. After about 30 or 40 minutes more steam starts to rise from the vent, and a little water appears at the surface.
4. Water and steam rise and flow out of the vent in a series of small outpourings. Some of this water runs off, but most goes back into the vent.
5. Several small eruptions then occur, throwing bubbling water out of the vent to a height of several feet above the ground. This continues for several minutes.
6. The main eruption starts, and a column of water and steam spurts forth as high as 250 feet occasionally. The eruption lasts several minutes, then dies down, and the cycle is repeated.

How can we account for such action? Some facts about these eruptions are well known. Beneath the surface of Yellowstone Park perhaps at a depth of several thousand feet there is almost certainly a mass of very hot rock, perhaps a cooling magma. Heat from this mass rises to the surface, heating the ground water. The water coming from Old Faithful and other geysers is mostly rain water. It contains only very small quantities of the common volcanic gases and solutions. Surface waters flow into

Fig. 18-12. Old Faithful in eruption, Yellowstone Park. (Photo by courtesy of the Union Pacific Railroad.)

Fig. 18-13. Geyserite, a deposit formed around the openings to geysers. Most of these deposits are siliceous. (Photo by E. W. Spencer.)

the fractured and porous igneous and volcanic rocks that underlie the soil in Yellowstone Park. Beneath the surface the vent of the geysers is probably connected to a very irregularly shaped network of fractures and cavities dissolved out by the hot waters. It is from these cavity networks that the ejected water comes. So, after the eruption, time is required for the water to percolate back into the channels and refill them. The water, which has just been cooled by its ascent into the air, is warmed immediately. Since the heat in the rocks increases with depth, the water in the lower parts of the network becomes hot more rapidly than that higher up. Water boils when it reaches 100° Centigrade at the surface, but that water at the bottom of the system is under the pressure of the weight of the column of water above it, so it must be heated much more before it will begin to boil. Eventually the boiling point is reached at some point in the network, and steam forms. This exerts pressure, expansion accompanies boiling, and water is forced out at the top of the vent. Just a little is forced out at first. Then more is forced upward. Finally enough water has been removed to lower the pressure on the network, and large quantities of water are suddenly converted to steam. The main part of the eruption starts when this almost explosive generation of steam occurs at depth.

A large amount of silica is carried in solution by the hot waters. This is dissolved from the underground cavities, and it is precipitated at the surface when the waters cool. Usually a colloidal gel is formed. This consolidates to an amorphous silica form and leaves a deposit known as geyserite.

Ground water in confined units (artesian conditions)

Under certain conditions water will rise to the ground surface from depth and flow out on the surface under pressure. In places wells drilled deep into the surface will strike units from which water will flow without pumping. It comes to the surface under pressure and will spout forth as a continuous stream of water. Such conditions are called artesian.

Artesian conditions arise from the hydrostatic pressure of water trapped or confined within a porous and permeable unit that is overlaid and underlaid by impervious units of rock. Water comes into such a unit, which is known as an aquifer, where it is exposed at the ground surface or where it is overlaid by other permeable rocks. The water moves down into the aquifer, gradually fills it, and thereby builds up hydrostatic pressure. If the aquifer is tapped at some elevation lower than its intake area, then water will flow from it under the pressure of the hydrostatic head above that point. Under natural conditions an artesian spring may originate where a fault cuts the unit; a well drilled into the aquifer is called an artesian well.

The most common aquifers are very exten-

Fig. 18-14. Artesian conditions. Water percolates into the aquifer at the mountain front. When a well is drilled in the plains, water flows to the surface and almost up to the level of saturation in the aquifer.

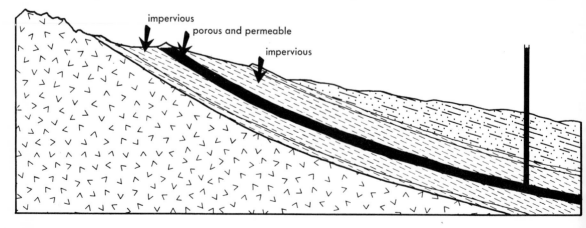

sive sedimentary units of sandstone or some other porous and permeable rock. They have great lateral extent and they are either tilted up or folded where they have been deformed after their initial deposition. After the deformation erosion usually lays the units bare around the margins of domes or mountain ranges so that they collect the runoff from the mountains. Water flows from the intake area through the unit toward wells drilled into the unit if they are being pumped. It is driven by two forces, the hydrostatic head and the compression of the unit under the weight of the overlying rocks. As the water is lowered in the aquifer the weight of the overlying mass compresses the aquifer and may partially destroy the porosity.

Artesian conditions may also arise in smaller bodies of rock such as lenticular sand bodies surrounded by clay and silt, such as you might find in old river channels, and in the cone-shaped aggregates of rock formed where streams leaving mountains deposit part of their load on the edge of the plains. These are not of great importance as water supplies, but artesian conditions may arise within them due to changes in permeability.

Caverns

In an active cavern you are very much aware of the moisture that drips from the ceiling, seems to pop out on the sides of the cave, and forms pools and streams on the floor. This moisture is ground water which seeps into the cavern from the surface. The cavern is in the zone of aeration (it would be filled with water if it were below the water table). Here a mixture of water and air is percolating through the rock which, if typical of most cavernous regions, is a limestone. Limestone is often a dense massive rock with relatively low porosity and permeability. Thus a great deal of the water moving through limestones flows along fractures. Indeed many caves are found to be eroded fracture zones which have become channels for underground streams. Water may be seen dripping from the straight line of a crack in the ceiling of the cave. The points from which it drips become the sites of calcite de-

posits which at first take the shape of thin straws. They are called stalactites and may be seen in various stages of development:

1. A drop of water hangs from the ceiling. Some of the water within the drop evaporates, leaving a thin ring of calcite around the drop.
2. After a long period of time this ring is lengthened by more deposits until it becomes a long straw.
3. Finally the inside of the straw becomes so filled with calcite that the drops can no longer flow through it.
4. Then the water moves as a thin film over the surface of the outside of the straw and slowly builds up layer on layer of calcite until a large tapering cone is formed.

The water that drops from the end of the stalactite falls to the floor of the cave where it may rest for a while evaporating further and precipitating more calcite. Slowly then a stump-shaped deposit rises from the floor. These are stalagmites. Usually they have a small saucer-shaped top into which the drops of water fall from the ceiling. Overflow from this saucer goes down the sides of the stalagmite building them out. Eventually the stalactite and stalagmite may grow together to form a column.

Other formations may grow from the sides of the cavern where droplets of water seem to hang. There they evaporate, leaving small rounded knob-like projections of calcite from the walls.

Where did the calcite being deposited in these cave formations come from? The obvious answer is that it was dissolved from the limestone through which the ground water moved. The ground water was originally rainwater. That means it contained carbon dioxide, which in combination with water forms a weak acid, carbonic acid. This acid dissolves limestone. The exact nature of the reaction has been outlined under chemical weathering; refer to Chapter 14 if you do not remember the process. The precipitation of the calcite as cave deposits comes from the loss of carbon dioxide and reduction in the water content when it reaches

Fig. 18-15. Drapery-like cave formations composed of calcite hang from the ceiling of this limestone cave. (Photo by courtesy of Luray Caverns, Virginia.)

Fig. 18-16. Stalactites, stalagmites, and columns in Carlsbad Caverns. (Photo by courtesy of the New Mexico State Tourist Bureau.)

Fig. 18-17. Travertine deposits here were built up to form stalactites and columns. Some of these earlier structures are now being covered by more massive cascade-like deposits. (Photo by courtesy of Luray Caverns, Virginia.)

Fig. 18-18. Formation of cave deposits. The photograph shows stalactites, stalagmites, and columns of various stages of formation. The sequence of events in the formation of a column like that at the left is described in the text. (Photo by courtesy of James F. Quinlan, Jr., Mineral Industries Journal.)

Fig. 18-19. Tunnel formed by the collapse of the roof of a cavern. A river flows out of this cavern entrance. Location is Shangri-la in New Guinea. (Photo by courtesy of the U.S. Air Force.)

Fig. 18-20. Natural Bridge, Virginia. The natural bridge may have once been a long tunnel such as that in Fig. 18-19. The stream, which once flowed as an underground river, is again flowing on the ground surface as a result of the collapse of the roof. (Photo by courtesy of the Natural Bridge Company, Virginia.)

Fig. 18-21. Hot spring deposits of calcium carbonate being built up as terraces. This deposit is at Mammoth Hot Springs, Yellowstone National Park. (Photo by E. W. Spencer.)

the cave, so the remaining water is saturated with calcium and carbonate ions. The rate at which these formations are built is highly variable. In active caves supplied with large quantities of water the rate is high—as much as a centimeter a year—but where the supply of water is limited the rate is slow, or formation may have ceased altogether. These calcareous cave deposits are usually known as travertine.

Caves may form through long-continued solution along fractures by water moving downward toward the water table or by waters moving near the water table. The process is somewhat analogous to the solution of a cube of sugar produced by dropping drops of water on it. The lime is slowly etched away along fractures until blocks are freed. They fall or shift, and solution continues. Eventually solution has removed enough material to cause a subsidence in the level of the ground surface. This may create a depression with no outlet on the surface. This enclosed depression, called a sink hole, forms a small drainage basin, catching all the rain that falls into it and a large part of that coming down slope into the sink. Once this process starts the cave is supplied with large quantities of water, and solution is accelerated. If the cavity extends far into the ground a path is available for the movement of large quantities of water. If enough water flows into the cave a stream is formed underground. Then the cave is enlarged by processes very much like the erosion by surface streams. This is a much faster process than solution by ground water. A great many caves have streams flowing through them, and most of them show signs of stream erosion throughout.

Springs

Springs form where the water table intersects the land surface or where water under artesian conditions finds its way to the surface. The most common places for springs to occur are illustrated. Spring deposits are called tufa.

Fig. 18-22. Cross sections showing conditions in which springs may form. These are but a few representative situations which give rise to the formation of springs.

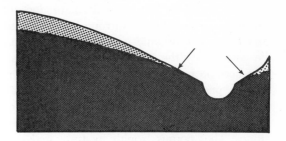
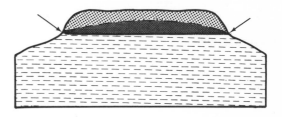
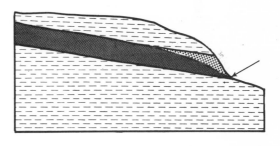
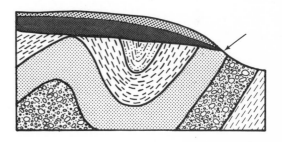
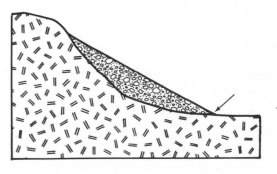

Most of them are calcium-carbonate deposits. Springs are commonly surrounded by plants and trees. The organic matter from these may be covered by the calcium carbonate deposits and become incorporated into the tufa making it very porous. Tufa is often poorly consolidated material. Where it has been firmly cemented it may be cut and used as a building stone. The porous rough texture makes it uniquely valuable for sound proofing.

REFERENCES

HUBBERT, M. K., 1940, The Theory of Ground Water Motion: Jour. Geology, v. 48, p. 785-944

LEGGET, R. F., 1939, *Geology and Engineering* New York, McGraw-Hill Book Co., 650 p.

MEINZER, O. E., 1939, Ground Water in the United States, A Summary: U. S. Geological Survey Water-Supply Paper 836-D, p. 157-232

MEINZER, O. E., Editor, 1942, Physics of the Earth Pt. 9, *Hydrology:* New York, McGraw-Hill Book Co., 712 p.

THORNBURY, W. D., 1954, *Principles of Geomorphology:* New York, John Wiley & Sons, 618 p.

TODD, D. K., 1959, *Ground Water Hydrology:* New York, John Wiley & Sons, 333 p.

TOLMAN, C. F., 1937, *Ground Water:* New York McGraw-Hill Book Co., 593 p.

U.S. DEPARTMENT OF AGRICULTURE, 1955, *Water The Yearbook of Agriculture,* 1955: Washington, D.C., U.S. Government Printing Office 751 p.

19   Wind Action

Wind

During a wind storm you see bits of paper or leaves blown by the wind. If you have noted the path of their movement you have seen a turbulent flow of air as it occurs near the surface of the earth where there are many obstructions setting up eddies, whirlwinds, updrafts, and downdrafts. The movements observed in the dust and smoke coming out of a smoke stack are a fair representation of movements in convection currents in the air. However, most natural convection comes from heating of the surface of the ground. Where the ground absorbs heat from solar radiation it heats the air directly above it, and this creates upward movements in the hot lighter air. This too is a form of turbulent motion. Turbulence extends high above the ground, as you know if you have ever flown a kite, but still higher it tends to decrease as effects of the irregularities of the surface become less pronounced. At high altitudes the wind moves in steady currents without a great deal of turbulence. This type of flow is laminar flow, consisting of movement of one layer over adjacent layers.

The effective forward velocity of wind is greatly reduced near the surface of the ground by turbulence set up by the movement of the wind around irregularities. Higher, the velocity becomes a steady directed stream.

Transportation

In a desert covered with sand you may stand in a strong wind and watch the wind-blown sand sweep across the ground. If the velocity of the wind is fairly constant the sand seems to be confined to a certain level above the ground. This zone is usually a few inches high, and only during storms does it reach more than 18 inches above the ground surface. Below this level the sand is actively blown, but above it the wind may be almost completely free of sand. If you look closely you will see sand grains rolling along the ground rapidly. These hit other sand grains and bounce a little way into the air. Once in the wind they are carried forward, and their velocity is increased, but unless the wind is very strong the pull of gravity on the grain will overcome any upward thrust on the grain from the wind, and the

Fig. 19-1. Sand dunes in the great sand-covered plains of Algeria. These are highly complex longitudinal dune ridges. The wind direction is variable, but appears to come predominantly from the northeast. (Photo by courtesy of the U.S. Air Force.)

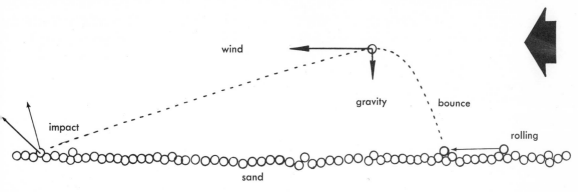

Fig. 19-2. **Sand movement.** The movement of sand is started by rolling grains which on impact with other grains bounce into the air. They are carried along in the wind but fall back to the ground because the force of gravity directs their path. When they hit the sand surface the impact causes other grains to bounce and the process of saltation is begun.

grain will follow a slanted path back to the ground. The increased velocity will give it more energy in the form of momentum. When it hits the surface again the impact dislodges other sand grains which may start rolling or may bounce into the air. Soon a chain reaction has been established, and transportation is under way through a series of bounces. The process is called saltation. Most of the material transported in this way is sand and silt, the size range of about 2 mm down to 1/16 mm. As the sand is moved it tends to become rounded and sorted, and small pits that resemble a sandblasted piece of glass begin to form on the wind-blown grains.

Larger sizes may be lifted from the ground during unusually intense wind storms. Tornadoes are known to pick up roofs from houses, toss cars into trees, overturn railroad cars, and blow down trees along their paths, but tornadoes are not common enough to be an im-

portant agent of gradation. Hurricanes and typhoons also have localized effects, although in the long run the effect may be comparable to other forms of wind action.

Pebbles may be rolled along the ground surface during normal high winds, but they are rarely lifted from the surface. Larger boulders may be moved by a combination of wind and mass movement. The wind blows the finer supporting material from beneath the boulder, which then rolls forward.

The finer sediment sizes are the main load of the wind. Wind carries sand and silt in saltation, but the finest particles such as dust, cloud particles, smoke, and haze are moved in a very different way. These particles are so light that the force of gravity exerts a very slight pull on them. In addition, they are large relative to their weight. Dust is often composed of flat tabular particles with large surface area. This makes it possible for the force of upward

Fig. 19-3. **Grains of sand in the process of saltation.** Note that ripple marks are formed in the sand, and that only one side of these is hit directly.

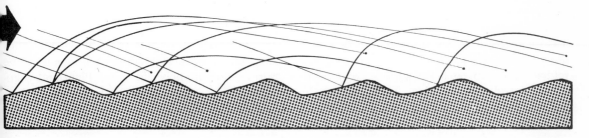

Fig. 19-4. Dust storm in New Mexico. "The day had been relatively calm with light wind from the south east. The dust storm rolled in on a very light wind, but about 15 minutes later a regular hurricane struck which lasted about 30 minutes. Visibility was zero, and tightly closed rooms were filled with fine choking dust." Dust is so light that it remains in suspension in the air. (Photo by courtesy of the U.S. Soil Conservation Service.)

motions of wind currents to more than counter-balance the downward pull of gravity. The dust and smaller particles settle very slowly and are easily wafted back up higher in the air by the slightest updraft. They are in suspension in the air. Eventually they do settle back to the surface. Large quantities of volcanic dust carried aloft during the explosions of Krakatoa and Katmai stayed up for several years and were carried around the earth in the upper layers of the earth's atmosphere.

These smaller particles are blown directly into the air by the impact of the wind against their surfaces, or are lifted up by the pressure created by velocity differentials between layers. Take a piece of paper and fold the two ends down about an inch from the sides. Prop the folded paper up on a flat surface so it forms an open-ended box. Then blow under the paper. If properly done the paper will not be blown away, but the top will be pulled down

toward the surface. What has happened? The velocity of the air under the paper was greater than that above it, and this created a difference in atmospheric pressure on the two sides. The pressure dropped where the wind velocity was greatest, and the force of the pressure above pushed the top of the paper down. The same thing can take place in any fluid media. It happens in the wind and in running water. This pressure would be enough to lift small dust-sized materials into the air.

Sources of wind-blown material

Potential sources of wind-blown materials are found anywhere small particles come to the surface and are not held down. Plant and vegetative cover tends to prevent the removal of material by the wind, as does a lot of moisture in the soil, but once either of these is lost the particles may be carried away. Sources include the following:

1. Any place where loosely consolidated sandstone, siltstone, or shale rock units are exposed at the surface.
2. Weathering of almost any rocks will produce some small particles. Finely disintegrated rock is an excellent source either where it is residual or where it has been deposited after transportation by some other agent. Some of the places where large quantities of such material are found are:

   a. Flood-plain sediments.
   b. The deposits washed out of glaciers.
   c. Beach sands.
   d. Dried lake sediments.

3. Volcanic explosions have provided large quantities of dust. Unlike material from other sources, this material may be placed directly in the air. Old deposits of volcanic ash are also potential sources of sediment.
4. Man has often played an important role in making material available to the wind that would not otherwise have been exposed. This has come mainly through poor conservation practices in farming and in forestry. By plowing ground during years of drought the soil is turned up, and what moisture there is in the dirt is exposed to more rapid evaporation. Thus moisture is lost, the soil is loosened, plants die, and since the material sizes are small enough to be transported by the wind they are blown away. The results have been disastrous in some places, where fertile farms have been converted into deserts of wind-blown sand and dust. Similar effects

Fig. 19-5. Exposure of loess, wind-deposited dust, and silt, near Vicksburg, Mississippi. (Photo by E. W. Spencer.)

may be produced by removal of the forest cover from semiarid lands, thus exposing the soil to wind erosion.

EROSION BY WIND

The wind accomplishes erosion by three means:

1. Deflation (blowing away of materials).
2. Corrosion and abrasion.
3. Impact.

Deflation refers to the actual blowing away of the land. It would include the lifting and removal of dust and smaller particles, and the transportation of sand and silt which bounce into the air and are carried along by saltation. You abrade wood if you rub a piece of sand paper over it. In like manner the sand, silt, and dust act as tools in the wind, and as they move over surfaces they may bring about a scraping or abrasion of the surface. In wind erosion impact is more important than abrasion. Impact occurs when a sand grain is blown into or against a rock surface or into the soil. The momentum is used in dislodging other granular material, as when a sand grain is blown against a sandstone. The impact may break the cement freezing other sand grains. The nature of im-

Fig. 19-6. "Camel Rock." This oddly-shaped formation is located a few miles north of Sante Fe, New Mexico. It is one of the land forms typical of wind erosion processes. The impact of wind-transported sand has undercut the rock. (Photo by courtesy of the New Mexico State Tourist Bureau.)

Fig. 19-7. "Window Rock." This and other more delicate arches have been cut through these sandstone units. Much of the erosion is controlled by fractures in the sandstone. Note the undercutting at the base of the cliff and the holes to the left. (Photo by courtesy of the New Mexico State Tourist Bureau.)

pact can be seen in any sand-blasting operation. The old paint or stone is chipped away, exposing a new surface. The same method is used to frost glass and to cut letters in polished stones. Even granites may be cut by placing them in a sand blast. Letters and numbers are inscribed by cutting them out in a rubber overlay, covering the polished slab with the overlay, and directing a sand blast against it. Where the sand grains hit the surface of the rock it becomes chipped.

The evidence of impact can be seen in most samples of wind-blown sand. The surface of the sand grains is pitted or frosted as a result of repeated impact.

Where sand has been blown over rocks for a long time they become worn from the repeated abrasion, and smooth polished surfaces result. Such stones, which are commonly found in deserts, are called ventifacts. They have smooth sculptured surfaces which represent a streamlining of the rock. Ventifacts with one smooth surface are called einkanters; those with three, dreikanters.

Erosional land forms

There is some question as to just how important wind erosion is. It is most effective in

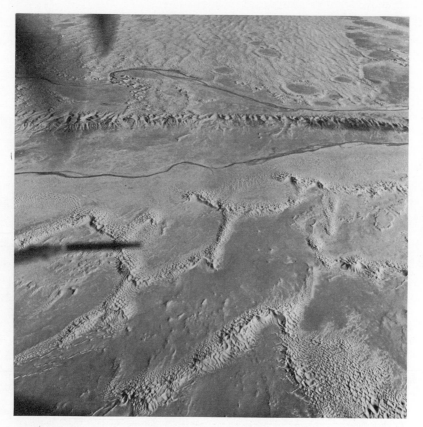

Fig. 19-8. Complex sand dunes in North Africa. Note the two streams which wind across the desert and the various forms of the sand dunes. Across the photo between the two streams a long outcrop of rock is visible. This may be the source of some of the wind-blown sand. (Photo by courtesy of the U.S. Air Force.)

the shifting about of debris that has been weathered from solid rocks. It keeps the land swept clear of this debris in places and shifts it and piles it up elsewhere as sand dunes or distributes it widely as sheets. Some land forms are due primarily to wind erosion. These include the following:

1. Broad shallow depressions in deserts where soil has been blown out by repeated movement of currents in one direction.
2. Broad shallow caves in the sides of hills where the impact and abrasion of sand have sculptured the lower slopes of the hill.
3. Mushroom, table, and pedestal rocks. These are isolated rocks from which the base has been partially cut by the undercutting of wind-blown sand. Some of these forms are quite spectacular, such as the balanced rocks. Often the top of the form is a different rock unit

from the bottom, which has been cut away because it is more susceptible to wind erosion.

Sorting

Wind is an excellent agent for sorting of materials. Sorting means the separation of the particles according to size, shape, or weight. The velocity of the wind determines just what maximum size of material it can transport by rolling, by saltation, and in suspension. Thus a very distinct separation is accomplished. The smaller sizes are suspended and carried away, the heavier particles lag behind on the ground, and the sand and silt are bounced along the surface. The loads in suspension and saltation are further separated. Of that in suspension only the lightest can be carried and maintained at extreme heights. Of the saltation load some will be moved more rapidly than others. Thus the wind's load becomes initially sorted while it is in transport.

When the wind begins to die down and its velocity drops, then critical velocities will be reached for each size, and that size will begin to settle. The result is a very well-sorted sediment.

DEPOSITION

Wind deposits take two general forms—piles and sheets. The piles are the various types of dunes which accumulate from sand and silt carried in saltation. The sheets are the dust deposits laid down over large areas. Within the sheets the thickness varies, generally thinning out farther away from the source, but the lateral extent is great. Two excellent examples of the sheet-like nature of some wind-blown de-posits are the deposits of volcanic dust from the eruption of Katmai and the layer of loess that covers most of the central United States. These sheet-like deposits cover much greater areas than do the sand dunes.

Travelers through the Mississippi Valley are often impressed by the fact that in many places the road cuts are nearly vertical. In most materials such a cut would almost immediately slump, and slides would develop in it very quickly. Examination of the material under a microscope shows that it is composed of very small angular particles apparently derived from a great variety of rocks including igneous and metamorphic rocks. The angularity of the particles is the clue to why the cliffs are stable in steep faces. The unit is unconsolidated or at best loosely consolidated; you

Fig. 19-9. Vertical air view of sand dunes which have become fixed by the growth of vegetation. The dunes would move very slowly. These are barchan dunes located near Fort St. John, Peace River District, British Columbia. They were formed by a strong easterly wind. It is thought that these dunes were formed late in the Pleistocene, when an ice sheet lay to the east, causing strong air currents to blow off the ice, toward the west. (Photo by courtesy of the Royal Canadian Air Force.)

can easily dig into it with your fingers. By digging into the loess it is possible to find a number of small snail shells, and these may be identified as a type of snail that lives on the surface of the ground. Thus the deposit which is known as loess has most likely been deposited by the wind. This conclusion is supported by the presence of many small tubes of calcite that apparently are fillings of the holes left after the decay of tall grasses. The wind-blown silt and dust sifted down over fields of grass so slowly that it was not forced down. It buried the snails at the same time. The composition of the loess found within the United States is such that it could be produced by grinding up rocks exposed in the northern part of the country and in Canada. A means of producing this material would be provided by the movement of glaciers over that part of North America within the Pleistocene. The finely-ground particles would be carried out to the areas in front of the ice sheet by meltwater. There they would be deposited over a broad outwash plain. Winds sweeping from the ice sheet could have dried them off and picked the material up, carrying it southward and depositing it over the Mississippi Valley region.

Sand dunes

Deserts are sometimes thought of as dry areas covered by drifting sand dunes. Actually, sand dunes are relatively rare features even in deserts, and they are by no means confined to deserts. Some of the most extensive accumulations of sand dunes in North America are found along the eastern coast and around the Great Lakes. Sand dunes may be formed anywhere these conditions are met:

1. Strong, constant, or intermittent winds.
2. A source of sand.
3. Obstacles that can initiate dune formation.

Fig. 19-10. A complex of prominent longitudinal dunes. In the foreground barchans stand out. Note the long ridges of dune sand in the background. (Photo by courtesy of the U.S. Air Force.)

Fig. 19-11. View of the slip face of a large dune. The wind blows from the right to the left. This dune is located on the Oregon coast. (Photo by courtesy of the Oregon State Highway Department.)

The sand sources are highly varied. Along coast lines the most common sand is quartz sand, but in Italy it is olivine sand derived from volcanic rocks, and in the Azores volcanic ash makes up its composition. In the Arctic and Antarctic there are large quantities of ice sand which forms dunes, and in the White Sands National Monument in New Mexico the sand is composed of gypsum.

Dune formation. Sand accumulations may start anywhere there is an obstruction in the path of the sand movement. Sand moving by saltation hits the obstacle or falls behind it when the wind velocity is suddenly decreased. A streamlined pile of sand forms. Once accumulation has started, the dune is likely to grow. On the windward side a very low slope forms up which sand moves in saltation. Just below the top of the pile beyond the crest, the wind velocity is reduced. Sand falling there is not readily blown. A back slope forms from the accumulation of sand, and it assumes the angle

Fig. 19-12. The formation of sand dunes. These two profiles show two stages in the evolution of a dune. The top dune is smooth and rounded as the wind flows over its entire surface, but below the sand has built up until the main stream passes over the slip face where eddy currents are shown. The sand is carried up the low sloping surface of the dune to the top where it is dropped over the side. The slip face has an angle equal to the angle of repose of the sand, usually about 35°.

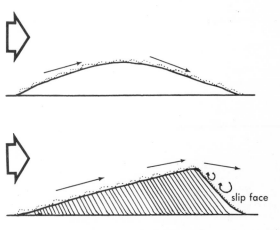

slip face

Fig. 19-13. Ripple marks in sand. Ripple marks caused by currents such as those in the wind or in runnin[g] water are asymmetrical in shape (one side is steeper than the other). The steep face is formed on th[e] side away from the direction from which the wind blows. (Esther Henderson Photo, by courtesy [of] *Arizona Highways.*)

Fig. 19-14. Cross bedding from ancient sand dunes exposed in cliff in Northern Arizona. (Photo by E. W[.] Spencer.)

f repose of loose sand, about 35° of slope. This surface is just barely stable. Any addition f sand at the top tends to cause small slides n the back slope. Sand moves up the windward slope in a series of bounces and rolls. At he top it is blown, falls, or slips over the crest nd down the back slope. Gradually the sand n the windward side is blown over to the uter slope. Thus the sand dune moves. Some unes move as much as 100 feet each year. Note the type of internal structures formed in and dunes. This is a form of cross-bedding.

Ripple marks. R. A. Bagnold in his experiments on the physics of wind-blown sand ound that sand surfaces with wind blowing ver them are not stable. After a short period f time irregularities will develop in an origially smooth sand surface. Once a depression r slight irregularity has formed, small ripples vill start to develop on the surface. These ripples are asymmetric in form. They may assume long rows or, if the wind direction is variable, they may become rhombic in shape. They move across the surface of the sand in the direction of the wind currents.

Dune forms

A great variety of forms may be assumed by sand dunes. The particular shape that is formed depends on these factors:

1. How much sand is supplied to the dune area.
2. The wind velocity.
3. The constancy of the wind direction.
4. The rate at which the sand is supplied.
5. Amount and distribution of vegetative cover.

Barchan dunes. These are the crescentic-shaped dunes with the points or wings directed

Fig. 19-15. Sand dunes in Death Valley. (Photo by courtesy of Santa Fe Railway.)

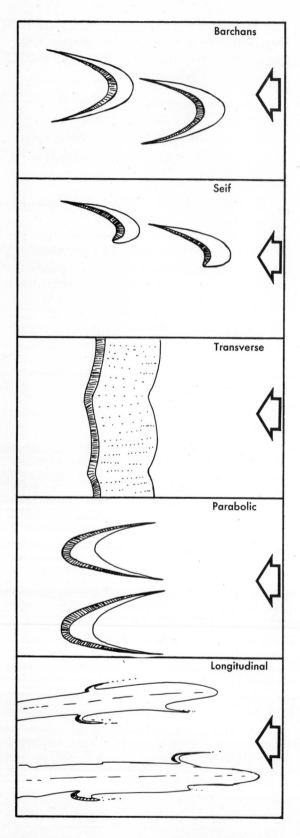

downwind. They are common where the wind direction is constant and moderate, and where there is little irregularity in the surface over which the sand is moving.

Seif. This dune is similar to the barchan except one wing is missing. This is caused by an occasional shift in wind direction but not in the direction from which the sand is being supplied. Seifs may form large ridges as much as 700 feet high and extending for many miles in length.

Longitudinal dunes. These form where sand is in short supply and the direction of the wind is constant.

Transverse dunes. These dunes are those aligned perpendicular to the wind direction. They are likely to originate when the wind direction is normal, at right angles, to an elongate source of sand. This condition is found along coasts and lake shores. These dunes may be very long, but they rarely attain heights of more than 15 feet.

Parabolic dunes. These result where vegetation is thick and at least partially covers the sand. In spots where the vegetation is missing a "blowout" will occur. A parabolic dune with the wings pointed upwind results. The shape is similar to that of the barchan, but the direction of orientation is reversed.

Dunes with regular shapes are not always formed. Where there is a great deal of sand, isolated dunes may be scarce, and the dunes coalesce, losing their individual characteristics.

REFERENCES

BAGNOLD, R. A., 1954, *The Physics of Blown Sand and Desert Dunes:* London, Methuen & Co. Ltd., 265 p.

RUSSELL, R. J., 1944, Lower Mississippi Valley Loess: Geol. Soc. America Bull., v. 55, p. 1-40

THORNBURY, W. D., 1954, *Principles of Geomorphology:* New York, John Wiley & Sons, 618 p.

Fig. 19-16. **Five common types of sand dunes.** The steep (slip) faces are indicated by the closely spaced lines. Wind direction is from the right.

20   Evolution of Landscapes

Running water, glaciers, wind, mass movements, and percolating subsurface waters are effective in bringing about modifications of the landscape. There is a reason why the landscape you see about you possesses the particular form that it has assumed. There is a causal relationship between land forms and the geomorphic agents which act on them. We have now considered the basic nature of these relationships in the discussions of the methods of erosion, transportation, and deposition by each of the

geomorphic agents. You should now be familiar with the erosional and depositional features produced by each of these agents. But one factor of major importance has not been emphasized. That factor is time. The agents that act to shape the land surface are usually extremely effective at their jobs. So long as there is any surface relief on which they can act they will erode the surface. Therefore, the landscape must undergo continual change with the production of new and different land forms.

The concept of the evolution of landscapes

A landscape altered by the action of the same geomorphic agents over a long period of time will undergo systematic changes leading to a sequential development of land forms. It is implied that it is possible to predict the nature of the land forms that will develop through time in any given area. Likewise it should be possible to extrapolate back through time and describe what has taken place in the past leading to the development of the present landscape. There are certain obvious limitations to this, and a great many situations which complicate the problem. For example, there is very definite evidence that climates have changed in the past. This means that regions which during part of their history were dominated by fluvial processes might suddenly have become the sites of glaciers. These would certainly modify or destroy the previous land forms. Other complications are caused by interruptions due to deformation of the crust accompanied by rising or lowering of the region, shifting of base level, and changing rates of erosion. Thus many problems are encountered in the application of the concept of the evolution of land forms to actual situations in nature; yet it can often be done with success.

Controlling factors. Many factors determine the particular sequence of land forms that will develop in a certain region. Certain geomorphic agents dominate erosion of the surface in any particular area, but they must function within a framework of other factors which they cannot control. These are:

1. *Base level:* This is the ultimate or temporary level toward which the land surface may be reduced, and below which the land surface cannot be reduced by subaerial agents of erosion. With this as the lower limit of effective degradation we can deduce that the ultimate or last stage in the evolution of land forms regardless of what combination of agents act will be the production of a broad, nearly flat erosion surface. Further evolution of a region which has been reduced to such a surface must await uplift or igneous activity to build the area up again.

2. *Deformation (diastrophism):* This factor is as important a part of the framework as is the base level. Uplift or igneous activity initially brings units of land into position above sea level where the cycle of erosion may commence to sculpture and reduce the land. Because diastrophic movements may be very slow they may continue over a great part of the erosional history of a region.

3. *Interruptions:* Of particular importance

Fig. 20-1. Erosional remnants in an Australian desert. These isolated masses of rock are all that remains of a formerly higher and more rugged topography. Note that the units of rock are stratified and that these strata are turned up on end, indicating that strong deformation once affected the area. (Photo by courtesy of Qantas Empire Airways Ltd.)

is the fact that because of diastrophism the sequence of development of land forms may be interrupted. This interruption might take any one of a number of forms:

a. It may be a very slow upward or downward warping.
b. It may be a very rapid upward or downward warping.
c. It may be an intense deformation, folding and faulting the crust.

4. *Structure:* The nature of the rocks exposed at the surface, their hardness, resistance to the weathering and erosive processes, and their geometric configuration and distribution all will play an important role in determination of what land forms are possible. The surface of any uplifted part of the crust has certain unique physiographic forms before the new cycle begins. Consider, for example, the initial differences in the surficial features of each of the following:

a. Sections of the marginal sea floors.
b. Folded mountain structures or faulted mountains.
c. Volcanic mountains and lava plateaus.
d. Glaciated plains.
e. Lake beds.
f. Deserts.

Obviously each of these will undergo at least initial differences in sequential development of land forms.

5. *Time:* Each stage in the evolution of the land is characterized by a particular group of land forms that are in harmony with the stage's place in the cycle of erosion within the limitations of structure, deformation, and base level.

LAND FORMS IN ARID AND SEMIARID CLIMATES

The nature and evolution of land forms in arid and semiarid climates are considered before those of humid climates for two reasons. First, the arid and semiarid regions of the world cover more surface area than those of humid regions. We have come to think of the landscapes of humid regions as being so-called "normal conditions." But this comes mainly from the fact that temperate humid climates are inhabited by more people than arid climates and consequently have been the subject of more study. Secondly, arid and semiarid regions have far simpler land forms than do regions with humid climates. Although the origin and evolution of land forms in different climates have long been a subject of controversy, there has been general agreement by most geomorphologists that the differences between land forms of humid-temperate, semiarid, and arid environments are differences primarily in degree, not in kind. This being the case it is much easier to proceed from the simpler forms of the arid climates to the more complex forms of the humid environments.

Deserts

So far the character of deserts has not been discussed. It is sometimes treated in connection with wind erosion, because the effects of wind erosion are most obvious in deserts. Nevertheless, the effects of wind erosion, transportation, and deposition are by no means confined to deserts. The wind-blown loess and volcanic deposits are not desert features, and sand dunes are as common along shore lines in any climate as they are in most arid and semiarid regions. But more important is the fact that most of the physiographic features of deserts are the result of mass wasting and running water—not wind erosion.

This gives us ample reason for asking: "What exactly is a desert?" There is no simple answer, and, in fact, most of us hold many misconceptions about the nature of deserts. Common fallacies are that: deserts have no vegetation, deserts consist mainly of mile after mile of drifting sand piled up in sand dunes, deserts are always hot, and finally wind is responsible for most desert land forms. Arid regions make up more than 30 per cent of the land surface of the world. They are regions characterized by scarcity of rainfall and consequently relatively thin vegetative cover. The rainfall in deserts is typically torrential; that is, it comes down rapidly in a short period of time. Many times, the

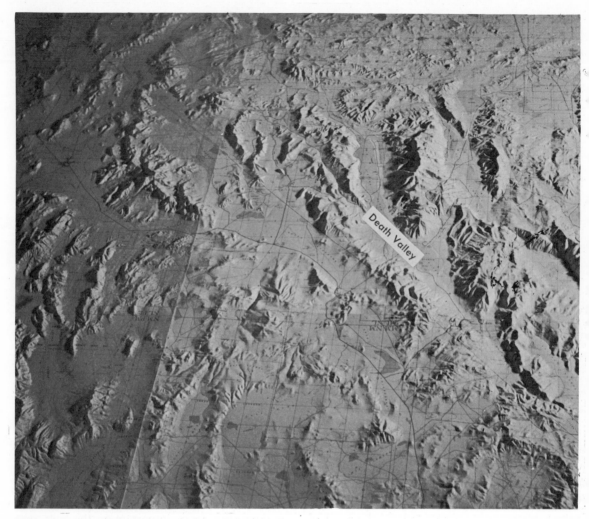

Fig. 20-2 Desert land forms in the Great American Desert. Death Valley is at the right. The region is located in California and Nevada. South is at the top of the page. The photograph is of a plastic relief map prepared by the Army Map Service.

entire year's rainfall will be concentrated in no more than three or four rains, but as much as several inches of rain may fall during each of these. The long dry periods between rains exclude most of the common plants of humid regions, but others adapted to the small supply of rain flourish. Tropical deserts may be hot or at least warm throughout the year, but those in the middle latitudes undergo temperature changes with the seasons that are very much like those of the humid regions. In the high latitudes the deserts may be cool or cold most of the year. Even in the tropical deserts there is a high daily variation in temperature. Be-

cause there are fewer leafy plants, less moisture, and few clouds, heat is lost rapidly from the desert at night. Temperature variations may range from over 150° Fahrenheit in the midday to near freezing at night in temperate or tropical deserts.

Many deserts are characterized by internal drainage. That is, the amount of rainfall is so small and the rate of evaporation is so great that a well-developed drainage pattern carrying water out of the desert is lacking. Of course many deserts are drained by large streams such as the Nile and the Colorado Rivers, but there are few tributaries within the deserts even in

Fig. 20-3. Desert landscape. Gently sloping valleys and steep cliffs are prominent features of the desert. This scene is in northern Arizona. (Photo by E. W. Spencer.)

Fig. 20-4. View across a pediment to a block-like mountain range. The centers of such valleys are filled with debris eroded from the mountains, but closer to the mountains there is only a thin veneer of sediment in transport across a solid bedrock, the pediment. This range is located near Las Vegas, Nevada. (Photo by E. W. Spencer.)

these instances. Particularly in the southwestern United States the deserts are basins that are almost entirely enclosed by mountain ranges. Within the desert, mechanical weathering is important just as wind erosion is where there are steady winds equipped with tools of wind-blown sand, but chemical weathering and erosion by running water are more important in bringing about alteration of the land. Thermal expansion and contraction resulting from the wide range of daily temperatures has been named as the cause of exfoliation, but many of the recent investigations have shown that chemical weathering is also an important aspect of breakdown and spalling off of boulders and exposures of massive bare rock. The result of weathering processes in deserts is the production of much greater quantities of broken rock debris than the available water and wind are capable of moving.

The weathered debris on the ground surface in deserts is moved by wind, mass movement, and by rain wash. The wind selects only the finest materials, mass movement is most effective where the relief is great, and erosion by streams is accomplished mainly through sheet floods or sheet wash. During a typical desert cloudburst, rills and sheets of water containing a very heavy load form almost immediately. The slopes are generally broad and smooth because there may not be enough water for streams to flow all the time and cut well-defined drainage patterns. Most of the streams flow for a brief time after a rain, but disappear soon afterward as the water evaporates or soaks into the ground. Channels formed during these rains are called washes or wadies. The slopes do not become dissected by prominent stream channels, so surface wash is a very prominent form of movement of the weathered debris.

Desert land forms

By far the most prominent land forms in deserts are plains. These have been formed in a variety of ways. In some arid regions there are rivers, and they have flood plains, although these are not nearly so common as they are in humid climates. In the Southwest and particularly in the Colorado Plateau there are prominent structural plains. Those are flat surfaces of structural origin such as uplifted sea floors. In addition there are plains formed through erosion and deposition, playas, bajadas, and pediments.

Fig. 20-5. Erosional features. The steep cliffs, the debris-covered, gently sloping surfaces around the mountain, and the rugged mountain outline are characteristic of erosional features in deserts. (Photo by E. W. Spencer.)

Fig. 20-6. A late stage in the evolution of the topography in this desert. All that remains of the former high topography are a few isolated masses. Note that these are still characterized by cliffs and talus slopes as are young high mountains. (Photo by courtesy of Qantas Empire Airways Ltd.)

Playas. In deserts that consist of basins enclosed by mountain ranges the drainage is toward the center of the basin from all margins. Where these drainage lines converge we expect to find a lake. In general there is a nearly level plain that has been built up by the gradual influx of sediment from the basin sides. When there is sufficient water this plain is covered by a broad shallow lake called a playa. Playas usually contain water only a short time after a rainfall. Water is lost through evaporation or by being soaked into the ground. The lake becomes the site of deposition of salts that have been precipitated from the waters of the lake. Such salt-covered plains are called alkali flats or salinas if there is a very high concentration of salt.

Bajadas. The playas occupy positions on plains that have been built up through successive deposits of alluvial material washed into the basin by sheet flooding and surface runoff. These are often the deposits of coalescing alluvial fans. The surfaces of these deposits change from the flat plain at the center of the basin to the very gradual slope up toward the surrounding mountains. These lower alluvial deposits at the base of the mountains and near the center of the basin are called bajadas. Their slope is generally in the range of 1° to 5°.

Pediment. Closer to the mountain the

Fig. 20-7. Topography of the Valley and Ridge province of the Appalachians. In the background is the Blue Ridge. Compare the smooth rolling shape of the landscape here with that of the deserts of Australia and Nevada. (Photo by E. W. Spencer.)

gently inclined plain that slopes up to the base of the mountains is often an erosional feature. The solid rock that lies close to the surface has been eroded as the mountain front has retreated back away from the center of the basin. The pediment surface may be covered by a thin veneer of debris that is in transport, but this is not a permanent deposit. It is material in the process of moving from the high slopes toward the center of the basin. Fig. 20-7 shows the general parts of the slope away from the basin and the position of the pediment relative to the bajada. The parts are:

a. Top slope.
b. Cliff face.
c. Debris slope or talus.
d. Pediment.
e. Bajada.

Evolution of land forms in deserts is primarily concerned with the formation and extension of pediments. There is considerable diversity of opinion regarding the specific details of both. A number of different processes probably play a part. These include lateral erosion by streams flowing out of the mountains and their small tributaries, unconcentrated sheet wash without definite flow lines, and erosion by small rills of water flowing across the ground surface. The net effect of all of these is to bring about retreat of mountain slopes through time. Fault scarps are prominent along the edges of some mountains in the Basin and Range province of the southwestern United States. Sharp folds and downcutting of streams through rock units of varying resistance also give rise to cliffs and steep slopes. Such steep slopes may retreat parallel to the original slope all along mountain fronts. Hillsides or mountain slopes may be divided into four elements. At the top there usually is a broad, nearly flat, somewhat rounded surface, the waxing slope. This passes into a cliff or steep face that has been washed clear of soil and debris. At the foot of this cliff talus piles or talus slopes form what is known as the detrital slope. In hard resistant rock there is a pronounced break from this rather steep slope to the low slope of the pediment, but in weak units there is a gradual lowering of the slope onto the pediment surface. Usually the most active of these slopes are the cliff or "free face" and the detrital slope. Mass wasting is most effective on them, and surface wash is most capable of moving debris across the steep surfaces. Material from these steep slopes is washed out across the pediment. In arid climates movement of debris is most active from the start of rain to shortly after rain falls. As the pediment is a smooth land form it permits discharge of sheets of water over all or at least large parts of its area. Farther downslope the amount of water moving on the pediment surface increases just as the discharge in streams increases downstream. Water becomes deeper, turbulent, and highly erosive. Wadies or washes form, and gullies or small channels may be cut into the pediment. Moving water is the dominant process responsible for transportation of material across the pediment.

If the steep slope becomes covered with vegetation or stops actively retreating for any other reason, then the slope above it (the waxing slope) will become smoothed off. It will gradually develop a convex form where it breaks away into the steep free face slope. This rounded form may become so pronounced that the free slope and the detrital slope appear convexly rounded at the top, and the profile across the cliff becomes concavo-convex.

Evolution of the physiography in an arid region, once pediments are formed, consists essentially of the parallel retreat of the steep face of the slope above the pediment. The slope of the pediment is maintained. If pediments occur on both sides of a mountain range they gradually converge. Eventually the range is reduced to a very broad dome with the slope equal to that of the pediment on either side of a crest that consists of a narrow ridge of small scattered domes. These residual hills are known as bornhardts. These forms appear near the ultimate stage in the erosion cycle. Once bornhardts are removed from the landscape further reduction of the land is negligible until the region is uplifted or otherwise deformed.

EVOLUTION OF LAND FORMS IN HUMID CLIMATES

Although a few authorities have completely rejected the concept that land forms may pass through cyclic evolution, most geologists and particularly those in the United States accept the concept that a sequence of land forms will develop on an elevated segment of the crust as it is progressively lowered by the dominant geomorphic agents of the region. Because the effectiveness of different processes is largely governed by the climatic conditions under which they operate, it has been assumed that different sequences will develop in different climates. One of the most recent schools of thought proposes that these differences are more apparent than real, and that the pattern of development of land forms in humid, semiarid, and arid climates is essentially the same; the principal difference is one of degree rather than a fundamental difference in type or kind of land forms. This school considers the evolution of land forms in the arid regions as already described to be the basic pattern of change both in arid and humid regions. The ideas of this group have developed largely from criticisms and additional studies of the original concept of cyclic evolution of land forms as expressed by William Morris Davis who is sometimes known as "the great definer and analyst" of geomorphology.

The idea of land-form evolution was first conceived by Major J. W. Powell, a one-armed Civil War veteran who headed the United States Geological Survey, studied the arid Southwest, and made the first trip through the Grand Canyon of the Colorado River. But it was William Morris Davis who developed the idea. A student of his, Douglas Johnson, applied and elaborated the application of the concept to the land forms of the world. Both Davis and Johnson concentrated on the application of the concept to the land forms in humid temperate climates of the central and eastern United States. Other regions and different land forms were treated as deviations from the cycle of evolution in the humid regions, or as climatic accidents. They visualized landscapes as passing through stages in development somewhat comparable to the stages of life—youth, maturity, and old age. Youth is a period following uplift, when erosion is most active on the land which has just experienced a shift in base level. Maturity is reached as the processes of erosion and deposition begin to become ad-

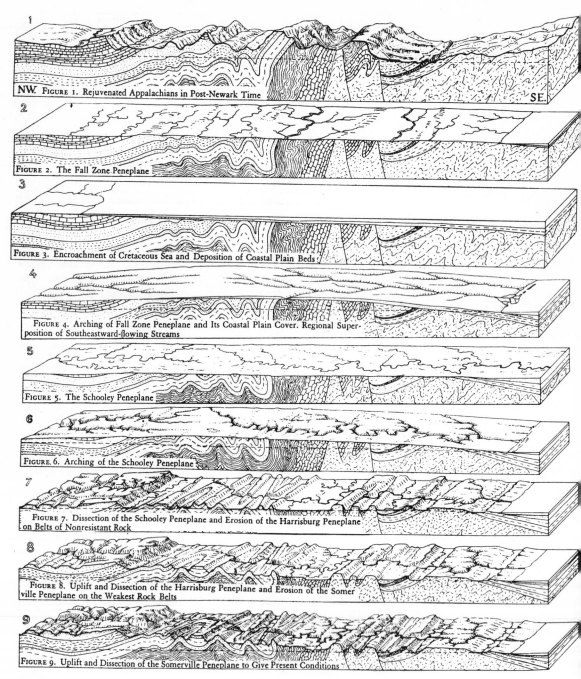

NW. FIGURE 1. Rejuvenated Appalachians in Post-Newark Time SE.

FIGURE 2. The Fall Zone Peneplane

FIGURE 3. Encroachment of Cretaceous Sea and Deposition of Coastal Plain Beds

FIGURE 4. Arching of Fall Zone Peneplane and Its Coastal Plain Cover. Regional Superposition of Southeastward-flowing Streams

FIGURE 5. The Schooley Peneplane

FIGURE 6. Arching of the Schooley Peneplane

FIGURE 7. Dissection of the Schooley Peneplane and Erosion of the Harrisburg Peneplane on Belts of Nonresistant Rock

FIGURE 8. Uplift and Dissection of the Harrisburg Peneplane and Erosion of the Somerville Peneplane on the Weakest Rock Belts

FIGURE 9. Uplift and Dissection of the Somerville Peneplane to Give Present Conditions

Fig. 20-8. Stages in the development of the Appalachian Region, as described by Douglas Johnson. (From A. K. Lobeck, *Atlas of North American Geology.* By courtesy of Edwin Raisz.)

justed to the topography, as in the case of graded streams. Old age is reached when the topography, after millions of years of gradual reduction, begins to approach a level, nearly featureless surface. Davis and Johnson recog-

nized that there would be interruptions in the cycle if uplift of the land lowered the regional base level at any time during the cycle. But if the cycle goes to completion, old age, then in the ideal case the cycle might be started once again by uplift, and the sequence of development would be essentially the same as in the previous cycle.

An ideal fluvial cycle

The erosion cycle of Davis commences with rather rapid uplift of a region above sea level. Consider a cycle in which there is a minimum of complication. Let us assume at first that the following conditions are met:

1. The rock units are sedimentary rocks composed of sandstones, limestones, and shales that are warped up above sea level from the sea floor.
2. There is no complex structure in the rocks such as faults, folds, or prominent angular unconformities.
3. There are no interruptions in the cycle such as would be brought on by renewal of uplift or down-warping.

What happens in each of these events will be considered separately. It is further assumed that the landscape evolves in a temperate humid climate in which erosion is accomplished mainly by running water, weathering, and mass wasting.

The uplifted landscape will first be dissected by stream erosion as the streams start to cut down toward the new base level. A number of deeply incised narrow valleys will be formed at first. Then, when the streams become graded, lateral erosion begins to become extremely important. A graded stream has already been defined as one that is delicately adjusted so that it has just the slope necessary to transport the debris supplied to it over a long period of time. When a graded condition is reached, most irregularities such as waterfalls and cascades will have been removed from the river channel. Likewise, at this time the landscape has become mature. The streams cut their channels lower very slowly after they become graded. The valley sides are then reduced by weathering, mass movements, particularly surface creep and wash, and lateral erosion by the streams. Gradually the valley sides are re-

duced to lower and lower slopes. The divides between drainage basins are likewise lowered until they are almost completely flattened. According to Davis, a lowland of faint relief remains at this time. This land form, which is the ultimate of the erosion cycle, is called a peneplain ("an almost plain"). The characteristics of each of the stages may be summarized:

YOUTH

1. As soon as the sea floor becomes exposed above sea level, rain falling on it runs off in sheet floods or rills. As the slopes on the surface become greater the rills come together to form larger streams. Streams flow downhill as a consequence of the slope. A few major

Fig. 20-9. Four stages in the evolution of a plateau according to the idealized fluvial cycle of Davis and Johnson. (After A. K. Lobeck, *Atlas of North American Geology.* By courtesy of Edwin Raisz.)

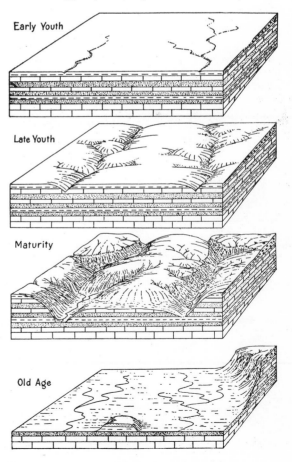

Fig. 20-10. The surface of the Colorado Plateau at the Grand Canyon. This high plateau surface is flat because the strata underlying it are horizontal. It has been dissected by the Colorado River, but there is not a well-developed drainage pattern. (Photo by E. W. Spencer.)

Fig. 20-11. Stream sculpture of horizontal sedimentary rock units. Note how poorly the drainage pattern is developed on the plateau surface. This is a recently elevated sea floor along the coast of Egypt. (Photo by courtesy of the U.S. Air Force.)

streams with dendritic (tree-like) drainage patterns develop. All of these streams have V-shaped cross profiles. Valleys are shallow near base level and deeper toward the higher elevations.

2. The V-shaped valleys have no flood plains or very narrow ones.
3. At first the major streams and their tributaries are widely spaced, leaving broad, nearly flat, and poorly drained uplands. The divides between streams are broad, and meandering streams may flow on these broad upland surfaces.
4. Along the streams there are waterfalls and rapids or cascades where local hard-rock units are exposed. These are especially numerous in the early stages of youth.

MATURITY

1. Maturity is reached when the streams become graded streams. Their courses will not be marred by waterfalls or rapids, which disappear as the state of equilibrium characteristic of graded streams is reached.
2. The valleys are broader, and there may be well-developed flood plains. The broad uplands of youth give way to sharper ridge-like divides between drainage basins. The drainage pattern becomes increasingly complex. If there are differences in the hardness of the exposed rock units the streams adjust their courses to follow the lines of least resistance.
3. With the disappearance of the broad upland tracts, most of the topography becomes either a part of the valley or the valley sides. Mass wasting gradually reduces these sides to lower slopes.
4. Most of the streams follow sinuous paths, and meandering streams are common.

OLD AGE

1. Most of the major streams are meandering streams flowing across broad, nearly flat flood plains characterized by natural levees, oxbow lakes, cutoffs.

2. The streams flow on very low gradients.
3. The divides between drainage basins are greatly reduced, and they are no longer sharp.
4. The adjustment of the drainage patterns to lithology disappears. There are few if any subsequent streams left.
5. All or a large part of the region lies very close to base level.
6. The ultimate form is a broad, nearly flat surface near base level called a peneplain.

Effect of interruptions in the cycle

At the beginning of this discussion we made three assumptions in treating the idealized cycle of evolution. One of these was that there would be no interruptions in the cycle. Interruptions do occur. It even seems probable that compound or multicyclic evolution is more common than single cycles. We can recognize such a change where the topography, which is generally characterized by features of old age or maturity, contains elements of the youthful landscape within it. This process by which the landscape begins to revert to youthful characteristics is called rejuvenation. It may occur in a number of ways:

1. Uplift: The old or mature topography may be uplifted as the crust is raised in relation to sea level.
2. Lowering of sea level: This changes the relative position of the base level just as effectively as lifting the land surface. The stream profile is steepened especially at the mouth of the streams, and a nick point moves up the stream as the channel is cut down toward the new level.
3. Change in hydraulic factors within the stream: If the load supplied to the stream decreases, or if the discharge (rainfall or stream volume) increases, the channel may be cut deeper.

Land forms resulting from rejuvenation. Two land forms in particular are characteristic of rejuvenated landscapes. These are entrenched

Fig. 20-12. A well-developed drainage pattern in loosely consolidated sedimentary rocks in China. This would represent a late stage of youth according to Johnson's fluvial cycle. (Photo by courtesy of the U.S. Air Force.)

Fig. 20-13. Scattered lakes and an intricate drainage pattern on a vast plain in Alaska. This extensive flat surface has most of the characteristics of a peneplain (a near plain); however, the most recent erosion here has been by ice sheets. (Photo by courtesy of the U.S. Air Force.)

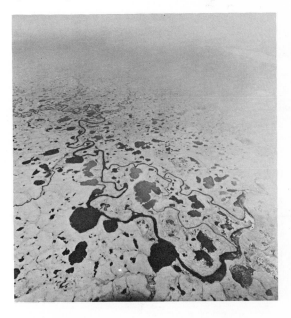

stream channels and river terraces. Many other forms may be found in rejuvenated landscapes. The features of youth may be superimposed on the forms of whatever stage the landscape had reached before rejuvenation. For example, you may see the features of a mature landscape with broad valleys and sharp divides in the uplands, but along the sides of the broad valleys there may be a sudden break in the slope and a distinct youthful V-shaped valley occupying the center of the older valley. Entrenched meandering streams are commonly found in the Appalachian Mountains. Here the streams follow broad meandering patterns, which in some places almost form cutoffs, but there are no flood plains. The valley sides rise steeply from the banks of one or both sides of the stream. It appears that these streams were once meandering on a broad flat flood plain like that of the Mississippi, and that this was interrupted by a regional uplift with consequent downcutting of the stream. This downcutting occurred so rapidly that the stream was unable to straighten out its path before it became en-

Fig. 20-14. Peneplain dissected by drainage channels. The divides throughout this area lie at about the same elevation. The strata are horizontal. Streams have dissected the vast plain, creating a complex drainage pattern. (Photo by courtesy of the U. S. Air Force.)

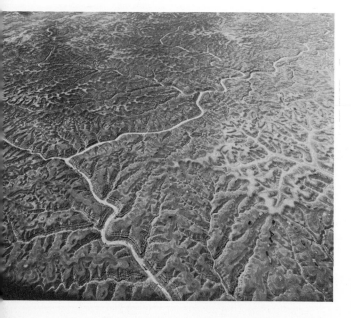

trenched. If a region is uplifted or if the sea level is lowered the gradient of the stream is steepest near the mouth of the rivers or where the flexure is greatest. A nick point forms as the stream cuts into the bottom of its channel at this point. Then this nick point migrates upstream until an adjustment has been made in the slope from the mouth to the head of the stream, and eventually to the head of all the tributaries.

Terraces. Profiles across many stream valleys show a number of flat level surfaces. These flat surfaces are stream terraces. They are formed by the lateral planation of the stream as it developed a flood plain and gradually migrated back and forth across that plain. The distribution of such terraces within a valley are illustrated in Fig. 20-17. In some cases there are an equal number of terraces on either side of the river, and these terraces may be paired off as they lie at the same level. In other instances the terraces cannot be paired. None of them lie at the same level. These two arrangements are interpreted as follows:

1. *Paired terraces.* The topmost terrace on either side of the river was the level of the original flood plain before rejuvenation began. That such a plain was formed is evidence that the landscape had reached maturity or old age. After the plain had developed, the region was rejuvenated; the stream in the valley cut down rapidly to a new position where it again reached a graded condition. The initial cutting was accompanied by the formation of a V-shaped valley. Then as a graded condition was approached the stream once again began to swing back and forth across its valley, cutting laterally in the older alluvial deposits. In this manner a second set of terraces may be formed within the older terraces which are partially (or completely) destroyed. The first uplift may be followed by a second and a third. Each of these may give rise to a new and lower plain and leave paired terraces as a remnant of the older flood plain.

2. *Unpaired terraces.* Where the terraces do not fall at the same level on opposite sides of the river we must conclude that they were not formed at the same time. This could easily happen if we have very slow rejuvenation of the area so that the stream continually cuts

Fig. 20-15. Complexly dissected region in the Big Bend National Park, Texas. The stream is the Rio Grande River. The plateau at left has been partially stripped of horizontal strata seen at far left. To the right of the prominent scarp in the center of the picture the dissection has been greatly accelerated. The Rio Grande is deeply entrenched in the plateau which is tilted in the background. The stream appears to have cut down as the plateau was uplifted and warped. Dissection has been more rapid and consequently more complete in the foreground to the right than it has been to the left or in the background. (Photo by courtesy of Jack Ammann Photogrammetric Engineers.)

Fig. 20-16. Santa Helena Canyon of the Rio Grande River. The river is covered by shadows in the bottom of the deeply cut canyon. The plateau is as yet relatively undissected. The plateau is still in a stage of "youth." (Photo by courtesy of Jack Ammann Photogrammetric Engineers.)

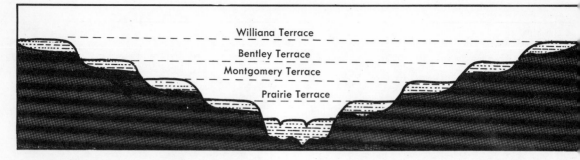

Fig. 20-17. Paired river terraces as seen in profile.

down, and remains at grade while lowering its channel. In effect, the stream does not stop and re-establish its lateral planation. Instead, while the stream occupies one side of its valley and cuts a flood plain laterally there, the other side is elevated relatively. Then the stream eroding laterally cuts back across the flood plain and cuts on that side while the other side rises in relation to the stream. The unpaired terraces are formed during periods of simultaneous lateral planation and rejuvenation. The paired terraces are formed by alternate rejuvenation and lateral planation.

Effects of deformed strata on the cycle; shifting divides

In the idealized cycle first described, we assumed that undeformed rocks were elevated from the sea floor. Let us now consider what happens if there is a sequence of folded and faulted sedimentary rocks of varying hardness buried beneath the flat-lying sediments. You will recognize that this relationship implies the

presence of an angular unconformity. This un conformity might have formed as a consequenc of a strong deformation of the crust followe by the development of an erosion surface whicl was then submerged where it might accumu late a layer of flat-lying sediment. If this seg ment of the crust is warped up by a broa uplift, rain water initially flows from it as consequence of the slopes of the land surface The cycle commences just as in the idealize case. Deep V-shaped valleys are cut into th uplifted area. The divides are broad and fla and drainage is poorly developed at first. Bu as the streams cut down into the sediment the begin to encounter the deformed rocks tha have very different hardnesses and resistance to erosion. The sediment veneer is soon strippe from the surface because this material is easil eroded and moved by the surface wash an sheet floods. The positions of the main strean channels become fixed if they have establishe channels in the consolidated rocks before th surface covering of sediment is removed. If thi has happened then they will cut their channel.

Fig. 20-18. Unpaired river terraces seen in profile. See text for discussion. (Modified after H. N. Fisk.)

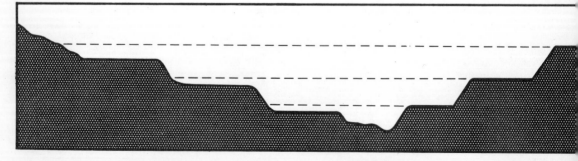

ig. 20-19. The Colorado Front Range. The structure of the strata along the margin of this range has een etched out by stream erosion, and the streams have become adjusted to the structure. In the distant ackground the mountain tops appear at about the same level indicating the presence of a widespread rosion surface. The land forms in the central part of the picture are called hogbacks. (Photo by T. S. overing, U.S. Geological Survey.)

ig. 20-20. High angle view of a relief map of the area around Harrisburg, Pennsylvania. Similar toography is found in the Appalachians from northern Pennsylvania southward into Alabama. The main ivers cut across the ridges through water gaps. These main streams flow toward the ocean. The tributaries are adjusted to the structure of the underlying rock. Note that the tops of the ridges are at about he same elevation. This erosion surface is thought to be a remnant of an extensive peneplain. South is at he top of the photograph. (Relief map copyright Aero Service Corp.)

Fig. 20-21. The law of unequal slopes governs the processes acting on this topography in Arabia. The cliff face is being eroded most rapidly on its steepest side, and drainage toward the northwest is being diverted to the east. (Photo by courtesy of the U.S. Air Force.)

across rocks of varying resistance. Thus they may flow across the structures of the deformed rocks.

The tributaries to the main streams tend to assume positions on the less resistant rocks, along fault zones or other lines of weakness. Weathering is most effective on the less resistant units exposed at the surface, and these are lowered much more rapidly than the harder units. Streams may become established in the weaker units regardless of their position on the structures. If weak units are exposed along the crest of an anticline, the crest will be lowered, and an anticlinal valley will be formed. Likewise, if the resistant units are exposed in the

center of a syncline, a synclinal mountain may form. In similar manner there may be synclinal valleys and anticlinal mountains etched out by weathering, mass movement, and running water.

Law of equal slopes. Further development depends largely on the slopes of the ridges and valleys and on the gradient of the stream. Where a resistant rock unit is exposed as a cuesta, or on the flanks of an anticline or syncline, there is generally a difference in the slope of the two sides of the ridge. In low-dipping strata the dip slope is gentle, while the scarp is steep. In such cases the steeper slope of a rock unit will be cut back more rapidly than the low slope. The divide between the drainage on the two sides of the ridge will shift in the direction of the lower slope. This is the law of unequal slopes. If the divide at the head of a particular stream shifts rapidly across the lower slope of the adjacent drainage basin, it may cause stream piracy.

Stream piracy. This is the process by which a stream diverts the drainage from trunk streams of one drainage basin into streams of another basin. Consider this simple case. There are two parallel valleys separated by a ridge composed of tilted rock strata. The channels of the main stream in each of these valleys are at the same level, or one is slightly lower than the other. Somewhere along the side of the valley a small tributary flows from the steeper side of the ridge into the lower valley. Because this face of the ridge is steeper it will as a whole be cut back more rapidly than the other side of the ridge. Where this tributary flows, debris can be removed, and this stream cuts headward into the ridge. The top of the ridge is breached, and a notch is thus made in the ridge. As this notch is worn lower and lower by the headward erosion of the stream, the divide shifts toward the center of the second valley. Eventually, through continued headward erosion and lowering of the stream channel, the head of this tributary of the lower valley intersects the main channel of the stream in the upper valley. Now the path of movement of water from the head of the stream in the upper valley shifts, flows through the gap, called a water gap, in the ridge and into the main trunk of the lower stream valley. The process of piracy

s complete. The tributary of the lower stream
s called the pirate stream. The stream it has
liverted or captured is said to be beheaded.

The process of stream piracy does not nec-
ssarily require that the slopes of the separating
idge be different. Essentially the same steps
will take place if the streams on the opposite
ides of the ridge have different gradients. The
tream flowing on the steeper gradient will
ower its channel more rapidly and will erode
leadward.

By the time the landscape has reached ma-
urity the stream drainage has become subsequent. That is, the streams have become ad-
usted to the structure and in large part follow
he paths of least resistance.

SYNTHESIS

The evolution of land forms in arid and
humid regions has been treated as entirely sepa-
ate developments and as though the two are
governed by different processes. The essential
differences, according to the Davis concept, beween the humid regions and the arid regions
are:

1. The cycle in humid regions progresses
   by continual lowering of the land slopes,
   while in the arid region reduction of
   landscapes is accomplished by the retreat of scarps or cliffs.
2. Hillsides and mountains in the humid
   climates become rounded, smooth, and
   convex upward, but angularity of form

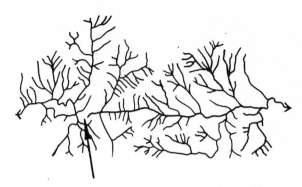

Fig. 20-22. Stream capture near Asheville, North Carolina. Note how the stream flowing eastward has captured the upper tributaries of the west-ward-flowing river.

characterizes desert land forms, and the
pediment is slightly concave upward.
3. The ultimate land form in the humid
   region is a nearly flat plain at or near
   base level. This plain is called a peneplain. In the arid climate the ultimate
   land form is a gently sloping plain worn
   down by scarp retreat. This is formed
   by the convergence of many pediments
   to form a pediplain.

In recent years a number of geologists
have stressed the idea that reduction of landscapes is not basically different in humid and
arid climates. The dominant processes in both
arid and humid climates are weathering and
the action of running water. The two types of
regions obviously differ in the amount of precipitation and in the extent of vegetative cover,
but it is difficult to believe that the nature of

Fig. 20-23. Slope retreat and slope reduction are the two ideas depicted here. They are discussed in the text. These are hypothetical profiles.

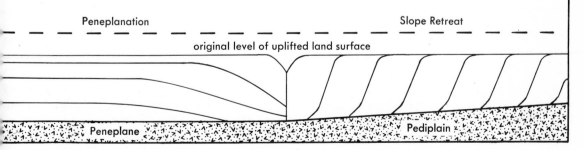

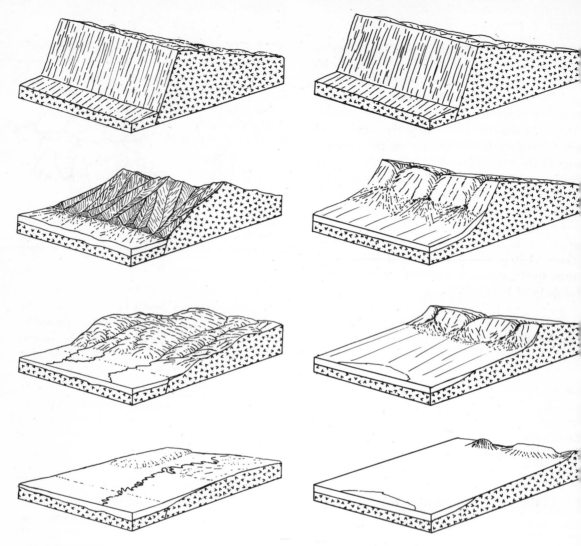

Fig. 20-24. Evolution of an uplifted block-faulted mountain according to the concept of slope reduction as visualized by Johnson. (After H. M. Davis.)

Fig. 20-25. This illustration depicts the evolution of an uplifted block-faulted mountain according to the concept of slope retreat.

hydraulic processes is dependent on climate. Therefore, since the same hydraulic and weathering processes are responsible for shaping the land in both types of regions, it seems reasonable to expect certain fundamental similarities in the forms developed.

Chauncey Holmes, Professor at the University of Missouri, summarizes the position of this school of thought:

Slopes are best classified into two fundamental types . . . : (1) wash slopes (graded surfaces of sediment transport), and (2) gravity or derivation slopes (surfaces which supply the sediment). In arid regions these two types occur in large-scale

units dominating the landscape as pediments of various dimensions, and prominent scarps and mountainsides. In humid regions vegetation impedes both erosion and rate of runoff, resulting in significant contrasts with arid-climate landscapes.

The contrast results because:

1. The pediment slopes in humid regions are controlled by the vegetative cover and by the amount of sediment being transported across them. Consequently they are steeper than the relatively bare slopes of the desert.

2. The humid climate has much greater

rainfall, and thus a much more complex and complete drainage network develops. It is more varied and intricate in pattern than the drainage network in the desert.

3. As the erosion cycle begins, rills, sheet runoff, and soil creep slowly lower the upland surface and round off the upper edges of the valley walls and scarps. This brings into existence the convex slopes which are so prominent in humid climates, but which also occur at the tops of the retreating scarps of the desert. In humid climates vegetation exercises some control on these scarps. Where vegetation is thick, the slope tends to be lower, but, where vegetation is lacking, an exposed cliff or bare rock is found. At the bottom of this scarp we find an accumulation of talus and debris washed down from the scarp face and from the top of the cliff.

This synthesis of the two concepts of landscape reduction in arid and humid climates is very appealing. It provides a unifying basis for understanding sequential development of land forms where fluvial processes are dominant. However, we must not accept an idea because it is simple or because it sounds theoretically correct. In geology every hypothesis must meet the test of observation in the field. We must ask if there is field evidence to support this theory. Although there has not yet been enough quantitative analysis of land forms to permit a conclusive answer, there is the following evidence to support this point of view:

1. Pediment-like slopes are found along the sides of many stream valleys in humid climates.
2. There is a striking resemblance between a large number of mountain profiles in arid and humid climates. These are especially numerous in the Appalachian highlands.
3. Pediplains, the ultimate land form created by scarp retreat, are well developed in many parts of the world. Peneplains, low surfaces of relief formed by

gradual reduction of slopes, are more difficult to prove. There are many nearly flat erosion surfaces in the Appalachians and in the Rocky Mountains, but criteria are lacking by which these surfaces can be definitely ascribed to peneplanation. Concerning these surfaces we find many points of view. Some believe all these surfaces are actual peneplains as described by Davis, others that all the surfaces are pediplains. Still others think the ultimate answer must lie somewhere in between, with scarp retreat and reduction of slopes both playing a part in the story. We can only conclude

Fig. 20-26. Stages in the erosion of a terrace in which solution is an important process in shaping the land forms. (Armin K. Lobeck, 1929, The geology and physiography of the Mammoth Cave National Park: *Kentucky Geological Survey,* ser. VI, v. 31, pt. 5, pp. 327-399.)

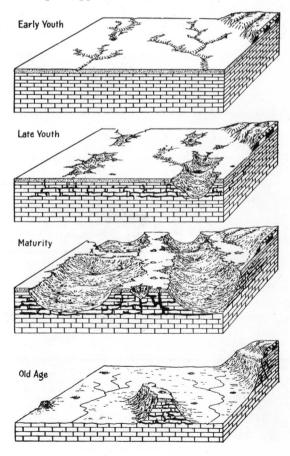

Early Youth

Late Youth

Maturity

Old Age

that further study, and particularly a more quantitative approach, is necessary to solve this problem.

KARST GEOMORPHIC CYCLE

Features due to erosion by ground water include sink holes, caverns, underground rivers, and other solution cavities. Subsurface movement of water may become the dominant process causing alteration of the landscape, but it is never the sole factor. Wherever there is enough water for the formation of caverns there will be surface drainage as well, and mass wasting invariably plays a part in degradation. Karst topography is most likely to develop in humid climates where limestone or other soluble rocks are exposed or are near the surface of the ground. How these become exposed is important in determining the initial forms. The Ocala limestone of the Florida pen-

Fig. 20-27. A high plateau surface dissected by valley glaciers. Note how large portions of the plateau surface are still intact. No horns and very few cols or arêtes are present. Compare this with the more complete dissected mountains in Fig. 20-28. (Photo by E. W. Spencer.)

Fig. 20-28. Mt. McKinley. Note the sharp rugged features which have been etched out as a result of glaciation. (Photo by courtesy of the U.S. Air Force.)

nsula is broadly exposed over a large region after its uplift from the sea floor, but in the karst topography around the Mammoth Cave in Kentucky a resistant sandstone unit covers the soluble limestone. This resistant cover must be at least partially removed before karst topography can develop. In such areas, where the units are flat or tilted, the limestone is first exposed along valleys. Then exposure spreads as the overlying units are eroded away.

The erosion cycle commences with surface drainage on a limestone that is above the base level of the region. In many of the karst regions the cycle appears to have started with uplift that initiated downcutting of the surface streams and finally caused them to become entrenched in their present courses. At first a large part of the precipitation runs off on the surface of the ground, and a small part infiltrates into the ground, bringing about solution along fractures, faults, bedding planes, and any other zones of weakness. Underground drainage passages begin to develop. At the same time slow percolation and solution result in solution

Fig. 20-29. Sharp ridges and cols cut into the Northern Rocky Mountains in Canada. With continued erosion these sharp ridges would be reduced in elevation. (Photo by courtesy of the Royal Canadian Air Force.)

sinks in the ground surface, called dolines. Where solution beneath the surface leaves sizable cavities, collapse or subsidence forms sink holes. There are few and isolated sink holes and dolines at first, but through the years more and more of these enclosed depressions characterize the landscape. Of course one of the important consequences of the formation of more sinks is that a larger and larger amount of the surface drainage is trapped before it reaches the main trunk streams. The small tributary streams gradually become less prominent as the water originally carried by them is diverted to underground passages. This water eventually finds its way to the main streams. But, because the water table ordinarily outcrops along the sides of the channels of these streams, open caverns cannot exist below the water table.

After the subsurface drainage becomes well developed there are many large and small caverns. Sink holes become so numerous that the sides begin to touch one another. Surface drainage becomes limited to short sinking creeks, those that disappear into the ground. Along some such streams you can see the vortexes where water swirls into small openings

leading into caverns. Such holes are cal[led] swallow holes for they swallow the rivers. [?] called blind valleys may form. These are v[al]leys that lead into a hillside or gradually l[ose] the characteristics of a valley as the water fr[om] their streams is lost to subsurface channels.

In time more and more sink holes for[m]. Subsurface drainage channels and solution ca[v]ities etch out more of the limestone. Collap[se] features begin to dominate the surface of t[he] ground. Karst windows form where collapse [of] the surface over an underground stream [ex]poses the channel. These karst windows grad[u]ally expand with the collapse of the margins [of] the window and mass wasting of the sid[es.] When the depression becomes large, exposi[ng] the stream or caverns over a large area, it [is] called a uvala. At this stage streams flow f[or] long distances through karst tunnels, and the[re] are natural bridges where the tunnels have p[ar]tially collapsed. Mass wasting gradually caus[es] the overhanging or steep cliffs, formed whe[re] collapse has occurred, to retreat back aw[ay] from the streams.

As the cycle nears its completion, draina[ge] returns to the surface of the ground. The tu[n]nels, natural bridges, sink holes, and dolin[es] disappear. All that remains are a few more [or] less isolated rounded hills of the limestone [in] which the caves initially formed. These hi[lls] may stand out above a relatively flat surfa[ce] into which the stream channels are cut. T[he] surface may be flat because it is at or near t[he] regional base level, or it may be that a very r[e]sistant insoluble unit is exposed beneath t[he] limestone. It should be emphasized that the[re] may be more limestone, even part of the sa[me] stratigraphic rock unit, below the level of th[e] surface on which the streams flow. In this ca[se] the further reduction has been stopped by t[he] position of the base level, and uplift would [be] necessary to start the cycle over again.

SEQUENCE OF LAND FORMS IN MOUNTAIN GLACIATION

As soon as the amount of snowfall in t[he] winter exceeds the amount of melting in t[he] summer, glaciers begin to form. Potentially the[se]

an reduce a high mountain range to nothing more than a mass of low hills. Of course a very important factor in the realization of this potential is that the foot of the mountain must have a climate that is cold enough to keep the snow and ice from melting. The word "potentially" is used because actually there appears to be no example in the world of a mountain system that has completely eroded away as a result of mountain glaciation. There is no way to tell even if such has been the case, but there is much evidence that mountains undergo sequential development of land forms resulting primarily from glaciation, and these are worthy of consideration.

As glaciation begins, snow fields form on the high mountain tops which are more often broad plateau-like surfaces than they are masses of rugged peaks. Stream valleys are almost invariably the sites of the tongue-like masses of snow and ice that make up the valley glaciers. After a considerable thickness of snow and ice has accumulated in the valleys the glacier begins to move downhill, carrying with it the stream alluvium and the talus piles from the sides of the valley. So the cycle begins with cleaning out of the debris from the stream valleys. Where the glacier pulls away from the snowfield near the head of the valley, a large crevasse forms. This site becomes subjected to increased erosion by glacial plucking, and the rocks beneath this crevasse, the bergschrund, are eroded rapidly. Soon the head of the valley has begun to develop a semicircular shallow bowl-like form at the head of the valley. This is the initiation of the glacial cirque. Down the valley the glacier is found to erode most rapidly on the inside of all the curves in the former stream valleys. This is accomplished by undercutting the sides of the valley. The long-term tendency is to straighten out the path of the valley and streamline it for the movement of the solid mass of ice. The nose-like projections between tributaries are called spurs. These spurs become truncated or cut off on both sides of the valley as the valley begins to assume a broad U shape. The spurs on the inside of curves are truncated more than those on the outside. There is less ice in the tributaries to the main glaciers so they are somewhat less

effective in accomplishing erosion and they do not cut down as deeply into the valley floors. This brings about the formation of hanging valleys.

Once the above pattern has become established, continued glaciation tends to bring about most rapid change in forms near the head of the glacier. The cirques become enlarged through time and may eventually become large amphitheater-shaped features a mile or more across and with walls that slope steeply down for several thousand feet. Plucking or quarrying of the cirque wall as the glacier moves away periodically makes the cirque walls retreat toward the drainage divide. Through this headward erosion the glaciers on either side of the divide eventually reduce the divide to a narrow sharp ridge, an arête. Similar ridges may develop along the top of divides between two essentially parallel glaciers. Where the glaciers are eroding headwardly they will cut into the ridge. If two glaciers are directly opposed

Fig. 20-30. This topography, like that in the last three figures, has been shaped by glaciation. We do not know how high these mountains may have been when glaciation started in the Pleistocene, but no remnant of the previous topography is left here. Sharp arêtes divided all of the major valleys. These may have been lowered considerably from their former heights. (Photo by courtesy of the U.S. Air Force.)

to one another the divide will be cut down as the two cirque walls continue to be lowered. This brings about the development of a pass or col in the ridge. The cycle continues as the ridge is slowly cut down by the headward erosion of the cirques. Finally the original divide is gone with the exception of a few high peaks. These are called horns. They too will eventually disappear, and the entire mountain range will have been reduced in level.

Glaciers will continue to move as long as the slope of the floor of the valley is sufficient for the available amount of ice to flow down it. And as long as this movement continues, more debris will be removed. The divides be-tween glaciers and between cirques will continue to be lowered by a combination of glaciation and mass wasting.

REFERENCES

COTTON, C. A., 1948, *Landscape as Developed by the Processes of Normal Erosion,* 2nd ed. New York, John Wiley & Sons, 509 p.

DAVIS, W. M., 1899, The Geographical Cycle: Geog. Jour., v. 14

KING, L. C., 1953, Canons of Landscape Evolution: Geol. Soc. America Bull., v. 64, p. 721-751

THORNBURY, W. D., 1954, *Principles of Geomorphology:* New York, John Wiley & Sons, 618 p.

21   Coasts

n July of 1958 an earthquake rocked the upper nd of Lituya Bay on the southern coast of laska. Rock falls and slides from the sides of he mountains on either side of the bay poured nto the water. Astonished fishermen in three oats near the mouth of the bay watched as a uge wave moved down the bay. Two of the oats were unanchored and were raised by the pproaching wave until the men could look lown on the 80-foot fir trees below before they vere dropped as the wave passed. Geologists ater examined the sides of the bay and discov- red that the wave crest was 100 feet high. The

wave had swept the sides of the bay, knocking down trees and washing away the soil.

Directly across the bay from one of the large slides there is a narrow inlet. Water moved into this inlet with such force that it washed 1700 feet up the side of the mountain. Trees were knocked down and washed into the forest at the top of the swash, and water con- tinued to run off the mountain side for several hours.

Only rarely are the effects of wave motion along the coasts so dramatic, but the constant impact of breaking waves along shore lines can drastically modify the landscape. Sea cliffs develop and are cut back, beaches are formed and destroyed, and thus the coasts are, like other elements of the earth's surface, undergoing constant change.

MOVEMENTS OF SURFACE WATERS OF THE OCEANS

The near-surface circulation of ocean water has long been of interest and importance to man. The study of ocean currents began soon after the first attempts at navigation on the seas, but the complexity of the movements of even the near-surface water of the oceans is such that there are still many unanswered questions.

Factors in surface-water movement

The illustration of important surface currents (Fig. 21-2) clearly indicates that the near-surface movements of oceanic currents do not have a simple explanation. Anyone who is familiar with the sea is well aware of the great variety of its moods. It is sometimes whipped into huge waves by storm winds, and at other times it is quiet and calm. Twice daily it responds to the gravitational pull of the moon as tides come and go. Many factors play important roles in the movements of the seas. The most important of these are:

1. The slope of the surface of the ocean.
2. The effects of wind blowing over the water.

Fig. 21-1. Vertical photograph of a portion of Nova Scotia. Prominent bedding shows up on the island which is partially surrounded by sand beaches. On the west side (left) of the island there is a tidal mud flat through which a stream flows. (Photo by courtesy of the Royal Canadian Air Force.)

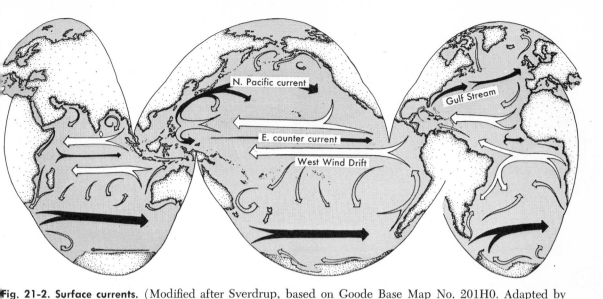

Fig. 21-2. Surface currents. (Modified after Sverdrup, based on Goode Base Map No. 201H0. Adapted by permission from *The Oceans: Their Physics, Chemistry, and General Biology,* by H. V. Sverdrup, Martin W. Johnson, and Richard H. Fleming. © 1942. Prentice-Hall, Inc. Reproduced by permission of the Department of Geography, from the Goode Base Map Series, copyright by the University of Chicago.)

3. Density variations within the water.
4. Coriolis force.
5. Gravitational attraction of the moon and sun.
6. The configuration of the ocean floor.

The slope of the surface of the ocean. At one time the currents of the oceans were attributed largely to the fact that the surface of the oceans of the world are not at exactly the same level. For example, the waters in the Gulf of Mexico are nearly 7 inches higher than the water of the Atlantic on the opposite side of the Florida peninsula. Some such differences appear to be relatively constant, while others are transient. There is much more rainfall in the equatorial regions than in the middle and higher latitudes. Thus water tends to pile up near the equator, elevating the surface. Where ocean currents drive water into bays or gulfs the surface tends to become elevated. The same effects are produced by the tidal currents, which pull water into embayments. In all these instances the level of the ocean is raised differentially, and surface movements are initiated which tend to restore the level. A perfectly level surface is not necessarily ever obtained. Instead, a balance is reached so that the rate of movement away from the elevated area is

approximately equal to the rate at which water is building up.

Effects of wind in contact with water. When a strong wind blows across a pond or lake we see waves set up on the surface, and a wave current in the direction of the wind is generated. These effects are often attributed to the frictional drag of the wind on the surface of the water. A very strong wind is required to start this motion if the wind is moving in laminar flow, but as we have already seen there is usually turbulence in the wind motion. The eddies, minor updrafts, and irregularities in the flow pattern of the air over the water surface initiate depressions and rises in the surface of the water. Once such motion is started, only a slight wind is needed to continue the action. If the wind is consistently from one direction then it exerts a more or less continuous pressure on one side of the wave form, tending to push it along. Then as the wind passes the crest of the wave it exerts a pull on the other side of the wave, a sort of suction. In this manner wave currents are established in the oceans where the wind directions are consistent. This is particularly important in the belts of the trade winds of the tropics and along the equator where the wind directions are predominantly from east to west. In the middle lati-

Fig. 21-3. Divers preparing for underwater current studies. Such studies are restricted to near-surface currents. (Photo by courtesy of the U.S. Coast and Geodetic Survey.)

tudes, on the other hand, the westerly winds set up a drift of the currents from west to east.

Density variations within the water. Variation in the density of sea water is one of the most important factors in the circulation of the deep seas. It is important to a lesser degree in determining surface movements. Density is highly variable in sea water.

1. Density varies with salt content (amount of dissolved solids in solution).
2. Density varies with temperature (cold water is more dense).

Such variations are the result of four factors: evaporation which concentrates salts, precipitation which tends to dilute the sea water, heating and cooling of the surface waters due to climatic conditions, and the inflow of waters from the continents. The effects of density are closely tied in with the Coriolis force.

Coriolis force. G. G. Coriolis, a French mathematician, demonstrated that any object in motion on a rotating sphere experiences a force that tends to pull it to the side. This force is such that objects in motion in the northern hemisphere are pulled to the right of their path, and those in the southern hemisphere are pulled to the left of their path. This

force, although small, affects all objects, including wind currents and water currents that move across the face of the earth. In most cases the force is so small that it has little effect, but in the case of wind and water movements the other forces acting on them are so small that the Coriolis effect is influential. It is at a minimum along the equator where the ocean currents follow most closely the wind direction and it increases toward the poles. The effects are such that surface motion in the northern hemisphere is generally along a path at 45° to the right of prevailing wind directions in the open sea.

The Coriolis force also makes it possible to predict that more dense water will lie to the right of the prevailing current direction in the northern hemisphere and to the left of the prevailing current direction in the southern hemisphere. Thus, when a body of water of increased density rises to the surface from depth, or develops from increased evaporation, it will tend to be deflected to the right of the path of movement in the northern hemisphere and to the left in the southern hemisphere.

Gravitational attraction of the moon and sun. The waters of the oceans experience a gravitational pull toward the moon and the sun. Twice during each lunar month the sun and moon are situated along a direct line from the earth. At these times the force exerted along a single line on the earth reaches a maximum. The water on the side of the earth facing these bodies bulges out toward them. The greatest elevation is at the point closest to the moon. A somewhat lower bulge is produced on the opposite side of the earth. As the earth rotates, these bulges move around the earth giving rise to the familiar tides twice daily. The influence of the moon is about double that of the sun in spite of the vast difference in their masses, because the moon is much closer to the earth, and the force of gravitational attraction varies inversely with the square of the distance.

$$F = k \frac{m_1 m_2}{d^2}$$

Configuration of the ocean floor. The shape of the ocean bottom and the coast of the continents provides a framework within which the other factors can operate. Surface movements are confined within this framework and deflected by its form. For this reason the surface movements within the southern hemisphere, which has very little land area in it, are much simpler than those in the northern hemisphere, which is irregularily broken up by odd-shaped continental masses which make up four-fifths of all the land on the earth.

In the southern hemisphere the west-wind drift causes the prevailing surface currents to follow a simple circular pattern flowing from west to east. The only obstacle is that formed between the tip end of South America and Antarctica where the currents are constricted. In the northern hemisphere the equatorial currents follow the equatorial drift from east to west, but they are broken up in the Atlantic where the currents are deflected north and south by the eastward protrusion of South America.

Ocean currents

The very complicated details of the movement of surface water in the oceans of the world can be reduced to a relatively simple picture. Surface currents flow from west to east in what is called the west-wind drift in the middle latitudes of both the northern and southern hemispheres in all oceans. Along the equator the currents flow from east to west in the equatorial drift of the Atlantic, Pacific, and Indian Oceans. Between the prevailing westerly drifts and the equatorial drift, currents are deflected to the right in the northern hemisphere and to the left in the southern hemisphere. Where islands or irregular coast lines intersect these currents they are deflected both right and left in streamlined patterns around the land.

In the northern Atlantic the northern equatorial current flows from east to west across the Atlantic. It strikes the northern coast of South America and is deflected to the north (also to the right in this case) where it flows through the Caribbean and into the Gulf. In the Gulf of Mexico the warm water is backed up and augmented by flow from the Mississippi River. Here the well-known Gulf Stream emerges from the Gulf through the strait between Florida and Cuba, where it flows at the rate of almost 3 miles per hour. This segment, known as the Florida Current, flows northward along the coast of the Southern States, where it is

Fig. 21-4. Density flows. These flows of water containing a high amount of dissolved salts pour out of the strait between the Rock of Gibraltar and the North African coast. The water in the Mediterranean has a high concentration of salts because of the rapid rate of evaporation. The sketch at right shows a decrease in salinity of ocean water away from the strait. At the left a cross section through the strait shows dense water from the Mediterranean flowing over the sill separating it from the Atlantic and down the continental shelf into the ocean basin. At the surface in the strait ocean waters of normal salinity flow into the Mediterranean. (After G. Schott, 1942.)

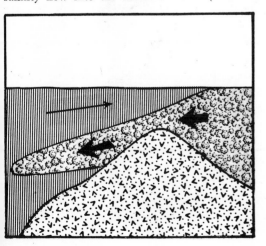
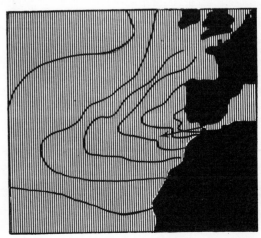

joined by currents that are deflected to the northern side of the Caribbean Islands. This stream of warm equatorial water moves northward as a body as much as 50 miles wide and well over 1000 feet deep. It follows a meandering course at times and is occasionally broken up into several threads flowing in a braid-like pattern. At about the latitude of Washington, D.C., the stream diverges more from the coast and flows eastward as the North Atlantic Current almost all the way across the Atlantic. It is broken up by the irregularities off the western coast of Europe and splits into two parts. One part moves southward to the right back toward the equator; the other component moves northward along the coast of Norway.

The second important current along the eastern coast of North America is the Labrador Current, which flows southward from the Arctic Ocean between Greenland and Labrador. It mixes with the Gulf Stream south of Newfoundland and is largely broken up there.

Along the western coast of North America the principal current is the North Pacific Current, which flows from the west to the east and impinges on the coast at Washington. Here it is

partially deflected northward to form the Alaska Current along the western coast of Canada and the southern Alaskan coast. The other component is deflected to the right and to the south as the California Current. This water moves southward and rejoins the equatorial drift.

Tides

Along the Hangchow River in China a wave 16 feet high rushes up the river at the rate of as much as 16 miles an hour once each day. It is easy to imagine the damage that such a wave could inflict. It is called a tidal bore and is driven by the surge of water from the oceans into the river as the ocean waters are pulled along following the path of the moon and sun. Tidal bores of this sort are not uncommon, although few reach these dimensions or rates. Tidal effects are most notable where the shore lines are of such shape that water from a large area is forced to converge in a confined section of the coast. Thus water is piled up as the tidal current moves in toward the shore. In some places the amounts of water

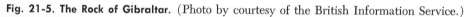

Fig. 21-5. The Rock of Gibraltar. (Photo by courtesy of the British Information Service.)

mporarily confined in this manner are great.

the Bay of Fundy, between New Brunswick
d Nova Scotia, the difference between high
d low tides reaches as much as 70 feet, and
e rate of movement of the water both as it
mes in and as it flows out reaches 8 to 12
iles per hour. Velocities of this magnitude
e capable of moving any of the granular sedi-
ents likely to be found on the continental
elves. Where the range between high and
w tide is great, the outgoing tidal currents
e undoubtedly responsible for much erosion
the sea bottom.

The force of tidal attraction on the hydro-
here is not confined to the surface of the
eans. Water at all depths experiences the
ll, and it is likely that deep tidal currents
sult. It is unlikely that these are responsible
r much submarine erosion. The principal
fects of these currents might be found where
e deep waters off the continental slopes are
illed landward onto the continental shelf.
hus they would be effective at the outer edges
the shelves and may be responsible for the
ifting and grading of the sediments on the
a floor near the margins of the shelves. The
coming tidal currents would bring with them
ry little or no sediment at all, but as they
versed direction they could carry away the
ier sediments. This may very well explain
hy we so often find that the sediments at the
iter edge of the continental shelf are some-
hat coarser than those closer to the coast.

AVES

Most of the alteration of the shore or sea-
ape by marine agencies is accomplished by
aves and the currents set up by their motion.
ost ocean waves are elongate humps sep-
ated by irregular troughs. The wave motion is
arted by surface-pressure variations and fric-
onal drag on the water surface by turbulence
the air. Once the motion is started, the
aves are propagated in the direction of the
evailing wind. They become aligned approxi-
ately perpendicular to the wind direction and
parallel rows if the wind is continuously
om the same general direction. Where the air

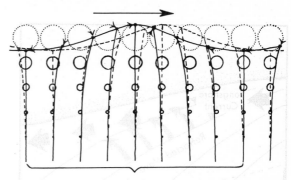

**Fig. 21-6. Theoretical wave form seen in cross sec-
tion.** The movement of water beneath the wave
surface dies out at a depth equal to about one
third of the wave length. Particles of water in the
wave move in slightly elliptical paths.

is very turbulent the waves are short and
choppy. They may change their direction of
motion or die out altogether. A model of a
theoretically perfect wave is illustrated. This
model is approximated very closely in nature
by a large majority of the waves moving toward the coasts except that they are not necessarily continuous over a long distance. The profile of the wave is a sinuous curved surface.
The top of the wave form is called the crest,
the depression between two crests is the
trough. The distance between two crests or two
troughs is called the wave length. The vertical
distance between the top of a crest and the
bottom of a trough is the wave height. The
time required for a crest to progress one wave
length is called the period of the wave motion.

If you have ever watched a cork bob up
and down on a water surface you know the
nature of the movement of the water in a wave.
The water does not move along with the wave
form. If it did the seas would be impassable to

Fig. 21-7. Profile of waves approaching shore. As
the wave approaches shore the height of the waves
increases until breakers form. Then the water is
thrown forward onto the shore.

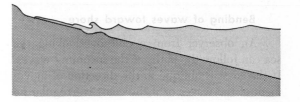

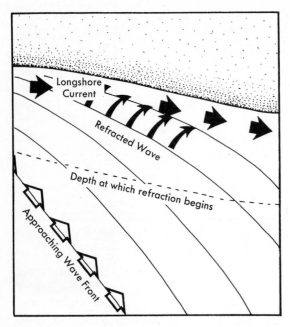

Fig. 21-8. Refraction of incoming wave fronts. The refracted waves do not come in perpendicular to the shore line. For this reason a component of movement is set up along the shore. The long-shore current is indicated by the heavy black arrows.

most surface vessels. Instead the water travels in a nearly circular path. At the crest of a wave the motion is directed in the direction of the wave's movement, but in the trough the motion is in the opposite direction. At depth the motion is also almost circular, but the size of the orbits decreases with depth until at a depth equal to about half of the wave length the motion is negligible. Below this depth the effects of the wave movements are not felt in the water or on the bottom. A submarine submerged to this depth may experience no movement due to even violent storm waves on the surface. However, the wave length of some swells and storm waves is very great—several thousand feet—and these can be felt on the bottom at depths of more than 1000 feet.

Bending of waves toward shore

An observer from a cliff overlooking the sea can follow the paths of the incoming waves. If the coast is oblique to the direction of movement of the waves or if the coast is irregular he

will see the waves bend as they approach tl shore. They are bent so that they tend to a] proach the shore straight on, perpendicular the shore line. If we could watch a long wav strike a beach obliquely we would notice th as one end of the wave approaches the shore becomes slowed down, appearing to wait fe the rest of the wave to swing into a position the same distance from the shore before mo ing in. What actually happens is that the wav is slowed down in the shallow water whe there is interference with the movement of su surface water involved in the wave motio That part of the wave which is moving deeper water continues to travel at its origin rate until it too is in shallow water.

This bending or refraction of the waves they come obliquely into shallow water is e tremely important. Because they are not con pletely bent in perpendicular to the sho there is a component of motion in the wat directed down the shore line. This establish the longshore current. It is important in tran porting sand and silt along the shore. The r fraction is also of importance in that it focus

Fig. 21-9. Refraction of incoming waves along rugged shore. Contours of the sea floor are draw in by dashed lines. The energy possessed by tl wave at the position first shown is equally di tributed along the wave, but as the wave front bent the energy is spread over areas of varyin sizes. Thus a much larger portion of the wave energy is dissipated on the headlands than alor an equal distance of bay shore.

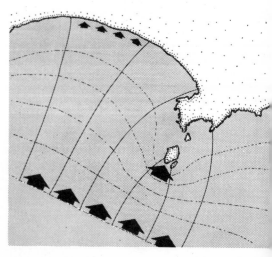

g. 21-10. Breaking wave. The water in the foreground is returning to the ocean under the breaking ave as an undertow. Such an undertow does not ordinarily create a strong current. (Photo by E. W. pencer.)

he energy of the waves on parts of the shore nat protrude into the ocean, the headlands, nore than on the bays or recessed parts of the hore. How this is accomplished is shown in ig. 21-9. The energy of the wave is evenly istributed along the wave front while it is out t sea, but as it comes into the shore and is efracted that part of the wave's energy that nters a bay is spread out and distributed over long shore line. That part of the wave's nergy which is directed against the headlands concentrated along a short portion of the hore. For this reason the headlands become roded back by wave action much more rapidly han does the shore line as a whole.

Breakers

As the wave enters increasingly shallow vater the subsurface movement begins to be nhibited by the sea bottom. The wave form is estricted to a body of shallower water, and as result the wave form becomes deformed. The vave height increases, and the velocity of the vave decreases. This change takes place rapid- y and at a specific depth for waves of par- icular characteristics. The velocity of the top art of the wave begins to exceed the forward velocity of the wave motion as a whole, and for his reason the top part of the wave outruns

the rest of the wave and spills over in front of it, forming the breaker. Once the wave begins to break, the water spills forward. The wave form is lost, and the water is thrown, often with great force, onto the shore as a rushing

Fig. 21-11. Wave movement. After the water from an incoming wave is thrown on the beach it be- gins its return to the ocean directly down the slope of the beach as indicated by the parallel lineations. (Photo by E. W. Spencer.)

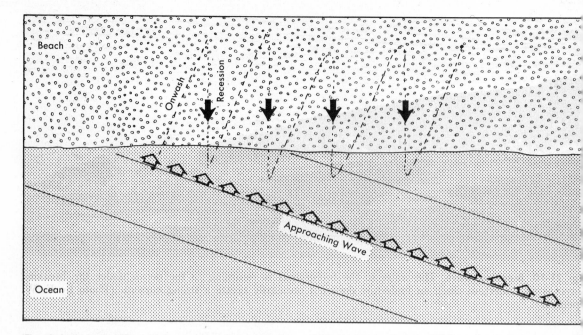

Beach

Onwash

Recession

Approaching Wave

Ocean

Fig. 21-12. Path followed by sand grains which have drifted along a beach. With each incoming wave th grain is moved obliquely across and up the beach. It then rolls and is washed back down the beach a water returns to the ocean.

turbulent mass. Where the waves break there is a great deal of movement of the sediments on the sea bottom. Out beyond the zone of breakers there is little more than a slight shifting of sediment back and forth by the wave movement, but within the zone of breakers sediment is churned up into the water. A slight depression or trough may form along this zone. The sediment removed from the depression is piled up on the landward side to build a bar and eventually an offshore beach in some instances.

Rip currents

Once a wave breaks, the water in it rushes onto the beach, stops, and then reverses its direction and begins its return to the ocean. That the water from a dissipated wave slips under the incoming wave and goes back out to sea as an undertow is a popular misconception. Recent studies have revealed that the undertow is neither common nor is it responsible for large-scale movement of water. Instead, the water from a wave finds its way back to the sea by moving along close to the shore and al-

most parallel to the shore line as part of th longshore current until it reaches a currer moving rapidly out to sea. These are called ri currents (also rip tide or "sea puss"). The ri currents are probably responsible for most c the drownings attributed to undertow. The ri current is a rapid movement certainly capabl of knocking the unsuspecting wader off his fee Rip currents are usually more or less confine to channels running perpendicular to the shor So the best way to escape one is to swim par allel to the shore across and out of the curren rather than to try to swim directly back t shore against it. A rip current is fed almost con tinuously as each successive wave breaks, pil ing up more water along the shore.

TRANSPORTATION

Deep sea

The most important aspect of the surfac currents moving across the deep seas is tha they are too weak to transport sediment ver far out to sea. Even in the rather extreme cas of the Gulf Stream, which flows in places witl velocity of 1 or 2 miles per hour, only very small particles can be carried in suspension. The other oceanic currents are much too weak to move even the smallest sands and silts out far. Only clays may be carried in ocean currents, and most of these sink to the bottom soon after they enter salty sea waters. Most of the load in the currents beyond the continental shelves is composed of floating and free-swimming marine plants and animals, and these are microscopic in size. In spite of their size individually they make up a very large percentage of the marine sediments on the deep sea floors.

Shallow sea

Incoming waves are capable of moving sediment as soon as the depth of water is about half the length of the waves, but until the waves begin to break this does not account for much erosion. Sediments are sorted by this agitation and shifting. Long-period sea swells can affect the bottom at depths of hundreds of feet in this manner.

Most movement of sediment is accomplished by the breaking waves and the longshore currents set up by these waves as they are refracted. Even after refraction the incoming waves hit the shore at a slight angle. Let us trace the path of a pebble in succeeding waves. Because the wave hits the shore at an angle, the water is thrown on the beach obliquely. A pebble or grain of sand is rolled or tossed along in the water up on the beach. When the water returns to the sea it initially moves directly down the slope of the beach, which is usually perpendicular to the shore at that point. The pebble is carried down with the water. When the next wave comes in obliquely the pebble is again moved up on the beach obliquely. Thus with each new wave there is a general tendency to move the sediment along the beach.

The water from the waves is capable of moving the finer sizes of sediment in suspension, and they may be carried into the longshore current until the current velocity diminishes. This usually leaves the beaches bare of the smaller sizes of sand and silt.

Fig. 21-13. Rocky shore along the California coast. When large waves break along such a shore, water is thrust into the fractures and wedges them loose. The loose fragments may be hurled against the shore—this is an unusually effective type of erosion. (Photo by E. W. Spencer.)

MECHANICS OF EROSION

The destructive power of waves is impressed on us every year as we read in the newspapers about the destruction of boats, buildings, and property along the coasts during storms. The coasts themselves are undergoing an almost constant attack by waves. Frequently small volcanoes rise from the sea and build up cones as much as several hundred feet high, but, when the activity dies down or ceases, the cone disappears sometimes almost overnight under the erosive power of waves.

The erosion by waves is accomplished mainly through two processes:

1. The impact of sediment picked up by the water as the wave breaks and is thrown against the shore, and
2. The force of the water itself as it is thrown forward in the breaking waves.

Where erosion is active, waves are able to break down even the most solid rocks. Armed with the sand, pebbles, or even blocks that form rocky shores, the waves rapidly break down loosely consolidated rocks exposed along the shore. Weak rock units are broken, sometimes undermining the more resistant units, but the impact of large boulders that may be moved or even thrown by large waves is capable of breaking up the most resistant granites and massive sedimentary rock units.

Erosion is most rapid when there is a supply of "tools" for the water to use in cutting into the land, but the force of the water alone is enough to be effective in dislodging fractured blocks. Water is forced into the fractures and becomes highly compressed by the thrust of the water behind it. The amount of this pressure is greater than is generally recognized. A moderate-sized wave 5 to 10 feet high can exert pressures from 1000 to 2000 pounds per square foot against the rocks exposed where it breaks. This is enough to extend or enlarge pre-existing fractures and to dislodge any loose blocks.

There is some solution by the sea water but this is of relatively minor importance even where rocks such as soluble limestones are exposed along the coasts.

Fig. 21-14. Bay of Islands, Australia. The sea stacks are remnants of the cliff-forming rock units at the right. At the time this picture was taken a sand beach was present at the base of the cliff. During storms the sand may be quickly removed and the cliff may then be eroded more actively. The cliff will retreat through time under the attack from wave erosion, leaving a wave-cut terrace. (Photo by courtesy of the U.S. Air Force.)

Fig. 21-15. Uplifted coral terraces. Unlike the wave-cut terraces, these were formed by the growth of reefs to a position just below sea level. Like uplifted wave-cut terraces, these indicate a relative elevation of the land with respect to the sea. (Photo by courtesy of the U.S. Air Force.)

FEATURES FORMED BY MARINE EROSION

Erosion is the dominant process along the coast of New England and the western United States. In these areas wave action is gradually gnawing away at the land, reducing it to the level of the seas. The rate is not always slow. On the south shore of Nantucket Island the shore retreats as much as 5 or 6 feet per year. Along the west coast in California and along the Chalk Cliffs of Dover in England, wave action has undercut the sea cliffs bringing about large landslides and slumps, the products of which are broken up and graded by further wave action.

Cliffs and terraces

Wave-cut cliffs and terraces are two forms usually found where erosion is the dominant shore process. Almost all sea cliffs are steep, and, although not all are high, many are as much as several hundred feet high. At the foot of the cliff there is usually a sudden break in slope. The sea floor is nearly flat or gently sloping seaward. This platform or terrace is generally covered by the rocks that have been dislodged from the cliff. It is this material that is used as tools for further undercutting of the cliff. The rocks are hurled against the cliff repeatedly. Sand can always be moved by the incoming waves, and in moderate waves cobbles and pebbles can be picked up and hurled. In times of storm even the largest boulders may be smashed against the base of the cliff. The effect of the breaking waves is negligible below the surface of the water, so the cliff stops abruptly just below the level of the water. As we would expect, the width of the wave-cut terrace is limited by the fact that the water is shallow.

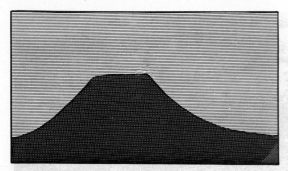

Fig. 21-16. Profile of a guyot. The vertical dimension has been greatly exaggerated.

As the terrace becomes wider, more and more of the wave energy is dissipated before the wave reaches the base of the cliff, so its ability to erode the cliff is reduced. Of course, if sea level is rising even slightly in relation to the land over a long period of time, then the terrace will become very wide because the part of the terrace formed early is increasingly submerged below the level of the wave action. With submergence the water depth near shore is maintained, so waves break near shore.

Guyots

Guyots are flat-topped seamounts foun[d] mainly in the Pacific Ocean. A large number o[f] them have been discovered, and most ar[e] covered by considerable depths of water, be[-] tween 3000 and 6000 feet. The most logical ex[-] planation for these features is that they are sub[-] merged volcanoes, which were truncated b[y] wave action to form a wave-cut terrace. Th[e] puzzling fact about them is the great depth t[o] which they are submerged. Sea level was un[-] doubtedly lower during the great ice ages o[f] the past million years, but it is unlikely that i[t] would be lowered as much as 3000 feet. Th[e] other explanation is that there have been fluc[-] tuations in the level of the bottom of the ocean[.] Perhaps a combination of arching and change[s] of sea level is responsible for these remarkabl[e] features.

Stacks, arches, sea caves, notches

As a sea cliff is eroded back, through th[e] years some irregularities in the coast develop[.]

Fig. 21-17. Sea arch formed by wave erosion along the west coast. Note the smooth surface above th[e] cave. This is a remnant of an elevated sea terrace. (Photo by E. W. Spencer.)

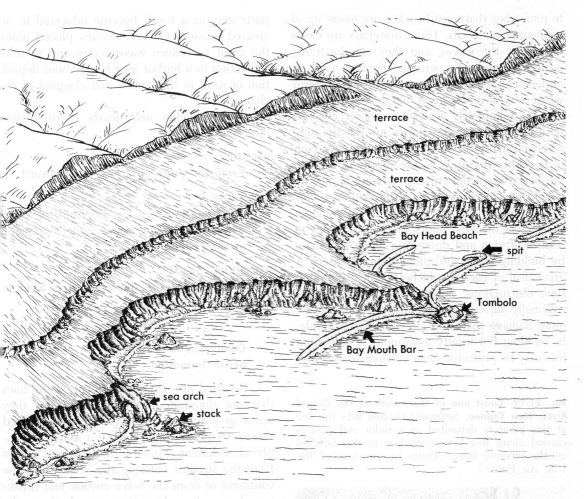

Labels on figure: terrace, terrace, Bay Head Beach, spit, Tombolo, Bay Mouth Bar, sea arch, stack

Fig. 21-18. Characteristic physiographic features found along a rugged coast.

These may be due to differences in the concentration of wave energy or simply to differences in the hardness of the rock, or to the structures in the units. Retreat of the cliff may leave some columnar masses of rock standing isolated as islands just off the shore. Because these frequently resemble smoke stacks sticking out of the water they are called stacks, although they are not necessarily small or round. Sea caves and arches are likely to develop when the rocks exposed in the cliff are stratified sediments of varying hardness. The weaker units are undercut rapidly, sometimes leaving the resistant capping layers as a natural bridge or arch over them. Such features, like the stacks, are transient. They will disappear and perhaps be replaced by similar features farther

inland at a later date. If the cliff is composed of some massive resistant rock type, the wave action may produce a notch near the base. Such features are the initial stages of undercutting, which will eventually lead to a mass movement as the cliff breaks away above the notch and falls into the sea.

MARINE DEPOSITS

Beaches

Beaches are transient features. The sandy beach which appears so permanent in the summertime may be reduced to a very narrow strip of coarse pebbles in the winter. It is important to remember that most beaches are made up of sand-sized materials. These materials are easily moved by the waves, and they can be transported in moderate currents. So it is easy to understand what can happen during a storm when waves reach great heights. The beach may be completely washed away or covered with coarse debris. But storms are not the only mechanism for the movement and destruction of beaches. Any upset in the supply of sand to the beach or in the currents moving along the beach may cause it to be built farther out or washed away. We are well aware of some of the factors involved and sometimes attempt to control erosion and deposition along the shore by building jetties and piers or breakwaters. A great deal of care should be taken in planning such obstructions, however, because they occasionally introduce side effects which cause more damage than they prevent. For example, in building out a jetty a segment of the shore line may be protected from erosion, while other parts may as a result become subjected to increased erosion. Or breakwaters placed along the coast to reduce wave action and to offer protection to a harbor may bring about deposition of sand in the harbor and clogging of the channels.

Most beaches are clearly divisible into three parts:

OFFSHORE
From the position of low tide seaward.

FORESHORE
The zone between low tide and the point where the beach becomes either horizontal or slopes landward.

BACKSHORE (BERM)
That part of the shore which is level or sloping landward.

Conditions favorable for beach formation

Beaches are characteristic of shore lines that are dominated by deposition, but they occur as patches along even the most rugged shores. Of prime importance is a source of supply of sediment. Most of the sediment comes from the streams entering the ocean from the continent or from the wave erosion and breaking down of rock units exposed along the shore. During storms some sediment from the sea floor may be brought in from deeper waters offshore, but ordinarily the movement of this material is minor. Locally the sediment may come from volcanoes, melting glaciers, or deposition by the wind.

A second condition that must be satisfied for the shore line as a whole or for small parts of it if beaches are to persist is that the rate of supply of sediment to the shore line must exceed the rate at which it is being removed either by storm waves or by longshore currents. If there is a great abundance of sediment, then the shore line may have a beach which extends for hundreds or even thousands of miles. If the amount of sediment available for transport and deposition is limited or if there is a high rate of transport, then beaches will develop only along protected stretches of the shore.

Fig. 21-19. Coast line at the mouth of the Golgal River, New Guinea. Sediment carried into the sea at this point is deposited as a delta and part is carried along this low shore line to the beaches on the offshore bars. (Photo by courtesy of the U.S. Air Force.)

Fig. 21-20. Australian coast line. This is a shore line of deposition. Note the spits, both modern and old, the marshes in which the river flows, the modern sand beaches, and the older beaches. The light color in the ocean water is caused by reflection of light from a shallow sandy sea bottom. (Photo by courtesy of the U.S. Air Force.)

Fig. 21-21. Vertical photograph of a rugged coast line at Cape Puget, Alaska. Stacks stand in the water off the headland. Beaches appear along the smoother portions of the shore. The white zones in the water are caused by breaking waves. (Photo by courtesy of the U.S. Air Force.)

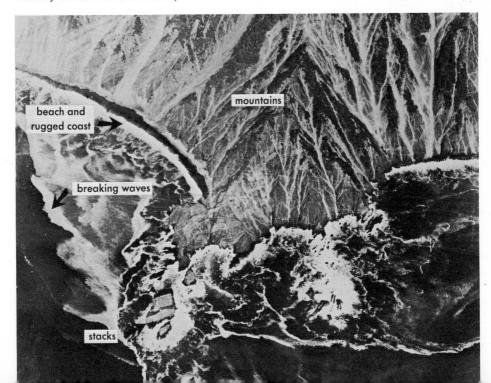

Fig. 21-22. Smooth, low coast line. Note the rhombohedral pattern of the waves, breakers at the shore, and the lunar-shaped sand dunes on the coast. This photo was taken in China. A river in the upper right corner may be the source of much of the sand being deposited along this shore. (Photo by courtesy of the U.S. Air Force.)

Fig. 21-23. Characteristic features found along low coast lines.

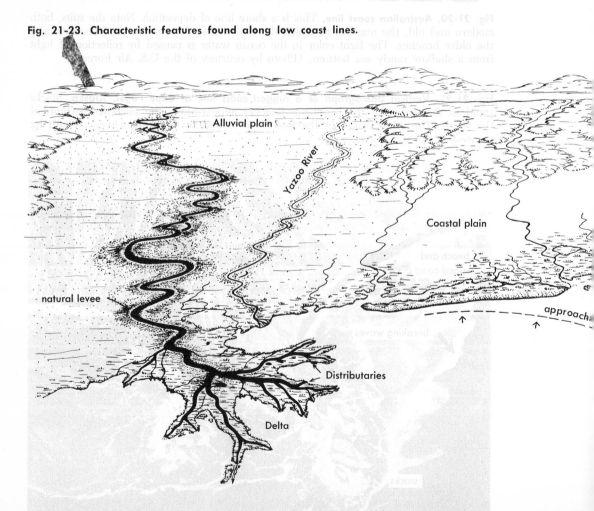

Along irregular coast lines the most common site for a beach is at the head of the bays or inlets. Here the beach is protected from wave action and at least partially from the longshore current. Headlands projecting out on either side of the bay prevent the rapid removal of beach materials by beach drifting and the longshore current. Protection from wave action in the bays comes from the fact that the wave energy is spread out over a long stretch of beach due to wave refraction along the sides of the bay. The headlands are the sites of most intense wave erosion, but when the supply of sediment is excessive beaches may develop even at the foot of the headland sea cliffs. These beaches are very likely to be destroyed during storms, and they will show the very marked influence of changes in the supply of sand. Beach sands from headland beaches will drift in the direction of the longshore current, and these sand beaches may even be built out across the mouth of the bay. At first a submerged bar is built out from the tip of the

headland beach. With the addition of more sand this may emerge and may form a projection out from the land mass into the bay. Such a feature is called a spit. The end of the spit is generally curved back into the bay, but with sufficient sediment supply it may continue to be built out even completely across the bay to form a bay-mouth beach. Such beaches are not likely to cross large bodies of water because rivers empty into most of them, and this water must find an outlet into the sea. The outlet may be no more than a narrow channel, however.

Tombolos are bars or beaches of sediment built between islands and the main land mass. The islands are usually small patches of land left as a result of wave erosion like sea stacks. When the rate of wave erosion is reduced or when the supply of sand is increased, this small strait between the island and the land interferes with the longshore drift of sand, and the strait becomes silted in. As more sand is brought into the zone the submerged bar rises above sea level. It is built up more during high

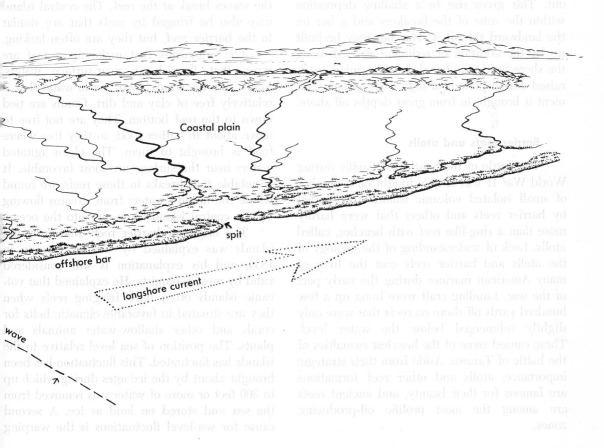

Coastal plain

spit

offshore bar

longshore current

wave

tides and then even more during periods of higher waves, provided they are not so high that they destroy it.

Offshore bars and beaches

Along most of the coast of the southeastern United States from New Jersey to Florida and in the Gulf Coast there are long bars and beaches that have been built up off the shore. There is generally a lagoon separating the offshore beach from the mainland, and occasional breaks through the bars or beaches where streams enter the ocean or gulf. Along coasts which have offshore beaches there is generally a submerged offshore bar beyond the beach. Where waves break, the water is extremely turbulent. The breaker is full of sand picked up from the bottom. This sand is rapidly dropped out as soon as the turbulence dies down. Since the initial direction of movement after the breaker forms is toward the shore, most of the sand moves in that direction before it settles out. This gives rise to a shallow depression within the zone of the breakers and a bar on the landward side of it. This bar may be built up by the addition of sediment carried along the shore inside the bar. Like the tombolo, it is raised during periods of high waves when sediment is brought in from great depths off shore.

Barrier reefs and atolls

The battle of the Southwest Pacific during World War II was largely fought on a number of small isolated volcanic islands surrounded by barrier reefs and others that were hardly more than a ring-like reef with beaches, called atolls. Lack of understanding of the geology of the atolls and barrier reefs cost the lives of many American marines during the early part of the war. Landing craft were hung up a few hundred yards off shore on reefs that were only slightly submerged below the water level. These caused some of the heaviest casualties of the battle of Tarawa. Aside from their strategic importance, atolls and other reef formations are famous for their beauty, and ancient reefs are among the most prolific oil-producing zones.

Although reefs are often called coral reefs they are in fact usually composed of the remains of many types of organisms. Corals may not even make up the largest part of the reef. Many of the reefs have as many bryozoans, marine bivalves, and plants in them as they have corals.

Barrier reefs

These reefs tend to encircle the island or island groups of volcanoes with which they are associated. They vary in width and distance off shore, but many are 100 yards or more wide and are separted by a lagoon that may be several miles away from the central island. On the oceanward side of the reef, debris broken off by storm waves lies at the base of the living reef. The reef itself is generally just about the level of the water and may be submerged during high tides and exposed at low tides. Fine sands and algal remains cover the bottom of the lagoon, which is relatively quiet water since the waves break at the reef. The central island may also be fringed by reefs that are similar to the barrier reef, but they are often lacking.

The organisms that make up a reef are types that flourish in near-surface waters. Many, like the corals, favor warm water that is relatively free of clay and dirt. Corals are tied down to the reef bottom. They are not free to move about to gather food, so they live where food is brought to them. The clean agitated waters near the surface are most favorable. It is notable that breaks in these reefs are found where the muddy waters from streams flowing off the central islands flow out into the ocean.

The origin of barrier reefs that surround islands was explained by Charles Darwin in 1839, and his explanation is still considered valid by most geologists. He explained that volcanic islands often have fringing reefs when they are situated in favorable climatic belts for corals and other shallow-water animals and plants. The position of sea level relative to the islands has fluctuated. This fluctuation has been brought about by the ice ages during which up to 300 feet or more of water was removed from the sea and stored on land as ice. A second cause for sea-level fluctuations is the warping nd movement of the sea floor. Consider what happens when a volcanic island with a fringing reef begins to become submerged for either of the above reasons. If the volcano is extinct it does not grow upward, but the reef, composed of living organisms that live in certain depths of water, will be built upward and will maintain a position near sea level. Thus over a long period of time the original fringing reef becomes a barrier reef, and the island is separated from it by a lagoon. With still further submergence the volcano disappears completely, and we are left with an atoll.

One of the most extensive barrier reefs is the Great Barrier Reef of Australia, which is located along the northeastern coast of Australia. It is separated from the mainland by a lagoon that varies in width; in places it is very narrow, but at other points the width is more than 200 miles. The reef extends for well over 1000 miles.

Atolls

One possible origin for the atolls has already been mentioned. Some almost certainly have been formed in this way. Others may be better explained by the theory put forth by R.

A. Daly in 1910. He suggested that there does not necessarily have to be a relative movement between the sea and the islands other than that caused by glaciation. During the Pleistocene, when sea level was at least several hundred feet lower than it is now, the waters of the ocean would have been cooler than at present and therefore less favorable for the growth of corals. As sea level dropped, volcanoes and their fringing reefs were exposed above sea level. Corals could not grow around the margins of the volcanoes fast enough to protect the islands from wave erosion. Thus the islands were beveled off to form platforms. When sea level began to rise after the periods of maximum glacier advance, and the oceans began to warm up, new reefs formed near the margins of the platforms, bringing into existence new reefs that maintained their positions during further rise in sea level and created the atolls with their relatively flat-bottomed lagoons. The details of the lithology of a typical atoll will be given in your study of Historical Geology.

Classification of shore lines

Coasts are among the most varied geologic features. We have touched on only a few of

Fig. 21-24. Configuration of Bikini Atoll. The atoll is at the right. A similar flat-topped submerged mountain lies to the left of the atoll. (After Emery, Tracey, and Ladd, U.S. Geological Survey.)

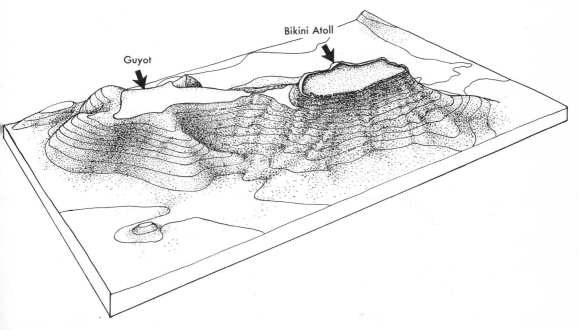

the most prominent features and types in this chapter. The following classification, devised by Francis Shepard, provides a most useful summary of the various types.

I. PRIMARY COASTS AND SHORE LINES, WHOSE CONFIGURATION IS PRODUCED CHIEFLY BY NON-MARINE AGENCIES

A. Those shaped by erosion on land and subsequently drowned as a result of rise of sea level because of deglaciation or epeirogenic downwarping:
   1. Drowned river coasts (Ria coasts).
   2. Drowned glaciated coasts.
B. Those shaped by deposits made on land:
   1. River-deposition coasts.
      a. Deltaic coasts.
      b. Drowned alluvial plains.
   2. Glacial-deposition coasts:
      a. Partially submerged moraines.
      b. Partially submerged drumlins.
   3. Wind-deposition coasts.
   4. Coasts extended by vegetation.
C. Coasts shaped by volcanic activity:
   1. Coasts on recent lava flows.
   2. Shore lines caused by volcanic collapse or explosion.
D. Coasts shaped by diastrophism:
   1. Fault-scarp coasts.
   2. Coasts on folded rocks.

II. SECONDARY COASTS AND SHORE LINES, WHOSE CONFIGURATION IS LARGELY THE RESULT OF MARINE AGENCIES

A. Shore lines shaped by marine erosion:
   1. Shore lines straightened by marine erosion.

Fig. 21-25. Tidal flats at Mont-Saint-Michel, France. During high tide the castle is completely surrounded by water. (Photo by courtesy of the French Cultural Service.)

Fig. 21-26. Coral reefs of the Bermuda Islands of the Caribbean. (Photo by courtesy of the Bermuda News Bureau.)

Fig. 21-27. The configuration of this shore line is determined by the structure of the rocks. The broad, open folds are clearly reflected in the shore line's irregular shape. (Photo by courtesy of the Royal Canadian Air Force.)

2. Shore lines made irregular by marine erosion.
B. Coasts and shore lines shaped by marine deposition:
    1. Straightened shore lines.
    2. Prograded shore lines.
    3. Shore lines with offshore bars and longshore spits.
    4. Coral-reef coasts.

EVOLUTION OF COASTAL FEATURES

Gradation on continents by running water, glaciers, and ground water is limited by the regional base level. In a similar manner gradation by wave action is sharply limited to the approximate level of the sea surface where wave erosion is effective and beach drift is made possible by the longshore currents. Sea

level has proven to be very unstable in the past. It rises and falls in relation to the land as the crust is warped and as periods of glaciation affect the balance between ice and water on earth. This is very important in considering the evolution of features along shores because it means that over a long period of time the forms that develop are not simply a result of continual wave action at a specific level against the continent, but that the wave action is intimately related to the relative rise or fall of the level of the sea. For this reason some of the earliest classifications of coasts were based on whether the coasts were coasts of emergence or submergence. This was highly desirable since it classed the coasts according to their mode of origin. Unfortunately this means of classification fails because the same features may develop along shore lines of emergence and submergence at different stages in their

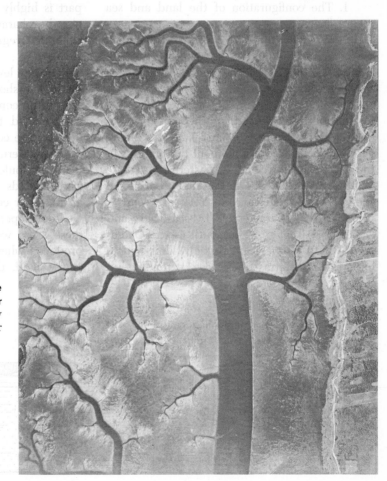

Fig. 21-28. Drainage pattern in the tidal mud flats at low tide, near Yarmouth, Nova Scotia. (Photo by courtesy of the Royal Canadian Air Force.)

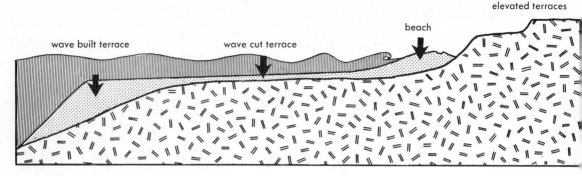

Fig. 21-29. Cross section through a typical rugged shore.

evolution. This makes it impossible to make positive identifications based on the observed features.

The forms that develop at the contact of the sea and the land depend mainly on three things:

1. The configuration of the land and sea floor.
2. Whether the sea shore is advancing across the land or retreating from it.
3. The nature of the processes of wave erosion.

The last of these is essentially the same throughout the world. Items (1) and (2) are highly variable. Consider for a moment the margins of the United States. Along the eastern coast there is a relatively broad, nearly flat continental shelf. From Maine to New York the coast is irregular; it is characterized by sea stacks and wave-cut sea cliffs. As far south as the Chesapeake Bay the rivers are partially drowned to form estuaries, arms of the sea, extending up the river valleys. The southeastern coast is marked by long smooth offshore bars. The sea bottom gradually slopes out onto the continental shelf from them. This is true of the coast along the western part of Florida and along Texas. The shelf is narrow along part of the Gulf coast off Alabama-Louisiana, and the outer part is highly irregular. The entire west coast may be characterized as marked by sea cliffs, general irregularities, and narrow irregular shelves.

If sea level should drop throughout the world, the shore line would take up a position out on the continental shelf. The entire eastern coast would then have a gently sloping sea floor off the coast. In the Gulf and along parts of the western coast some of the present irregularities would stand up above the water level as headlands. These would project out from an irregular coast into the ocean. Except for a well-developed system of submerged valleys, these areas would be essentially like features produced where the sea level has risen relative to the land, drowning river valleys and pro-

Fig. 21-30. Cross section through a typical low shore.

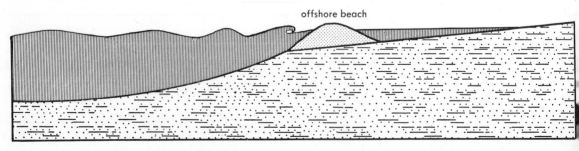

ducing an irregular coast line with islands and headlands that project out into the water. If there were no further relative change in sea level then we might expect exactly the same forms to evolve on physiographically similar parts of the emerged and submerged coasts. An altogether different pattern of evolution would occur where the sea floor is gently sloping into deeper water.

The concept of evolution of coastal land forms is best illustrated by considering two situations:

1. Evolution along rugged coasts such as are commonly formed when the coast has been submerged or has features of submergence, and
2. Evolution along low, smooth, gently sloping coasts such as recently emerged parts of the continental shelf.

In each of these examples it is assumed that sea level remains at the same position relative to the land throughout the cycle.

Evolution of irregular coasts (especially submerged coasts)

Imagine that a hilly or mountainous part of the country is lowered below sea level. What will the resultant coast be like?

1. The rivers will be drowned.
2. The coast line will be highly irregular as valleys are filled with water.
3. Islands will protrude offshore.
4. The sides of hills will drop off sharply into the water. Features similar to this are the fiords formed along glaciated coasts.
5. Initially at least there are no beaches, bars, or other marine deposits along the coasts.

Because water drops off suddenly to a great depth, the waves coming into the shore line will not break until they are almost against the land. This means that they will break with great force, and the maximum amount of their energy will be dissipated in cutting into the land. As a result, a cliff will form rapidly. The debris from the cliff will consist in large part of blocks too large for the longshore currents to move. They will be rolled and gradually broken up, but most of the debris will settle in the water just offshore as a deposit. This will in time build up to form a wave-built terrace. At the same time continued wave action and mass wasting will cut the cliff back, giving rise to a wave-cut terrace at the foot of the sea cliff.

More wave energy is concentrated at the islands and projecting headlands than along the more protected parts of the shore line, so cliffs and terraces will be built at these points first. After some time, however, a profile of equilibrium will have become established along most of the shore line. A profile of equilibrium is obtained when the slope of the sea floor just off the shore is just sufficient to permit the seaward movement of the material derived from the sea cliff and the shore to the edge of the marine or wave-built terrace. The effect of the concentration of wave erosion on the headlands is to produce a shore line with fewer irregularities. This is aided by the deposition of bars along the shore. Bars are built out from the headlands into the bays. Others form at the heads of the bays and along their sides. Eventually bars may entirely close off the bay, and the coast line becomes relatively smooth. Beaches that may form at the headlands become essentially continuous with the bay-mouth bars. The bays and lagoons left behind these bars are gradually filled in by sediments furnished from the land.

Of course a great deal of time is involved in the evolution of all land forms. Once the coast has attained the characteristics described above, it changes even more slowly. But it does not cease to change. The waves continue to break up the rocks exposed in the sea cliff, and longshore currents continue to move the material down the shore. The shore line gradually retreats. As it moves back, bars and beaches move with it. Eventually the shore line lies along the head of the drowned valleys. By this time, if there has been no fluctuation of sea level, there will be a broad wave-cut terrace, and the cycle of erosion will begin to approach what may be called old age. Actually there are

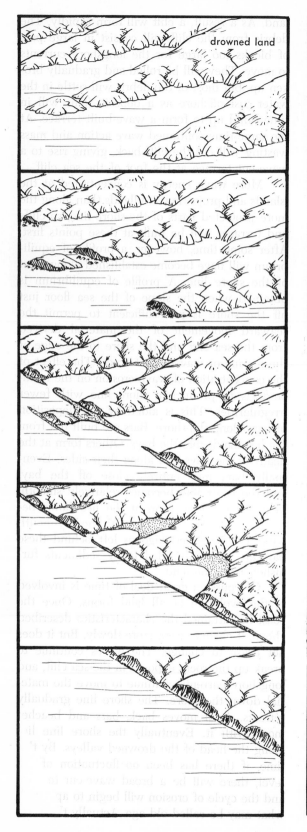

drowned land

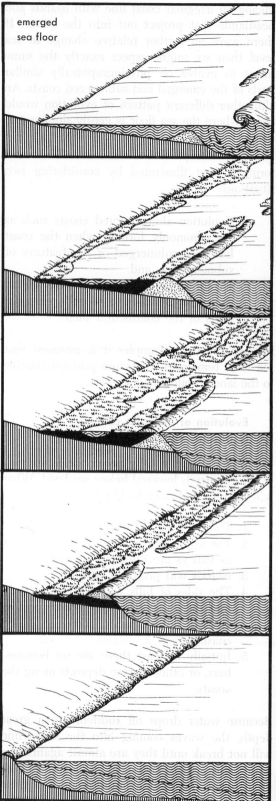

emerged
sea floor

ew if any instances where old age is reached. ea level has fluctuated too rapidly in the past or wave-cut terraces to plane off a large part f a continent, but the margins of every continent are partially beveled.

Evolution of coasts with gently sloping sea floor (emerged shore lines)

Emergence of the offshore continental opes would in most places bring to the surace an almost featureless plain that slopes ery gently into deeper waters. The slope of the ypical continental shelf amounts to only a few egrees. Wave motion affects water down beow the waves to a depth of between half and ne-quarter of the wave length. Interference ith this subsurface movement begins far offhore, and the waves break offshore. Where ney break, the bottom sediments are dislodged, nd since most of them are unconsolidated sands nd silts they are readily moved. A submerged ar begins to form on the landward side of he zone of breakers. This is built higher and igher until this bar emerges. It extends along arallel to the initially smooth shore. The almost continuous bars from Cape Hatteras outhward are of this origin. Once this bar ises above the surface, a lagoon forms behind . The lagoon becomes the site of a relatively till body of water that may first become a wamp and then later be filled with sediment. he only breaks through the offshore bar are idal inlets and outlets for the streams flowing rom the continent.

The permanence of the bar will depend largely on the supply of sand and the nature of the currents moving along the shore. If, over a long period, the currents are capable of moving more of a load than they are being supplied, then the sand from the offshore bar is gradually removed, the bar slowly disappears, and the shore line moves toward the land. The lagoon is drained and rapidly washed away, and the wave action is then concentrated on the mainland. Presumably the land slopes toward the sea shore. If this is the case the elevation increases farther inland, and, provided there is no elevation of sea level, waves will come in close to the shore before they break. They will cut a sea cliff and build a terrace, maintaining the profile of equilibrium. The profile of equilibrium is presumably attained after the offshore bar forms. Once this stage has been reached, further alterations are identical with those of the shore of submergence.

REFERENCES

JOHNSON, D. W., 1919, *Shore Processes and Shore-line Development:* New York, John Wiley & Sons, 584 p.

KUENEN, PH. H., 1950, *Marine Geology:* New York, John Wiley & Sons, 568 p.

MOORE, H. B., 1958, *Marine Ecology:* New York, John Wiley & Sons, 493 p.

SVERDRUP, H. U., JOHNSON, M. W., and FLEMING, R. H., 1942, *The Oceans, Their Physics, Chemistry, and General Biology:* New York, Prentice-Hall, 1087 p.

U. S. GEOLOGICAL SURVEY, 1954, Bikini and Nearby Atolls, Prof. Paper 260 (Issued in 5 parts, by many authors)

g. 21-31. Evolution of shores, according to the idealized cycle of W. M. Davis. he early stage is at top in both of these sequences.

22   Gradation in the Deep Sea

More than half the surface of the earth is covered by deep marine waters. These include the extensive abyssal plains located at a depth of 18,000 feet, the deep-sea trenches which extend to as much as 37,000 feet below sea level, and the continental slopes and rises which are covered by more than 600 feet of water. With few exceptions these areas are many miles distant from land. The exploration of them has until recently posed problems that were largely insurmountable. In the last decade, however,

our ideas concerning the deep sea have changed considerably. Before, it was an area about which very little was known. Even today we know far less about the oceans than about any other surficial part of the earth. This arises from the very limited access we have to the deep parts of the oceans. Skin divers are limited to the upper 150 feet of the oceans for all practical purposes. This is less than a quarter of the way down to the most shallow edges of the continental shelves. The diver wearing a uit may be able to work at depths of 500 feet, but this hardly reaches even the continental shelves. The bathyscaphs of Piccard, the French Navy, and the United States Navy have made it possible for man to descend deep into the deep-sea trenches, but many problems must be solved before these will become effective means of sampling and studying the deep seas. Most of our data have been obtained through indirect observations by means of cameras, core samplers, dredges, and echo-sounding devices. Thus the greatest problem of the deep seas is its inaccessibility, but other factors have been effective deterrents to the exploration of the oceans as well. These include the expense of work requiring an ocean-going vessel, the need for specially constructed equipment, most of which must be invented, designed, and constructed for use in the deep seas. Scientific work has often lagged for lack of technical advances. Much of the technical work of designing and making the necessary instruments has been done by the scientists themselves.

The old concepts

Whenever there is a lack of factual data we usually find a great abundance of hypoth-

eses, theories, or plain superstitions. This has certainly been true of the ocean basins. To most people the depths of the oceans have been veiled in an eerie cloud of mystery. The image is that of a vast all-consuming inky blackness. Into this realm a few have projected the light of reason. The views of many of the early oceanographers were well summarized in the words of Admiral M. F. Maury in 1855:

The geological clock may strike new periods; its hands may point to era after era; but, so long as the ocean remains in its basin—so long as its bottom is covered with blue water—so long must the deep furrows and strong contrasts in the solid crust below stand out bold, ragged, and grand. Nothing can fill up the hollows there; no agent now at work, that we know of, can descend into its depths, and level off the floors of the sea (quotation from Heezen, 1959).

Thus Maury visualized the world beneath the sea as a naked abyss bare of modern-day sediments, marked by the absence of processes of gradation. He reasoned that there would be no currents at depth, no wave action, no glaciers, wind, or running water which could bring about gradation as we know it on the

Fig. 22-1. "Sandfall." This "fall" was photographed in the Cape San Lucas submarine canyon, Baja, California, by Conrad Limbaugh, a diving specialist at the University of California's Scripps Institution of Oceanography. The "fall" is about 30 feet high. Currents feed sand from the nearby beaches into the canyon. (Photo by courtesy of the University of California, La Jolla, Scripps Institution of Oceanography.)

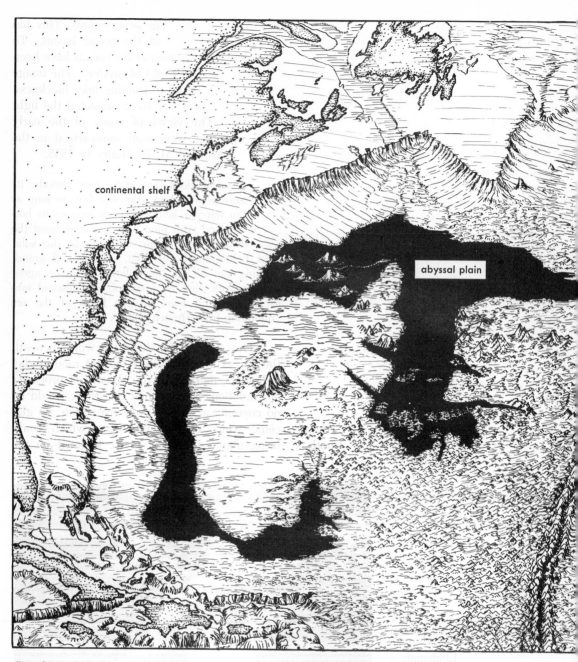

continental shelf

abyssal plain

Fig. 22-2. Physiographic diagram of the North Atlantic Ocean Basin. (Redrawn after B. C. Heezen, Geol

continents. Because the deep seas lie beyond the shelves, none of the sediment transported into the oceans would settle out in the deep water. All of the sediment from running water and glaciers would be caught on the continental shelves. The shape and extent of the shelves have been known for a long time since they are shallow enough to be sounded by old-fashioned methods of lowering ropes or wires.

Later, the concept depicted by Maury gave way to a very different idea—that deep-ocean basins are dominated by deposition of sediments. This came about when it was recognized that surface waters of the oceans are

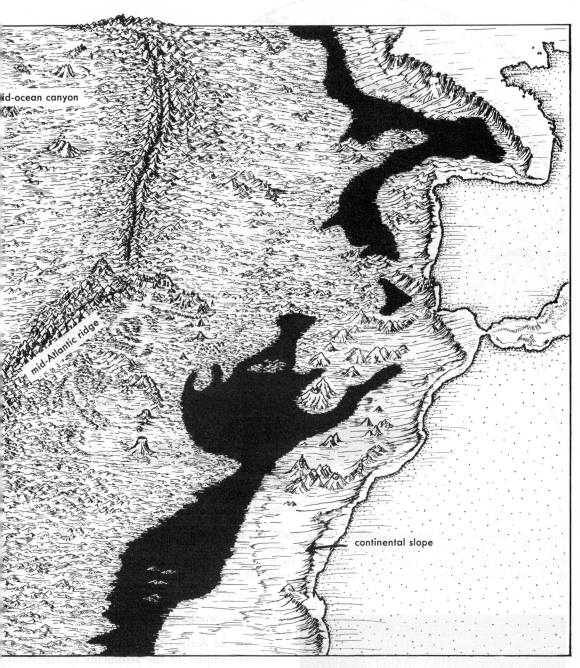

mid-ocean canyon

mid-Atlantic ridge

continental slope

Soc. Am., Special Paper 65.)

literally filled with very small free-floating and swimming plants and animals. These are microscopic in size, but if there are no processes of erosion on the floor of the ocean then through the eras of geologic time their remains should slowly accumulate. Rachel Carson depicts this concept in her book *The Sea Around Us*:

When I think of the floor of the deep sea, the single overwhelming fact that possesses my imagination is the accumulation of sediments. I see the steady, unremitting, downward drift of material from above, flake upon flake, layer upon layer—a drift that has continued for hundreds of millions of years, that will go on as long as there are seas and continents.

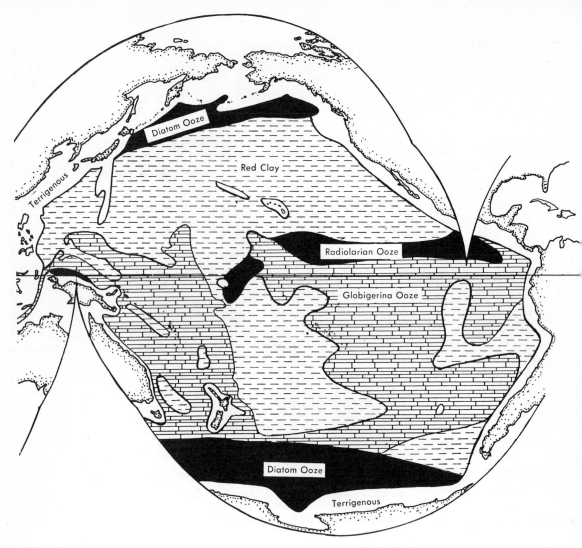

Fig. 22-3. Distribution of marine sediments in the Pacific Ocean. (Adapted by permission from *The Oceans: Their Physics, Chemistry and General Biology*, by H. V. Sverdrup, Martin W. Johnson, and Richard H. Fleming. © 1942. Prentice-Hall, Inc. Reproduced by permission of the Department of Geography, from the Goode Base Map Series, copyright by the University of Chicago.)

New methods—new discoveries

In the early 1900's attempts were made to obtain samples of the sediments on the continental slopes. These were greeted with some success. Cores of the top layers of the sediments in the oceans were obtained, and it came as a great surprise that some of these cores were

Fig. 22-4. Globigerina. This is one of the foraminifers the remains of which make up a large part of the sediment on the ocean floors in the middle latitudes. (Photo by courtesy of the American Museum of Natural History.)

stratified. This means that there must be some reason for changes in sedimentation in the deep sea, but the prevailing views were that the deep seas were not sites of change. Processes of gradation that might cause stratification were not thought to be effective in the deep seas. The problem became even more serious when it was discovered that layers on the bottom were composed not only of layers of shell fragments of microscopic marine animals, called oozes, but that these were interbedded with layers of silt and sand, sediments thought to be formed only at shallow depths on the continental shelves. Cores were obtained with various types of coring devices. One of the most effective is illustrated (Fig. 22-13). This is called the piston corer. It consists of a long section of heavy steel pipe with a sharp rim at the bottom and a large weight attached to the top. The corer is lowered to the bottom on a long steel cable. Just above the top of the device the cable is looped and locked by a clamp, which is released when a small weight hung from it hits the bottom. This triggers the clamp, releases the pipe and weight, which fall freely into the sediments of the bottom. Inside the pipe a small piston moves up through the pipe as a core of sediment is forced into the pipe. This prevents loss of the top part of the core and eases the movement of the cores. Cores 60 to 70 feet long have been obtained with this instrument.

About the same time, a second major discovery was made. It was well known that submarine canyons extend across the continental shelves. These in general lie at the mouths of

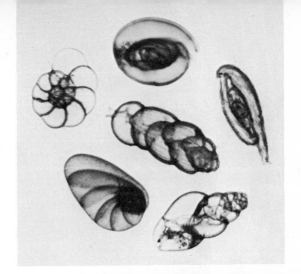

Fig. 22-5. Foraminifer shells such as those found on the ocean floors. These protozoans are about the size of a grain of wheat, but many are much smaller. (Photo by E. W. Spencer.)

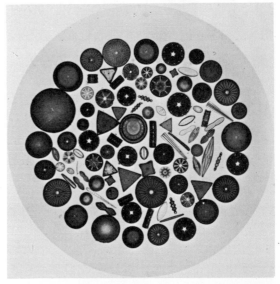

Fig. 22-6. Diatoms. The siliceous remains of these microscopic-sized plants are important constituents of marine sediments. (Photo by courtesy of the General Biological Supply House, Chicago.)

Fig. 22-7. Radiolarians. These are important constituents of marine sediments, particularly in very deep water and in high latitudes. (Photo copyright by General Biological Supply House, Inc., Chicago.)

Fig. 22-8. Deep diving dredge This dredge is designed to skid along the ocean floor while the ship is under way collecting rock samples and specimens of living creatures. Note the metal skis on either side of the vane. (Photo by courtesy of the University of California, La Jolla, Scripps Institution of Oceanography.)

Fig. 22-9. Bathyscaph. The Trieste is one of the modern bathyscaphs which are capable of descending to the bottom of the ocean even at its deepest parts. The sphere beneath the vessel contains a window from which pictures can be taken and undersea life observed. In 1960 this vessel set a record when it descended 37,800 feet to the bottom of the Marianas Trench in the Pacific Ocean. (Official U.S. Navy Photo.)

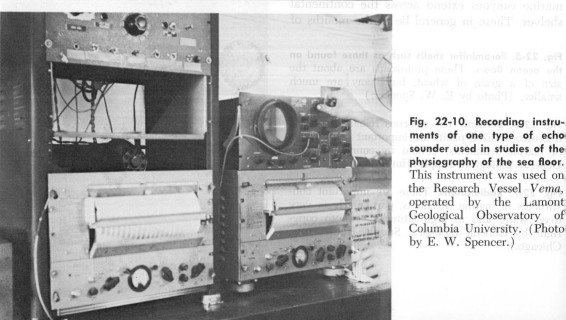

Fig. 22-10. Recording instruments of one type of echo sounder used in studies of the physiography of the sea floor. This instrument was used on the Research Vessel *Vema*, operated by the Lamont Geological Observatory of Columbia University. (Photo by E. W. Spencer.)

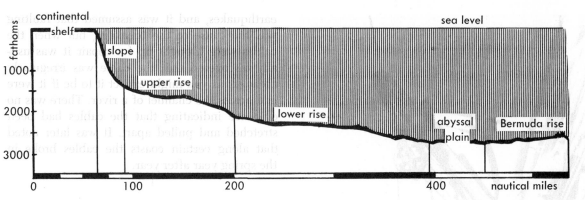

Fig. 22-11. A typical profile of the sea floor off the northeastern U.S. (After B. C. Heezen, Geol. Soc. Am., Special Paper 65.)

rivers. They were thought to be seaward extensions of the rivers during the ice ages when the water levels of the oceans were lower. But with the improvement of sounding devices it was found that these canyons extend beyond the continental shelves. In fact they extend down the slopes and across the rises, and a few may even be traced into the abyssal plains.

How could such features be accounted for? Certainly sea level could not have been lowered far enough to account for channels 18,000 feet below sea level.

A third important discovery was made when the Atlantic cables laid across the deep-sea floor were repeatedly broken. In some instances these breaks were accompanied by

Fig. 22-12. Profiles of the ocean floor. The top record was made during a crossing of the Mid-Atlantic Ridge. The 2200-fathom line is indicated. The lower profile is across the continental rise west of St. Nazarre, France. (From B. C. Heezen, Geol. Soc. Am. Special Paper 65.)

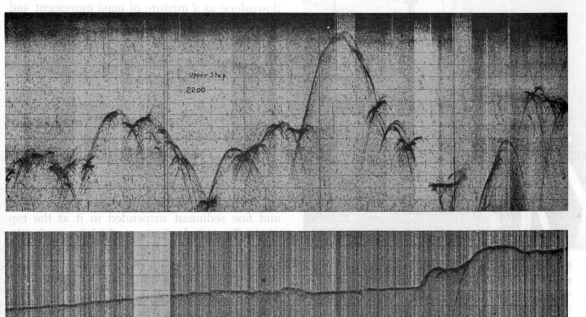

earthquakes, and it was assumed that faulting was the cause of the breakage, but when the cables were brought up for repair it was usually discovered that the cable was irregularly abraded, as you might expect it to be if it were laid across the channel of a river. There was no evidence indicating that the cables had been stretched and pulled apart. It was later noted that along certain coasts the cables broke in the spring year after year.

The concept of the turbidity current

The concept of turbidity or density currents has proved to be a unifying explanation for the previously unrelated problems. The idea of turbidity currents is very old, but its application to the gradation of the deep seas is recent. A turbidity current is a mass of water highly charged with material in solution or suspension which flows with turbulent motion down slopes through normal marine waters. The name "density current" is often used instead of "turbidity current." The turbidity current flows beneath water by virtue of its density, which is greater than that of the surrounding water. As a whole it sinks and flows downslope as a mixture of mass movement and stream flowage.

Experimental evidence

The nature of turbidity currents has been studied by Ph. H. Kuenen, 1937, and by many others. In the first experiments a tilted flume was used. The bottom of the flume was covered with sediment, and the rest filled with water. Turbidity currents were induced either by introducing mixtures of water with colloids and fine sediment suspended in it at the top of the flume or by laying a thick layer of sediment at the upper end of the flume and increasing the tilt until a slump or slide occurred. When small amounts of muddy water were introduced, a slow current was produced which did flow downslope, but very little erosion or deposition accompanied the flow. With an increase in the amount of load in the current,

Fig. 22-13. Piston coring tube over the side of the ship ready to be lowered to the sea floor. The weight is used to drive the pipe into the soft sediments on the sea floor. This is a scene on the Research Vessel *Vema* of Columbia University's Lamont Geological Observatory. (Photo by E. W. Spencer.)

however, the velocity was greatly accelerated, and the stream of turbid flow eroded the sediment on the bottom and carried it rapidly down into the lower end of the flume.

Evidence of turbidity currents in nature

Cable breaks. In November of 1929 a series of cable breaks occurred on the sea floor off the Grand Banks of Newfoundland. The exact time of each break was recorded, since the communication along that cable was disrupted at that moment.

A full-scale investigation of the breaks was made in the early 1950's by the Lamont Geological Observatory. Bruce Heezen and Maurice Ewing advanced the hypothesis that the breaks had been caused by a turbidity current. The idea was that the turbidity current was initiated by a slump or landslide from the steep edge of the Grand Banks. This might have been caused by the earthquake, or the quake may have simply been a shock produced by the slump. The movement of the unconsolidated sediments from the edge of the Grand Banks set much of the sediment into suspension, and it moved down across the slopes as a density flow traveling at very high rates. The velocity could be calculated from the times of the cable breaks. It required a movement of 50 knots or about 60 miles an hour. These rates have proved to be the greatest point of controversy about the theory. The turbid flow extended all the way down the slopes a distance of 450 miles into the abyssal plains.

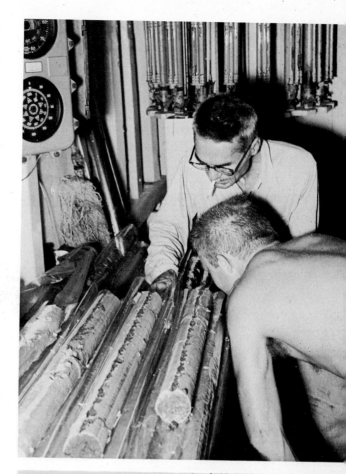

Fig. 22-14. Cores taken from the sediments at the bottom of the sea. The sediments most commonly found are red clay, calcareous and siliceous oozes, and fine silts. (Photo by courtesy of the University of California, La Jolla.)

Fig. 22-15. Underwater camera used to make photographs of the sea floor in great depths of water. The camera is in the top of the frame. Below is a flash unit and a motor. The weight on the deck serves to trigger the flash unit as the camera is lowered to the sea floor. This camera, which is on the Research Vessel *Vema* of Columbia University, was used to take the pictures in Fig. 22-16. (Photo by E. W. Spencer.)

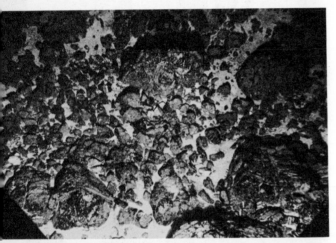

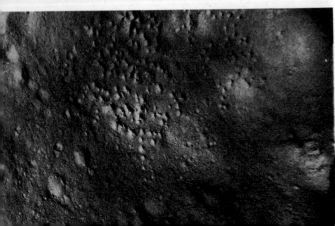

Proof of the theory

It is now generally accepted that the hypothesis stated above is an accurate account of what happened. The proof lay in the following discoveries made through extensive studies of the area:

1. Deep-sea cores were taken throughout the area. It was found that a layer of graded silt almost 4 feet thick covered the normal deep-sea sediments, and that this layer contained shallow-water micro-fossils. This layer was over a normal deep-sea sedimentary unit, such as red clay.

2. It was possible to outline the lobate form of the turbidity current from the core samples.

3. On top of the hills located near the foot of the continental slope no sign of the turbidity-current deposits could be found. Because of its high density, the flow moved along through the low places in the submarine topography and did not go over the small hills.

4. Photographs obtained by use of a specially designed underwater camera showed that the silty sediment was covered by ripple marks—a definite sign that some relatively strong current must have been flowing over them.

Further evidence has been obtained from a number of other sites. A notable case is that of the cable breaks off the mouth of the Magdalena River. These breaks occurred year after year just about the same season. Invariably the breaks took place during the highest flood stages of the river. At these times the river car-

Fig. 22-16. Photographs of the sea floor in the North Atlantic Ocean. These photographs show some of the variety in the sediment types. Photo (a) shows a rough sea floor partially covered by sand. A number of large cup-shaped sponges are visible. Photo (b) shows a rocky sea floor covered by volcanic debris. A little sand is visible. Photo (c) is a view of a sea floor which has a few rocks on a finer sediment. Photo (d) shows some very fine muds. Tracks of small animals are visible. (Photos by E. W. Spencer.)

ried large quantities of debris out from the continent, deposited it in the waters off the mouth of the river, and usually built up an alluvial cone of debris in the submarine canyon of the river. During the floods it was noted that the top of these deposits disappeared just before the cable broke. In 1935 when the cable was brought up from its position 12 miles off shore in nearly 5000 feet of water, it had green grass wrapped around it—dramatic proof that the river debris had been carried out to the cable and almost certainly played a major role in its failure.

Ocean canyons

That the submarine canyons which make such prominent features on the continental shelves continue seaward has already been noted. These canyons would be quite impressive features if they were exposed where we could see them. Several are as deep as the Canyon of the Yellowstone River in Yellowstone Park, 1100 feet. They are usually although not always located off the mouths of rivers and they are characteristically V-shaped valleys with tributaries. They often wind in sinuous curves across the continental shelves. A large number of such canyons are well known. One of the most prominent is the canyon of the Hudson River, which extends out across the shelf and down the continental slope. It has been traced into the abyssal plain. Others have been mapped and studied along the coast of southern California by the Scripps Institution of Oceanography. Among the California canyons are the La Jolla canyon, the canyon off Cape San Lucas, and the Carmel and Monterey Bay canyon. Of course, canyons are not confined to the United States. Others have been found on the continental shelf off the mouth of the Congo River, the Amazon, and many others.

The canyon off the Scripps Institution pier at La Jolla has been described by skin divers and has been mapped in detail by means of echo soundings. This has been described by Francis Shepard of Scripps Institution as follows:

. . . You would start your descent in a shallow sand chute where the water is only about 15 feet deep. As you swam down the axis of the little valley, the walls would get higher and you would see great masses of kelp and eel grass along the floor. At a depth of 50 feet the valley walls steepen until a rock gorge is encountered. Looking up from the floor of this gorge, you would see that the walls were overhanging in places and almost vertical elsewhere . . . . Beyond the juncture of the two tributaries the floor of the canyon . . . continues to have precipitous rocky walls much steeper than most of the land canyons in the southern California mountains. (From *The Earth Beneath the Sea*).

The lower parts of the canyon have not been seen by skin divers. They are much deeper.

Some of these canyons undoubtedly were eroded during the Pleistocene by streams which flowed on the continental shelves during the ice ages. But then, as now, the cutting of the canyons beyond the shelves must have been the result of density flow and turbidity currents. It may be that the loads of streams are carried farther out into the oceans than we think, but it seems likely that much of the erosion of these canyons is accomplished when the deposition of loads from streams in the canyons builds up steep piles of debris in alluvial cone-like deposits. When these become oversteepened they are unstable. Then slight earthquakes or the addition of more load may bring about a slump or submarine landslide which causes the debris to flow on down the canyons very rapidly, eroding the canyon walls and floor.

Form of turbidity-current deposits

Soundings of the deep-sea trenches show that alluvial cone-like deposits are accumulating on the sides of the flat bottoms of some of these trenches. It stands to reason that the trenches which almost completely encircle the Pacific Ocean are collecting most of the sediment which would be carried out into the Pacific Ocean by turbidity currents. This seems to be verified by the absence of turbidity-type deposits. Large areas of the Pacific Ocean bottom are covered by scattered nodules of manganese. The nodules are estimated to form at the rate of 1 mm in 1000 years. These nodules

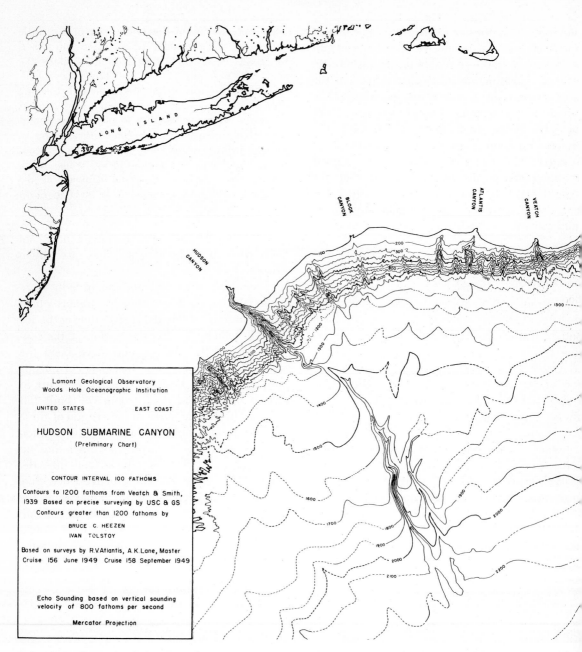

Fig. 22-17. Chart of the Hudson Submarine Canyon. A contour interval of 100 fathoms is used. This chart was prepared by the Lamont Geological Observatory and the Woods Hole Oceanographic Institution. (From B.C. Heezen, Geol. Soc. Am., Special Paper 65.)

often contain teeth of a Tertiary shark as nuclei. Thus it is possible to say that there has been either very little deposition or a good bit of movement of sediment in the time since the teeth were first deposited. If the trenches continue to receive the turbidity-current deposits, we may expect that they will become filled.

And it is in this light that certain seismic observations of the Atlantic margins must be viewed. The seismic studies reveal great thicknesses of unconsolidated sediments in trough-like depressions beneath the continental slopes. Could these have been old trenches that are now filled? The answer may very well be yes.

Once the trenches are filled, the next step would be for the turbidity currents to transport their loads into the deeper oceans. This is not expected nor found in the Pacific, but in the Atlantic there are few trenches to intercept the sediment at the present time. The material carried into the ocean deeps in this fashion may well be the main factor in the formation of the abyssal plains. They may be plains of deposition covered by the combined processes of the slow accumulation of shell fragments and extraterrestrial dust, and the rapid deposition of mud carried by turbidity currents.

This view helps to explain the fact that the mid-ocean canyon in the Atlantic has sides slightly raised above the level of the ocean floor. The physiographic form is very much like a river levee and probably formed in the same manner. The turbidity currents flowed down the canyon, overflowed the sides of the canyon, and the debris-laden water deposited sediment near the sides of the canyon in a wedge that thinned out away from the main path of flow.

Deep-sea circulation

Another of the recent discoveries has been that the sediments on the floor of the oceans commonly contain current ripple marks. Before, it was always assumed that there would be no currents strong enough to move the sedi-

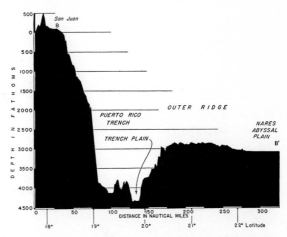

Fig. 22-18. A profile of the Puerto Rico Trench. (From Maurice Ewing and B. C. Heezen, 1955.)

ments on the ocean bottom. Not only have the ripple marks been found in connection with turbidity currents where they are readily explained by the rush of the flowing density current, but they have been found in places where no downslope movements could have contributed to their formation. This poses a serious problem. One suggested explanation is that the sea bottom has been lowered from a level near the surface of the ocean to its present depth. But there is very little other evidence for such a hypothesis. Ripples have been photographed on almost all the seamounts. The only logical

Fig. 22-19. Formation of a density or turbidity current by experiment. A layer of fine sediment was first placed in the tank. Then a pile of sediment was laid down at the right end of the tank to approximate the continental slope. As the tank is tilted the oversteepened slope slumps and a turbidity current is started.

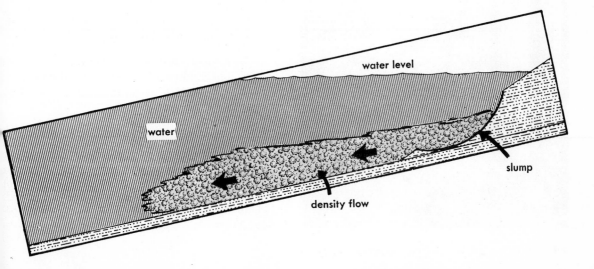

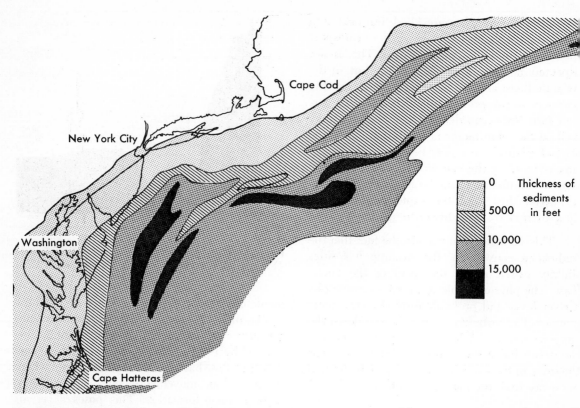

Fig. 22-20. Sediment thickness off the eastern coast of the United States. The inner margin is the coastal plain. The black areas are those in which more than 15,000 feet of sediment and sedimentary rocks overlie the basaltic layer of the ocean floor. (Modified after C. L. Drake, Maurice Ewing, and G. H. Sutton, 1959. Reprinted with permission from *Physics and Chemistry of the Earth*, v. 3, 1959, Pergamon Press, Inc.)

explanation for them seems to be that relatively strong deep-sea currents must exist. It has long been recognized that the currents associated with the Gulf Stream extend down to depths of over 3600 feet. Other means of deep-sea circulation which may be strong enough to produce ripples are being studied.

Movement of water in the deep sea is controlled by the following factors:

1. Temperature of the water.
2. The amount of material in solution.
3. Shape of the ocean bottom.
4. Surficial currents.
5. Internal tides.

Fig. 22-21. Temperature and salinity are two important factors in the deep-sea circulation of oceanic waters. Here the temperature and salinity of samples obtained at various depths is checked. (Photo by courtesy of the U.S. Coast and Geodetic Survey.)

Water near the poles is cooled at the surface where it comes in contact with the polar ice caps. Cold water is more dense than warm water, and it sinks, sliding down the slopes into the deep sea and forcing bottom water ahead of it into the equatorial latitudes where it converges and rises to the surface. This is just one example of the density differential that sets deep waters in motion. Other movements are caused by the sinking of water that has become heavily laden with salts produced by the evaporation of surface waters in the equatorial latitudes. The path of the sinking waters is determined by the shape of the bottom.

Internal waves and currents are little-known characteristics of the oceans. The nature of internal waves can be seen by filling a container with two liquids of different density and color. The heavier one will sink to the bottom. If then the container is slightly tilted back and forth waves will be set up in the liquids. They will be apparent not only at the top surface of the container but also at the boundary between the two liquids. Thus waves are set up within the liquid, and these ordinarily have greater amplitude than those at the surface. Recent studies of internal currents lead to the conclusion that internal tides are as common as surface tides, that the amplitude is much larger, and that they may establish internal currents sufficient to explain the observed ripple marks and scour marks seen around the manganese oxide nodules in the Pacific and Atlantic Oceans. The first important steps have been taken, but we are still just beginning to unravel the mysteries of the deep seas.

REFERENCES

DALY, REGINALD A., 1943, *The Floor of the Ocean:* Chapel Hill, University of North Carolina Press, 177 p.

HEEZEN, B. C., ERICSON, D. B., and EWING, MAURICE, 1954, Further Evidence for a Turbidity Current Following the 1929 Grand Banks Earthquake: Deep-Sea Research, v. 1, p. 193-202

HEEZEN, B. C., THARP, MARIE, and EWING, MAURICE, 1959, *The Floors of the Oceans. 1. The North Atlantic:* Geol. Soc. America, Spec. Paper 65 (122 p. and map in color)

KUENEN, PH. H., 1950, *Marine Geology:* New York, John Wiley & Sons, 568 p.

SHEPARD, F. P., 1959, *The Earth Beneath the Sea:* London, Oxford University Press, 275 p.

———, 1948, *Submarine Geology:* New York, Harper & Bros., 348 p.

SVERDRUP, H. U., JOHNSON, M. W., and FLEMING, R. H., 1942, *The Oceans, Their Physics, Chemistry, and General Biology:* New York, Prentice-Hall, 1087 p.

U. S. GEOLOGICAL SURVEY, 1954, Bikini and Nearby Atolls, Prof. Paper 260 (Issued in 5 parts, by many authors)

V OUR DYNAMIC EARTH

23   Metamorphic Rocks

ADJUSTMENT OF ROCKS

In spite of their hard and enduring appearance, rocks and minerals are not stable under all conditions. They will undergo changes in such a way as to become adjusted to the conditions in which they are placed.

An igneous intrusive may cool slowly deep in the earth's crust. As it cools, certain minerals crystallize out of the melt, and eventually the entire magma is reduced to a solid rock. This may be followed in the long periods of time following crystallization by uplift and erosion of the rocks above the igneous mass. Eventually the mass becomes exposed, first in the stream valleys, and later the entire surface of it may be laid bare. It becomes exposed to the atmosphere and its contents: water, oxygen, hydro-gen, nitrogen, etc. Some minerals of the igneous rock are not stable when they come in contact with these agents, and the rock begins to disintegrate. Some minerals react to form new minerals that are stable in the presence of water, such as clay. Other minerals dissolve and take on new forms. We call this process of disintegration and decomposition weathering. It is a process of adjustment of rocks formed within the earth or under water to conditions at the surface. Such changes are very similar to metamorphic changes.

Consider the rocks formed at the surface of the earth in streams, lakes, and in the oceans. If these become buried to depths of thousands of feet they are subjected to a remarkable change in their environment. They were formed under temperatures of about 50° C. and in pressures of only a few atmospheres. But at a depth of several thousand feet they are subjected to temperatures in the range of 100° C. to 600° C. and pressures of several thousand atmospheres. It is to be expected that these rocks will behave like their counterparts, the igneous rocks exposed at the surface, and certain of their component minerals which are unstable at high temperatures and pressures will tend to react with other minerals present to form new stable minerals. These adjustments of the rock to a new environment are called metamorphic changes. They are changes from less stable to more stable compositions and forms. Such changes may take place in igneous sedimentary rocks, in unconsolidated sediments, or in previously metamorphosed rocks which are subjected to a change in their environment. A definition of metamorphism:

The mineralogical and structural adjustments of solid rocks to physical and chemical conditions which have been imposed at depths below the surface zones of weathering and cementation and which differ from the conditions under which the rocks in question originated. (Turner and Verhoogen).

Fig. 23-1. Garnetiferous mica schist. The large crystals of garnet grew to their present euhedral form during metamorphism through recrystallization. (Photo by courtesy of the U.S. National Museum.)

Nature of metamorphic changes

Metamorphic changes take place in soli rocks. If the temperatures become high enoug to melt the rocks and a silicate melt evolve then the newly formed rocks are igneous, no metamorphic. Thus, there is a fine line of distinction between igneous activity and metamorphism. In fact the two phenomena grade s imperceptibly into one another that it has give rise to one of the most controversial question in modern geology—the problem of how to distinguish some igneous rocks from metamorphic rocks, and particularly how to tell whether th rocks called granites are igneous or metamorphic in origin. When metamorphism take place at lower temperature, there is little doub about the nature of the changes.

The original solid rock is transformed into a entirely different metamorphic rock. The new rock usually contains different minerals, but th bulk chemical composition of the metamorphic rock is the same as that of the rocks from which it was formed. Thus most metamorphic change take place without the addition or removal o elements. They are isochemical changes. Wha does happen is that new minerals form, old one are recrystallized, new textures develop, and the internal structure and fabric of the rock may change. These changes are influenced by number of factors which play a part in metamorphism.

Factors in metamorphic changes

The effects of temperature and pressure have already been emphasized, but a numbe of other factors play a role in influencing the nature of metamorphic changes and in deter mining the type of new rock that will be produced. These factors include not only the weigh of overlying rocks, called rock pressure, but di rected stress as well, the presence of chemically active fluids, the presence or absence of water the size of the grains in the rocks before it is metamorphosed, porosity and permeability of the original rock, and the original composition

1. *Temperature.* Elevated temperatures accelerate most chemical reactions; therefore, thi factor is important in any metamorphic change

aking place in the presence of heat. We may say it facilitates chemical changes. It is particularly important near the contact of igneous intrusions where the temperature may become the dominating factor in metamorphic changes. The name "pyrometamorphism" is applied in such cases. The country rock may be burned or baked, without melting. This type of alteration is found at the contact of large intrusives such as sills, dikes, batholiths, and in the fragments of country rock which may become broken off the sides or top of an intrusion and fall into the magma.

2. *Rock pressure*. Rock pressure is almost exactly like hydrostatic pressure. If you place an object in water it is compressed by the pressure of the water at that depth. The compression acts on all the surface contacts of the material and tends to cause a reduction in volume. The pressure on the bottom of the object upward is exactly equal to the pressure from above. Pressures from opposite directions tend to balance one another. The amount of pressure is dependent primarily on the depth of the rock in the earth. Pressures increase rapidly with depth, but few of the rocks we see exposed at the surface have ever been at depths of much more than 10 miles. These are exposed at the surface in regions where uplift and folding have forced these once deeply buried rocks up as mountains.

3. *Directed pressure (stress)*. If pressure is exerted on a rock or mineral so that the rock or mineral tends to move, or so as to change the shape of the material, it is a directed stress. Such stress is an important factor in bringing about textural recrystallization changes. Riecke's principle applies in such cases. It states in effect that if directed stress is applied to a mineral there will be a migration of material from the points of high pressure to points of low pressure. Solubility increases under pressure. Perhaps you have seen a piece of wire with weights tied to either end placed across a piece of ice. The wire will cut through the ice and eventually fall out at the bottom of the block, but the ice will still be a solid mass. What has happened? The points of greatest stress under the wire have been the sites of solution (i.e., the solubility of a mineral is in-

creased by pressure). The solutions moved around the wire, and then the water recrystallized above the wire in a position of less stress. The same can happen in rocks. Granular rocks have points of greatest stress where the individual grains touch one another. The points of less stress are the pore spaces around the grains. Under stress the grains may go into solution at the points of contact, and the material moves into the pores where it recrystallizes. In stratified rocks the lines of easiest movement are parallel to the beds, not across them. Thus we might expect that when a stratum is metamorphosed under pressure there is a tendency for elongated bands of the new minerals to form parallel to the old bedding surfaces.

A second important aspect of the role of directed pressure is that it tends to cause the rocks to become sheared if the magnitude of the stress is great enough to overcome the strength of the rock. Such shearing will break up the rock or bring about slippage parallel to the direction of the shearing. Some metamorphic rocks formed in the absence of high temperatures and active fluids or waters but under extreme directed pressures will become ground up without the formation of new minerals.

4. *Chemically active fluids*. The presence of such fluids may be extremely important in initiating chemical reactions and in providing a means by which the products of these reactions may be moved through the rock. The fluids that move through solid rocks and achieve the recrystallization must move along grain or crystal boundaries and through interconnected pores. The presence of any fluids facilitates this movement. The chemically active fluids may be introduced, as in the case of magmatic activity when gases and fluids produced in the rock melt escape into the surrounding country rock. In effect, this changes the net chemical composition of the surrounding rock and increases the chances of the formation of new minerals.

5. *Presence of water*. The presence of water in rocks, either introduced or that which may be initially in sediments, has an important influence on what chemical reactions take place, the rate at which they take place, the movement of materials through the solid rocks undergoing change, and, therefore, what new min-

Fig. 23-2. Banded metamorphic rock, gneiss. The light bands are composed of feldspar and quartz; the dark bands are composed of biotite mica. During metamorphism the minerals have become segregated into bands. Flowage also accompanied the alteration of these rocks. (Photo by E. W. Spencer.)

erals form. For many years the importance of water in metamorphism was overlooked. It was assumed that the main factors were temperature and pressures. But early in the 1950's a series of experiments were run at the Geophysical Laboratory in Washington, D.C. Metamorphic rocks were reproduced experimentally by varying the temperature and pressure applied to certain sedimentary rock minerals. The results of these studies showed that it is possible to produce different metamorphic rocks by varying the amount of water present even if temperature and pressure are held constant. With high concentrations of water and water vapor the so-called lower grades of metamorphic rocks were produced, while lower water concentrations at the same temperature and pressure yielded high-grade metamorphic rocks. Until these experiments were run it was generally assumed that high-grade metamorphism meant high temperatures.

6. *Grain size.* Since chemical reactions tak place at the surface of the fragments or crystal. the amount of surface area exposed determine the time needed for the completion of the re action. A given volume of rock is found to in crease in surface area as it is broken into smalle and smaller pieces. It is thus not surprisin that powdered sugar dissolves faster than larg crystals do. Similarly, fine-grained sediment such as clay or shale are sensitive to man slight metamorphic changes that might nc affect coarser rocks.

7. *Original composition.* The compositio: of a rock places certain limitations on the pos sible metamorphic reactions. Rocks of any give: composition subjected to different metamorphi processes and conditions can be altered to forr a number of different metamorphic rocks. shale, for example, initially composed of quart: mica, chlorite, hydrous aluminum silicates, an amorphous iron oxides, will become a dens

ard fine-grained rock called a hornfels if it
comes in contact with a very hot magma. The
new rock formed is composed of the minerals
quartz, andalusite, cordierite, biotite, and feldspar. If the same shale had been subjected to
deformation and if directed stress had played an
important part in its metamorphism, we might
find it changed to a rock composed of quartz,
muscovite mica, biotite mica, and garnet, called
a garnetiferous mica schist.

Processes of metamorphism

We have seen what factors play a role in
bringing about metamorphic changes, and the
ways in which these factors act has been suggested. Four processes taking place during
metamorphism are responsible for most of the

observed features of metamorphic rock textures,
composition, and structure. These are:

1. Rock flowage.
2. Granulation.
3. Recrystallization.
4. Recombination.

The particular geologic circumstance causing
metamorphism to occur and the particular group
of factors that control the metamorphism determine which of the four are most effective.

1. *Rock flowage.* Things we are accustomed to thinking of as solids are often
pseudosolids or pseudoviscous materials. Old
glass window panes are thicker at the bottom
than at the top. Although they look solid, and
even behave as brittle materials they will, over
long periods of time, flow. At higher temper-

Fig. 23-3. Locally the banding in these gneisses is almost obliterated. (Photo by
E. W. Spencer.)

atures this flowage is increased. Likewise most rocks will deform slowly without the development of fractures or breaks. The rock flowage which accompanies metamorphism is accelerated by movement of solutions and the migration of elements in the solids toward points of less stress.

2. *Granulation.* When directed stress becomes great enough on a rock to fracture or break it down, granulation may occur. Usually this takes place under such great pressure that visible open fractures do not occur, but the mineral grains become flattened out as though smeared between two surfaces pressed together. The grains may tend to rotate as they break up, crushing off the irregular corners or eventually forming a powdery substance resembling mortar. Granulation is favored by intense directed

stress, high rock pressures, and the presence o[f] brittle, hard, insoluble minerals that do n[ot] have a tendency to flow or recrystallize.

3. *Recrystallization and recombination.* Co[n]sider the changes that may take place in a roc[k] subjected to high temperatures and pressure[s] in the presence of water, but from which not[h]ing is removed and nothing is added to the tot[al] composition. A complete reorganization of th[e] elements of the original compounds may tak[e] place. Unstable minerals may slowly brea[k] down into their constituent parts, while at th[e] same time these elements recombine to for[m] new minerals that are stable. A reaction of th[is] sort might be diagrammatically represented a[s] follows: AB + CD → A+, B-, C+, and D- ions which recombine to form AD + BC. Th[e] compounds AB and CD were unstable, whil[e]

Fig. 23-4. Mixed rocks. Complexity is often characteristic of metamorphic rocks such as these. Flowage, recrystallization, and folding of these Precambrian metamorphic rocks all contribute to the complex pattern. Such mixed rocks as these are often called migmatites. (Photo by E. W. Spencer.)

Fig. 23-5. Complex flowage, recrystallization, and segregation are evident in this outcrop. Note the way in which the feldspar (light-colored) stringers are aligned. (Photo by E. W. Spencer.)

Fig. 23-6. Detail of a metamorphic rock in which the feldspars have become segregated in irregular bands. (Photo by E. W. Spencer.)

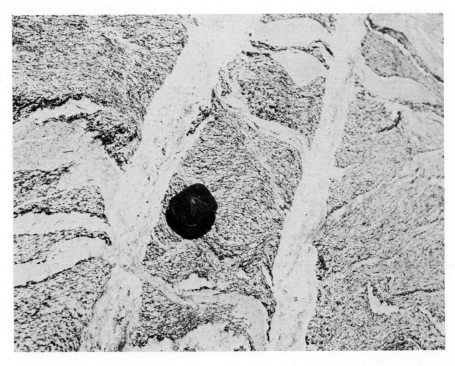

AD and BC were stable under the metamorphic conditions. The alternative reaction may be that the original minerals recrystallize into larger crystals or slightly different forms of the same minerals.

$CaCO_3$. in limestone + heat $\rightarrow$ CaO + CO_2 $\rightarrow$ (on cooling) $CaCO_3$. That these processes go on in metamorphism is well established since many minerals are known only in metamorphic rocks, and these are often seen to grade gradually into the sedimentary rock or sediment from which they were derived. In these cases it is possible to trace the changes accurately and in detail.

Types of metamorphism

We must now turn our attention to the special geological circumstances that bring about metamorphic changes. There are three such conditions:

1. Metamorphism at the contact of an igneous body.
2. Regional metamorphism.
3. Dynamic metamorphism resulting from deformation.

Contact metamorphism. Metamorphism may occur near the contacts of a magma. Gases and liquid from the magma may not be introduced into the country rock, but, if these are present and if the country rock is susceptible to them, they may play an all-important role in the outcome of the contact phenomena. Among our principal considerations must be:

1. How hot the magma is.
2. What fluids and gases are present.
3. What the country rock is.

But other things such as the size of the intrusion, the rate of cooling, and the composition of the magma may also prove important. Rocks are not very good conductors of heat; therefore, it is to be expected that contact effects will be fairly localized near the margins of the magma. Of course, if there are fractures in the country rock near the contact or if the country rock is very porous and the magma contains much gas and liquid, then the effects may be extended far beyond the margins. Since the temperature

is greatest at the marginal contact and creases outward, zones of different metam phic effects are established. Such zones are se in the Steiger slate of Alsace where it comes contact with a granite intrusive. At the margi contact the shale was metamorphosed to andalusite hornfels, a thoroughly recrystalliz fine-grained aggregate of andalusite, bioti muscovite, and quartz. This grades into second zone characterized by hornfelses wi spots in them. The slaty cleavage is obliterate The spots are incipient crystals of andalusi and the groundmass is a recrystallized mass mica and quartz. This zone grades into spotted slate in which the spots are segregatio of carbonaceous matter. Most of the rock practically unaltered.

Carbonate rocks are particularly suscep ble to metamorphism. Calcite and dolomite a very easily recrystallized, and they are high reactive chemically. When calcite is heat under pressure, dissociation into carbon dioxi and calcium oxide occurs. If the carbon dioxi a gas, cannot escape it will recombine with t CaO upon cooling, to form a recrystallized c cite or marble. Many unusual metamorph minerals occur in marbles. These are forme when limestone is heated liberating carbon oxide. If the carbon dioxide can escape then t reactive calcium oxide may combine with t impurities of the lime to form some of the minerals: garnet, wollastonite, diopside, trem lite, epidote. An example of such a reaction the combination of limestone and quartz form the contact-metamorphic mineral wo lastonite.

$$CaCO_3 + SiO_2 \rightarrow CaSiO_3 + CO_2 \text{ (a gas)}$$

Regional metamorphism. Essentially, r gional metamorphism is the chemical adjus ment of rocks to temperatures and pressur imposed on them by the depth of their buri: Certain parts of the earth's crust are mo stable than others. Some have had a tenden over long eras of geologic time to move up a down. They are mobile belts ranging up thousands of miles in length and hundreds miles in width. Within these belts great thic nesses of sediments have accumulated. In son instances we know these are as much as 50,0(

et or more thick. From near-surface observa-
ons we would conclude that as you descend
to the earth the temperatures increase at the
te of 1° Centigrade per 100 feet. If this rate
ntinues to a depth of 50,000 feet then the
cks buried to that depth are subjected to
mperatures of at least 500° Centigrade, cer-
inly enough to bring about drastic reorganiza-
on of the unstable constituents of the rocks.

addition, pressures increase with depth at a
ry rapid rate. Consider the weight of a
lumn of rock 50,000 feet high. This would be
e confining pressure on rocks buried at that
epth.

In addition to elevated temperatures and
gh confining pressures, rocks in the mobile
lts are subjected to movements under di-
cted stresses, and at great depths it is almost
rtain that some gases and liquids invade the
cks from the earth's mantle. Ultimately, when
at is locally concentrated, the metamorphic
cks may melt to form a magma.

Metamorphic facies. It should be possible
relate certain metamorphic rocks or assem-
ages of rock types to the temperatures and
essures under which they originate. One such
heme devised by Eskola is based on the idea
at a definite set of minerals characterize a
ven combination of pressure-temperature con-
tions. These minerals will have arrived ap-
oximately at equilibrium and thus will tend
undergo no further change under the given
mperature-pressure conditions. Thus each as-
mblage of minerals in a metamorphic rock is
group that was stable under the conditions
ring metamorphism.

The concept of grade of metamorphism. This
ea is that the degree of metamorphism is in-
cated by the first appearance of certain guide
inerals. In sequence from low to high grades
metamorphism the diagnostic minerals are:

ow temperature or high water pressure
   chlorite
     biotite
       garnet
         staurolite
           kyanite
             sillimanite
High temperature or low water pressure

The granite problem

Granite is defined as a plutonic rock consisting essentially of alkalic feldspar and quartz.
This definition places granites in the class of
igneous rocks. However, this has not always
been the case, for the first textbooks in geology
listed granite among the metamorphic rocks.
Today there seems to be a trend back to this
position. Many of the granitic rock masses appear to have formed through metamorphic
processes. Actually there is a very fine line of
distinction between igneous and metamorphic
rocks. If a silicate melt is produced, the rock
resulting from its cooling is an igneous rock. If
temperatures almost reach the point necessary
to form a melt, but instead the rock remains
intact although it may be permeated with gases
and liquid solutions and may be thoroughly re-
constituted, it is a metamorphic rock. It is no
wonder then that it is often difficult to make
the distinction.

Granites occur mainly in folded mountain
belts, the belts of mobility, and for many years
it was assumed that these represented intrusions
of magmas. In some cases this is undoubtedly
true. There are contact-metamorphic effects
around the margins of these intrusions; in places
the contacts are sharp, and the granites cut
across as they intruded the other rocks. But all
occurrences of granite are not so clearly
igneous. Students of many of the largest batholiths have made observations that pose very
difficult problems for those who support an
igneous origin for these batholiths:

1. Although some batholiths cover more
than 16,000 square miles of surface area and
are at least more than a mile thick, there is
little evidence that they have displaced any
rocks which originally occupied their present
positions. There is no evidence of crowding
aside of rocks on their margins, no folding, and
there are no certain inclusions of the country
rocks. The question then is how is it possible to
displace more than 16,000 cubic miles of rock
without affecting the surrounding units.

2. Many of the supposed igneous granites
may be mapped in detail on the basis of the
orientation of biotite and other platy minerals.
These have been shown to grade into rocks that

Fig. 23-7. Photomicrographs of gneiss showing the alignment of the platy minerals.
(From Engel and Engel, Bull. Geol. Soc. Am., v. 71.)

are undoubtedly of metamorphic origin. Thus the structure of the original stratification of the sediments which were metamorphosed may be traced into the granites. These structures would have been lost in the flowage if there had actually been a silicate melt.

3. Granites or small granite bodies of rock are commonly found completely isolated from any magmatic source. It would appear that they also formed in place as metamorphic rocks.

4. In the regions around granite batholiths very few if any of the compositional equivalents of granite are found. It would seem very likely that rhyolites, and other textural varieties of similar composition, would come to the surface or extend out from the enormous masses of granite.

5. Finally, there is no mineralogical evidence that proves granites to be igneous. The same feldspars may occur in both igneous granites and metamorphic gneisses.

The evidence from these observations indicates that many of the rocks called granites must be considered simply "granitic," meaning

of the composition of a granite. Many of th granitic rocks are partially foliated, and son are well banded. The name "granitic gneiss may be applied to such rocks. The granit gneisses appear to have been formed in plac (where they are). The process would be metamorphic or metasomatic replacement alteration in which solutions are very active bringing about the transformation. The origin sediments are recrystallized and recombine with the progressive development of feldspa and the growth of biotite and quartz. Usuall the more mobile constituents are concentrate in vein formations called pegmatites.

Since this is a problem presently receivin a lot of attention it is not possible to evaluat the final outcome of the dispute, but the mo widely accepted point of view is that som granites are definitely of igneous origin, and tha others have originated by a process of infiltra tion, permeation, and alteration called granitiza tion or progressive feldspathization. Finall there remain many areas of granitic rock which must be carefully studied in detail b fore their origin can be ascertained. The whole problem should caution us against jumping to conclusions.

Metamorphic textures

Most metamorphic rocks may be classed in one of two textural groups, those that are foliated and those that are unfoliated. The terms "foliation" and "schistosity" are applied to any parallel or nearly parallel structure or mineral fabric that induces a tendency in the rock to break easily along those planes. A number of structures may be responsible for this planar fissility. They include:

1. The parallel orientation of masses of tabular, platy, or prismatic minerals such as micas, chlorite, and sericite. If all of these are oriented so that they lie in parallel planes the rock produced will break much more easily along that plane.

2. Finely spaced planes of slippage or fracture, produced if directed stress has been applied to the rock.

3. Bands or layers of different minerals giving it a laminated structure. This may come about as a result of segregation of certain mineral assemblages.

Both the foliated and the unfoliated metamorphic rocks are crystalline. The term "crystalloblastic" is applied to the textural relations from the growth of crystals during metamorphism. Unlike a magma, in which the early crystals grow in a liquid melt, the metamorphic crystals must compete for space in an already solid rock. Nevertheless, many of the metamorphic rocks contain large perfectly shaped crystals. Studies of the crystals have led to the observation that certain minerals will seem to have preference in growth and development of crystals. The series is called the idioblastic series (an idioblast is a mineral bounded by its own crystal faces in a metamorphic rock).

Fig. 23-8. Hand specimen of gneiss. Gneisses are banded metamorphic rocks. The bands are not always solid or as clearly defined as the streaks in this rock. (Photo by courtesy of Ward's Natural Science Establishment, Inc., Rochester, N.Y.)

1. Rutile, magnetite.
2. Tourmaline, kyanite, garnet, andalusite.
3. Epidote.
4. Pyroxenes, amphiboles.
5. Micas, chlorites, talc.
6. Dolomite, calcite.
7. Feldspars.
8. Quartz.

Rutile and magnetite are thus the most likely to be perfectly formed crystals, and quartz is the least likely. If rutile and tourmaline are side by side in a metamorphic rock, the rutile will develop the perfect faces. Likewise, any mineral higher in the series can develop faces against or in contact with any one lower in the series. This series, besides being interesting in its own account, provides a means of distinguishing igneous from metamorphic rocks. The idioblastic series does not correspond to Bowen's reaction series. Thus feldspars are likely to exhibit euhedral crystals in igneous rocks and unlikely to do so in metamorphic rocks.

One special metamorphic texture resembles the porphyritic texture of igneous rocks. It is called the porphyroblastic. Although the two have the same appearance they are formed in entirely different ways. Porphyroblastic texture, which is the metamorphic counterpart of the igneous porphyritic texture, consists of a large perfectly formed crystal in a matrix of finely crystalline material, but, instead of being an early-formed crystal or having cooled at different temperatures, the porphyroblast grows simultaneously with its surrounding matter.

The nonfoliates have mosaic-like textures with crystals growing together to form an interlocking pattern, or granulose textures such as the tightly cemented sand grains or a quartzite.

Description of the common metamorphic rocks

FOLIATED METAMORPHIC ROCKS

1. *Slates.* These are the most perfectly foliated metamorphic rocks. You are familiar with the common blackboard slates. These have been split out of large

Fig. 23-9. Cut and polished section of a brecciated marble. Marble is one of the most common nonfoliated metamorphic rocks. (By courtesy of the U.S. National Museum.)

blocks of slate taken from a quarry. The foliations or slaty cleavages, as they are called, are so closely spaced that a single piece of slate may be split into thinner and thinner sheets. Theoretically you could split them into sheets no thicker than a piece of paper. These foliations are caused by deformation of shales during which the clay minerals become altered to micaceous minerals, and aligned parallel to one another. These mineral constituents are so small that they cannot ordinarily be identified megascopically. In the process of deformation or dynamic metamorphism the original shale sediments become folded and tightly compressed. The minerals tend to become aligned in planes that almost bisect the folds.

2. *Schists.* Schists are strongly foliated rocks of medium to coarse crystalline texture. Most of the mineral constituents are easily identified without the use of a microscope. Foliation or schistosity is caused by parallel or nearly parallel alignment of micaceous minerals. The most common minerals in schists are quartz, feldspars, and micas. Usually the name of one or more of the principal constituents of the schists is attached to the name as a modifier: garnetiferous mica schist, quartz schist, hornblende schist, or chlorite schist. Most schists are products of regional metamorphism.

3. *Gneisses.* These are the most abundant of all metamorphic rocks. Their characteristic feature is banding of the constituents. Certain of the minerals are concentrated in bands probably as a result of segregation during metamorphism, although many are thought to reflect the original stratification of sedimentary rocks. Some gneisses are formed by metamorphism of igneous rocks, others from sediments. Quartz and feldspar are the most common minerals, giving gneisses a composition very close to that of granite.

4. *Phyllites.* Phyllites are fine-grained schistose rocks that are less common than

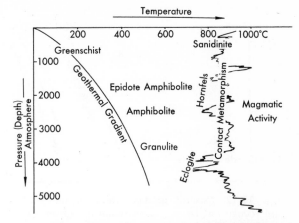

Fig. 23-10. Chart showing relationship between metamorphic facies and temperature-pressure conditions. Each facies is characterized by a certain group of minerals which reached stability under the metamorphic conditions in which they formed.

slates, schists, or gneisses. They are identified by the lustrous sheen which characterizes light reflected from chlorite and muscovite micas of which they are composed. They are usually greenish or red and they show the initial stages of segregation banding.

Fig. 23-11. The metamorphic equivalents of common sedimentary rocks.

Sediments	Sedimentary Rocks	Metamorphic Equivalents
clay	shale	dynamic metamorphism (slate)
mud	shale	regional metamorphism (phyllite, schist, gneiss)
mixtures (clay, sand, lime)	mixed rocks	contact metamorphism (hornfels)
limy mud (ooze)	limestone	marble
shell fragments	limestone	marble
calcareous sand	limestone	marble
quartz sand, gravel	sandstone	quartzite
	conglomerate	pebbly quartzite

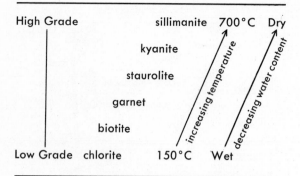

High Grade | sillimanite 700°C Dry

kyanite

staurolite

garnet

biotite

increasing temperature *decreasing water content*

Low Grade chlorite 150°C Wet

Fig. 23-12. Mineral grades. Metamorphic grades are recognized by the appearance of certain diagnostic mineral assemblages. Some of the important key minerals are given in this chart. Which of these are present depends on the temperature and pressure conditions and on the amount of water present. See text for discussion.

NONFOLIATED METAMORPHIC ROCKS

1. *Marble.* This is the metamorphic equivalent of calcite, limestone, or dolomite. Some marbles appear to be foliated, particularly if they contain large amounts of impurities that are micaceous, but most are unfoliated. The texture is usually that of large interlocking mosaic growth of calcite or dolomite crystals. Marbles of each locality tend to be slightly different either in color or in structures and patterns. Some are much more highly prized for their textures than others, although all are essentially similar in mode of origin.

2. *Quartzite.* Quartzite is the metamorphic equivalent of quartz sandstones. Sometimes the boundaries of the original grains of sand are visible, but they have become firmly cemented together. The cementing material is silica, and the bonds are so strong that, when quartzite is broken, fractures will cut indiscriminately across sand grains and cement. In contrast, when a sandstone is fractured, the fracture cuts through the cement and around the grains of sand.

3. *Hornfels.* There are nonfoliated dense, usually dark-colored metamorphic rocks formed near the contacts of igneous intrusions. The term does not apply to any particular compositional type of rock. It is much less common than marble or quartzite.

4. *Amphibolites.* As the name suggests, these rocks are composed of large amounts of the minerals that belong to the amphibole group, usually hornblende. They also contain plagioclase feldspars and biotite. These are sometimes foliated when the hornblende and biotite are aligned.

REFERENCES

AHRENS, L. H., RANKAMA, K., and RUNCORN, S. K., Editors, 1956, *Physics and Chemistry of the Earth,* v. 1: New York, McGraw-Hill Book Co., 317 p.

BUCHER, W. H., 1953, Fossils in Metamorphic Rocks: Geol. Soc. America Bull., v. 64, p. 275-300

GROUT, F. F., 1932, *Petrography and Petrology:* New York, McGraw-Hill Book Co., 522 p.

HARKER, ALFRED, 1939, *Metamorphism, A Study of the Transformation of Rock-Masses:* London, Methuen & Co., Ltd., 362 p.

MASON, BRIAN, 1958, *Principles of Geochemistry,* 2nd ed.: New York, John Wiley & Sons, 310 p.

TURNER, F. J., and VERHOOGEN, J., 1960, *Igneous and Metamorphic Petrology,* 2nd ed.: New York, McGraw-Hill Book Co., 694 p.

24   Deformation of the Crust

Stability and instability

Judging strictly from your own experience would you say that the crust of the earth is stable or unstable? If you are from the eastern or central states you probably consider the crust a very solid stable surface, but if you are from California, Japan, or any other part of the world's earthquake belts you have had the experience of feeling the crust give, sway, and roll, and at times exhibit characteristics of an unstable material. The surface of the crust is at times thrown into wave-like forms that resemble long ocean waves. Such instability is brought on by earthquakes and is usually of short duration, but effects of these movements are left in the rocks of the crust and over long periods of time they add up. The geologic record is filled with stories of long continued deformations of the crust. Sedimentary rock units, like those which cover the nearly flat continental shelves, are found folded and broken as though they were shoved together with tremendous force. In other places sea shores complete with sandy "beaches," scattered shell fragments, or wave-cut cliffs and terraces have been lifted high above the level of the modern oceans. We can only conclude that the oceans have either gone down or that the former beaches have been lifted up. Thus there is much evidence that the crust of the earth is not nearly as stable as it may appear.

Fif. 24-1. A sharp downward plunge of an anticline on the west side of the Big Horn Mountains in Wyoming. Folded structures of this nature indicate the magnitude of forces which deform the earth. (Photo by courtesy of the U.S. Geological Survey.)

Fig. 24-2. Uplifted wave-cut terrace. Epeirogenic deformation of the crust often elevates portions of the sea floor as it has here along the California coast where a wave-cut terrace has been uplifted. (Photo by E. W. Spencer.)

EPEIROGENY AND OROGENY

Two essentially different types of deformation are in evidence. The first type is that of broad uplifting or downwarping of the crust as indicated by uplifted beaches. These are called epeirogenic movements. They are broad movements of uplift or subsidence which affect all or a large part of a continent or sea bottom. Strata of sedimentary rocks are not crumpled or strongly folded in this type of deformation, although they may be tilted or warped.

The second type of deformation of the crust is orogenic. In orogenic deformation the crust is subjected to large stresses. Strata are crumpled and folded; they may become faulted by low-angle faults along which the rocks are displaced laterally over many miles. Usually orogenic movements affect long narrow belts of the crust which we shall call mobile belts. Orogeny refers to the processes of mountain building. Orogeny differs from epeirogeny in intensity of the deformation and in the general nature of structural features produced; the two are caused by different although related processes.

Evidence of epeirogeny

In the sixth century B.C. a large and rich city was built on the shore of the Bay of Taman on the northern shore of the Black Sea. The remains of this city, named Phanagoria, are now being excavated. The excavations reveal that some of the streets of the city now lie under the sea. Thus it appears that the region has been lowered in relation to sea level since the city was built. Similar evidence is found near Naples, Italy, in the ancient Roman public market known as the temple of Jupiter Serapis. Here holes have been bored in columns 18 feet above the floor of the temple by marine gastropods. The remains of some of these gastropods are still found in the holes. It is evident that the shore was submerged beneath the sea after the Romans built the temple and then again raised above sea level where it stands today.

Aristotle and other Greek philosophers noted evidence of large-scale movements of the crust, but one of the first efforts to measure the rates of such movements came in 1731 when special marks were made on rock cliffs along the coast of Sweden at the level of the sea. These marks are now about 2 m, almost 8 feet, above sea level. Such a rise is extremely rapid and could easily account for great uplifts of large areas if continued for long periods of geologic time. Such crude markings are not adequate to meet the needs of modern investigations. Now careful level surveys are made and checked from year to year to determine the rates of changes in level of the continents as a whole relative to sea level, and movements of parts of the continents relative to one another. Examples of the results are the discoveries that the Gulf Coast of the United States is subsiding at the rate of 6.6 mm per year, the coast of Newfoundland is rising .8 mm per year, the shield of Scandinavia is rising about 7 mm per year, the eastern coast of Australia is rising at the rate of .4 mm per year, and the eastern coast of India is subsiding at the rate of 1.2 mm per year.

One of the effects of erosion along sea shores that are under attack by wave action is

Fig. 24-3. Marine sedimentary rocks exposed in the cliffs on the sides of a high plateau in Venezuela. Such broad uplifts and upwarpings without strong folding are characteristic of epeirogenic deformation. (Photo by courtesy of the U.S. Air Force.)

that the waves eventually cut a nearly flat terrace, a wave-cut terrace, just below the level of the sea. Such terraces are cut by the impact of the rocks, sand, and gravel hurled against sea cliffs by waves. In 1946 it was discovered that a large number of flat-topped sea mountains lay submerged beneath the waters of the Pacific. These mountains, called guyots, are probably extinct volcanoes. As indicated earlier, the most logical explanation for their flat tops is that they were eroded off by wave action when the sea stood at the level of their tops. Along the northern coast of Africa row on row of wave-cut terraces are found above the level of the sea. Their step-like pattern shows repeated uplift, temporary stability while a new terrace was cut, and then renewed uplift. Either of these examples taken alone might be explained as a change in the level of the sea rather than epeirogenic deformation of the crust, but the relative movements in the two are in opposite directions, making sea-level movements alone an impossible explanation.

There is also evidence that the level of the seas has changed, as a result in the quantity of the water in the oceans. Even today great quantities of water are stored in the ice caps of the world. In fact there is enough ice on land to raise the level of the oceans 70–100 feet. More ice has been stored on the continents in the last million years of the earth's history. Within the last 10,000 years the sea has undoubtedly been lower than it is today. Some estimate that it may have been as much as 300 feet lower. Thus shifts in the relative position of the continents and seas result from two major processes, changing quantities of water in the oceans and through deformation.

Grand Canyon and epeirogeny. Epeirogenic movements are by no means confined to the present, nor even the recent periods of geologic time. One of the most remarkable records

Fig. 24-4. The Grand Canyon. (Photo by courtesy of the Union Pacific Railroad.)

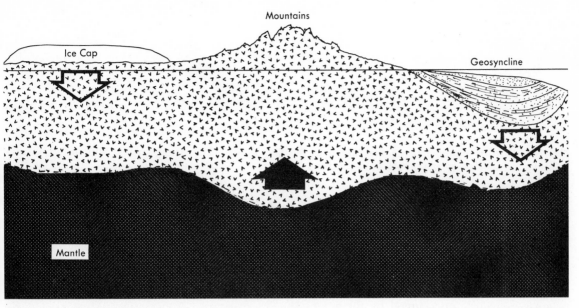

Fig. 24-5. Conditions disturbing the balance of the earth's crust. The crust of the earth is essentially in a state of isostatic balance. Different segments of the crust behave as though they are floating on a dense liquid. Conditions which tend to disturb the balance include the formation of ice sheets, erosion from mountain peaks, and deposition of sediment in deltas and geosynclines.

of epeirogenic movement of the crust is found in the section of strata exposed in the Grand Canyon of the Colorado River in Arizona. Near the bottom of the canyon extremely old rocks, more than half a billion years old, are exposed. These have been intensely deformed. They are folded and metamorphosed in what most certainly must have been an orogeny. Following the mountain building there was a long period of erosion. The mountains formed during the orogeny were reduced to a nearly flat plain. Such reduction would take place only above sea level where the mountains could be eroded by running water and other geomorphic agents. Then marine sedimentary layers were deposited across the edges of the older eroded rocks. The oldest of these layers is half a billion years old. During the millions of years represented by the strata exposed in the canyon, the region of the southwestern United States was beneath or just at sea level most of the time. Occasionally the region was uplifted, and some of the sediments were eroded off, but during most of that time new sediments accumulated on top of the older ones which continued to slowly subside. Today the marine sediments found in

the walls of the canyon nearly 1 mile above sea level are as flat lying as you might expect them to have been when they were initially formed on the floor of the ocean. Here, then, a segment of the earth's crust has been uplifted more than a mile without intense deformation of the rocks within the block. During the millions of years since these strata started to form, other epeirogenic movements preceded the one which brought the region to its present elevation, but at no time in that half billion years was the region of the Colorado Plateau complexly deformed.

Epeirogeny and isostasy

The theory of isostasy provides the best explanation of the cause of epeirogenic uplifts. The crust of the earth is known to be of variable thickness, of variable composition, and, therefore, of variable density. The crust is constantly undergoing change. This takes place through the shifting of loads of rock on the surface as a result of weathering, erosion, transportation, and deposition. Over a long period

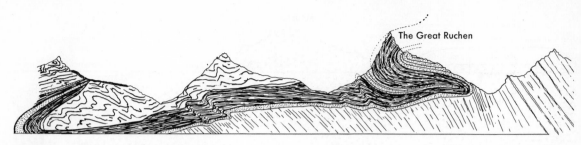

The Great Ruchen

Fig. 24-6. A cross section through the Alps near the Brunni Pass. The strong folding and distortion suggest a large-scale flowage of the rock units. (After A. Heim.)

of time mass is shifted mainly from the high mountains to the lower parts of the surface. Also, volcanoes and lava plateaus are constructed through igneous activity, and mountains are formed through orogenic processes. These processes throw up large masses of rock in areas previously unoccupied by them.

According to the theory of isostasy the earth approaches isostatic equilibrium. Loads on the crust are approximately balanced. If mass is removed from a certain area on the earth's surface, equilibrium is upset. Within the earth's interior, the mantle rock behaving like a plastic flows and exerts a pressure on the crust, tending to elevate the area from which mass has been removed and to restore what is essentially a flotational equilibrium.

The rates of epeirogenic uplift of the Canadian and Fennoscandinavian shields may be explained in these terms. During the ice ages both of these areas were sites of accumulation for large quantities of ice and snow. It appears probable that parts of Canada were overlaid by more than a mile of ice and snow. The weight of this ice upset isostatic equilibrium. The weight on that segment of the earth's crust caused it to subside slightly into the somewhat plastic zones of rock beneath the crust. Since the earth is a solid sphere, the material displaced by the downward extension of the area under the Canadian Shield had to move. This movement was either toward crustal segments which were becoming lighter, such as the ocean basins which would have lost water (to form the ice), or it would have caused a general upward exertion of pressure throughout the subcrust. When the ice melted away as the glaciers retreated, the weight was suddenly reduced on the shields, and equilibrium is now being re-established by compensating uplift of those areas.

STRENGTH OF THE CRUST

Compensation for uplifts and subsidence of the crust of the earth as accounted for by the theory of isostasy could take place only if rocks in the interior of the earth are much weaker than we ordinarily think they are. In fact we have already described the subcrustal movements as being those of fluids or plastics. Yet we think of rocks at the surface as being among the hardest and strongest materials in the earth. Examine the cross section through the Alps and Appalachians in this chapter. In these sections the strata of the mountains are folded and contorted in a way that we might ordinarily think impossible for rocks as hard and solid as limestones, sandstones, and metamorphic rocks. Yet the evidence is conclusive. Some of these sections have been drawn from exposures in the face of cliffs and in tunnels. These massive units of rock have been contorted and deformed more like a mass of wet clay than like a mass of hard brittle rock. We are forced to conclude that rocks do not always behave the way they do at the surface, and that, while individual hand specimens may be hard and brittle, sections of the earth considered as a whole are not.

The subject, strength of materials, is usually thought of as a branch of engineering. The engineer is interested in the strength and properties of building materials. Likewise, the geologist is interested in the strength and properies of the materials which make up the earth's crust and interior. These areas overlap, but the problems that confront the geologists are in many ways much more complex and difficult to answer than those facing the engineer. There are several reasons for this. First, it is impossible to produce artificially pressures equal to those found at great depths in the earth at the present. Secondly, the length of time required for the completion of an orogeny may well be many millions of years. Little is known of the behavior of rocks or other materials subjected to stresses over such long periods of time. Thus, there is no basis for accurately predicting what will happen. Thirdly, there is the problem of the scale of features such as mountain ranges. These factors make it difficult to simulate the conditions of their formation. For these reasons most of what we know of the nature of deformation of rocks during orogeny must be gained through field studies of mountain systems. These may be compared with the results of laboratory studies.

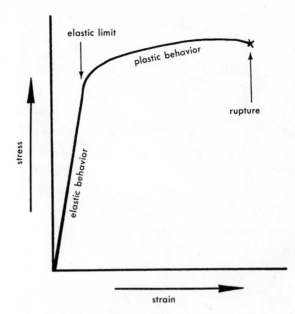

Fig. 24-7. Stress-strain curve. After the elastic limit is reached the addition of more stress causes the rock to deform almost continuously without the addition of more stress.

Behavior of rocks under stress

Several terms occur repeatedly in discussions of diastrophism.

1. *Confining pressure* (rock pressure) is the amount of pressure exerted on rock units as a result of their depth of burial. It is a balanced pressure like hydrostatic pressure, and it is applied equally on all sides.
2. *Stress* is here used in the sense of directed pressure. It is a force per unit area acting along a particular line.
3. *Strain* is the amount of change of shape that takes place in the body under stress.

Before delving into the behavior of rocks at great depth or under high confining pressures, it is useful to know how to describe the deformation of rocks or other material at the surface. In a laboratory stresses may be applied to a specimen of rock in three ways:

1. The rock may be put in a press and compressed. Here stress acts along the lines between the jaws of the vice, and the specimen is shortened.
2. The specimen may be stretched (put in tension) in which case it becomes elongated.
3. A stress may be applied along two lines in the rock so that the specimen tends to be twisted or sheared.

Most rocks, when subjected to one of these types of stress situations, deform as elastic materials for small stresses and strains. That is, if a limestone or granite specimen is put under

Fig. 24-8. Details of the structure of rock units exposed in the Simplon Tunnel in the Alps. (After C. Schmidt, 1907.)

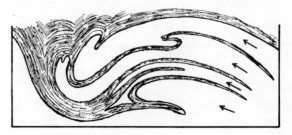

tension, the specimen will be elongated by an amount which is directly proportional to the amount of the stress. If the stress is released, the specimen will return to its original shape. Such behavior is that of an elastic substance. An experiment of this sort might be extended by increasing the amount of stress each time. Eventually the addition of any more stress causes a permanent deformation in the material, and it will not return to its original shape. This point is called the elastic limit. Beyond the elastic limit the addition of more stress is usually accompanied by much greater strains than would have been produced by the same increment of stress below the elastic limit. The material ceases to behave elastically and begins to exhibit the properties of a plastic. Plastic behavior is characterized by continuous deformation after a certain threshold value of stress is applied even without the addition of more stress. Of course, if the experiment is extended, failure of the material will eventually occur. Failure is accompanied by the formation of fractures or ruptures. Because most rock strata are fractured, the cause and nature of failures are of particular interest to geologists. In general, rocks fail under much smaller tensile stresses than compressive stresses.

From the above experiments it is apparent that under small confining pressures and small stresses rocks behave like elastic materials. It should be noted that the measure of the elasticity of a material is how fast it rebounds to its original shape after release of a deforming force. In this sense a piece of granite is much more elastic than a rubber ball. We are accustomed to thinking of rocks as behaving like rather brittle substances. But it is more important to an understanding of orogeny to know how these same rocks behave under the conditions within the earth's crust. The essential differences between conditions at the surface and at depth are:

1. Much greater confining pressure at depth (amount is proportional to depth).
2. Higher temperatures at depth, resulting from the geothermal gradient and from the possible proximity of magmas.

3. Possibility that solutions and gases coming from magmas will be present at depth. The reason for emphasizing this is that igneous rocks are found intruded into the strata of every major folded mountain belt.

Laboratory tests have been made on several rock types under high confining pressures. As the confining pressure is increased, the amount of stress necessary to cause failure is increased, the elastic limit is increased somewhat, and the range of stresses under which the rock will behave as a plastic is increased. Thus, rocks that exhibit little plastic behavior at the surface of the earth may be very plastic at depth in the crust. The effects of high temperatures are also to reduce the elastic behavior of the rocks. Likewise the presence of liquids facilitates solution and recrystallization, which tend to promote plastic rather than brittle deformation.

By far the hardest factor in orogeny to evaluate is time. On the campuses of some of the older colleges and universities, and especially in old graveyards, there are many marble benches. In areas where these benches have been standing supported at either end for hundreds of years it is not uncommon to find that the center of the bench has sagged. The amount of sag is sometimes pronounced and is easily measured. When these marble slabs were originally cut they were smooth and flat, so the sags must have formed in the time since the slabs were mounted. Here, then, is evidence that solid rock can be deformed under a confining pressure of 1 atmosphere with nothing more than the force of gravity acting as a stress, if enough time is allowed. With the knowledge that this is possible it is not quite as difficult to visualize the formation of the contortions in the earth's crust under high confining pressure, at elevated temperatures, in the presence of solutions, if even small directed stresses are acting over very long periods of time.

The patterns of deformation found in individual hand specimens and in whole mountain ranges often resemble flowage. There is so much compelling field evidence of this type of

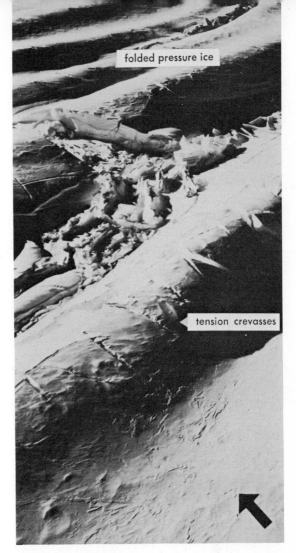

folded pressure ice

tension crevasses

Fig. 24-11. Folds in an ice sheet. Note particularly the regularity of the fractures on the crest of the fold. (Photo by courtesy of the U.S. Navy.)

Fig. 24-12. A folded mountain belt in North Africa. A plunging anticline is exposed at the bottom of the picture. Other plunging anticlines and synclines lie along the belt. (Photo by courtesy of the U.S. Air Force.)

Fig. 24-13. A structural dome. The top of this dome has been planed off through long continued erosion. The oldest rocks are exposed at the center and successively younger units are exposed away from the center. (Photo by courtesy of the U.S. Air Force.)

Fig. 24-14. A structural basin. A series of hogback ridges are exposed around the margins of the structure. The youngest units are exposed near the center of the structure. (Photo by courtesy of the U.S. Air Force.)

viscous deformation in rocks that we must properly think of rocks not as strictly elastic materials, but as elastico-viscous materials. Such substances exhibit the characteristics of elastic solids under some conditions and those of a fluid under other conditions. One of the most commonly known elastico-viscous materials is "silly putty." Its behavior is very much like that of the crust of the earth except for the time involved. The crust and "silly putty" have these things in common:

1. If subjected to a sudden sharp impact both will rupture.
2. If subjected to rapid small deformations both are elastic.
3. If subjected to slow continuous stress both will flow.

STRUCTURES RESULTING FROM DIASTROPHISM

Four major groups of structures are produced directly as a result of diastrophism. They are:

a. Folds.
b. Faults.
c. Fractures.
d. Unconformities.

There is no restriction as to the size or scale of these structures.

Folds

Folds rarely occur as isolated features but are more commonly found in belts or systems in which many folds exist together. Two prominent types of folds are:

1. Those with smooth regular geometric forms.
2. Those with irregular shapes. These are mainly found in unconsolidated sediments on steep slopes, in metamorphic rocks, and near intrusions, wherever flowage has been a prominent part of the folding process.

Fig. 24-15. Anticline with steep western limb in the Big Horn Mountains, Wyoming.
Granite is exposed in the foreground. The sedimentary rocks include units ranging in
age from Cambrian to Carboniferous. (Photo by courtesy of the U.S. Geological
Survey.)

Fig. 24-16. Fault scarp in the Precambrian rocks of the Canadian Shield. (Photo by
courtesy of the Royal Canadian Air Force.)

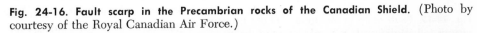

Although those of the second category are very common by virtue of the nature of their shape, they are not easily described. A picture is usually the best means of description. The first group is more easily described. These are found most often in the sedimentary rocks. Because they have regular geometric forms they may be bisected by an imaginary plane, called the axial plane. If the axial plane bisects the fold into two symmetrical halves, then the fold is said to be symmetrical; if not it is an asymmetrical fold. The fold may be divided into three parts, a crest or trough and two sides called limbs. If the axial plane is inclined so that any part of the upper limb is over the lower limb the fold is overturned. If the axial plane is horizontal the fold is a recumbent fold.

A line is formed where the axial plane intersects the top or bottom of any rock unit. This line is called the axis of the fold, and a projection of this axis on the surface of the ground is called the axial trace. In some folds the axis is horizontal for long distances, but eventually folds must die out, and then the axis becomes inclined. Where the axis of a fold is inclined, the fold is said to plunge. The amount of the plunge is the angle of inclination of the axis in relation to the horizon. The above terms are applied in the description of folds.

The following names are applied to folds of particular shapes:

1. Anticlines are upfolds in which the limbs dip away from the crest or axis.
2. Synclines are downfolds in which the limbs dip toward the axis.
3. Domes are circular uplifts. Strata dip away from the centers of domes.
4. Basins are circular downwarps or depressions.
5. Monoclines are flexures along which strata are bent. Because the units dip in only one direction, these have only one limb.

Faults

Faults are breaks in the solid crust of the earth beneath the soil cover along which there may be displacement of the two sides. Essentially they are fractures on which displacement occurs. During the displacement, rocks on either side of the fault become crushed. Long after movements cease along the faults they may become very inconspicuous and difficult to recognize. Some of the criteria by which they may be recognized are:

1. *Displacement of physiographic features.* Streams may be offset where they cross a fault zone. Frequently mountains, hills, and other topographic features are offset.
2. *Fault scarps.* Small escarpments mark the position of the displacement where one side moved up relative to the other.
3. *Displacement of geologic structures.* The outcrop of uniformly inclined strata may be displaced, or a structure such as a fold may appear distorted or offset across a fault.

Fault terminology. The fault plane is a zone within which the two sides have moved. It may be either a smooth plane produced by a sharp

Fig. 24-17. Fault scarp in Montana. (Photo by courtesy of I. J. Witkind, U.S. Geological Survey.)

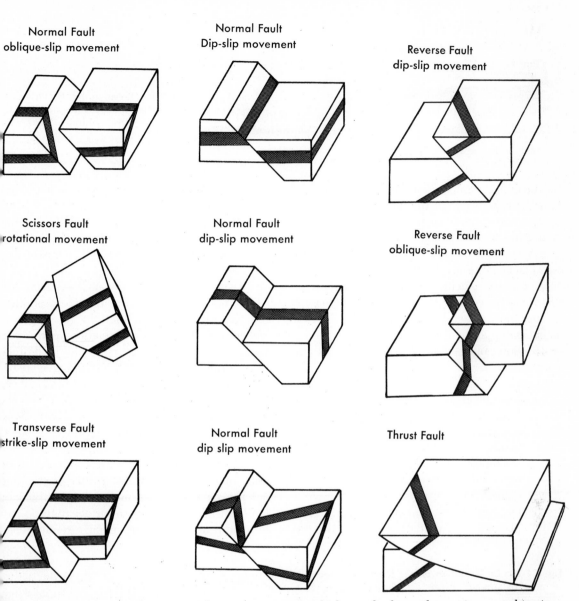

Normal Fault
oblique-slip movement

Normal Fault
Dip-slip movement

Reverse Fault
dip-slip movement

Scissors Fault
rotational movement

Normal Fault
dip-slip movement

Reverse Fault
oblique-slip movement

Transverse Fault
strike-slip movement

Normal Fault
dip slip movement

Thrust Fault

Fig. 24-18. Faults. Study the variety of outcrop patterns which result from the various combinations. Usually the upthrown side of a fault is eroded off more rapidly than the downthrown side. This brings about further alteration of the outcrop pattern.

break or it may be a wide zone of distortion as much as several hundred feet thick. Within the fault plane, crushed and brecciated rock is usually present. Sometimes the crushing is so complete that the breccia is reduced to a powdery-textured material. Usually rocks in the fault zone contain evidence of the movement of one side across the other. Striations and grooves appear where the two sides moved across one another. By running your fingers

along these surfaces, called slickensides, you can detect difference in roughness. Movement occurred in the direction in which the striations are smoothest. The fault plane either dies out, passes into a fold, or intersects another fault if traced. Faults locally divide the crust into blocks. If it is not vertical, one of these blocks must lie above the fault, and the other partially under the fault. The upper block is called the hanging-wall side, a mining term derived from

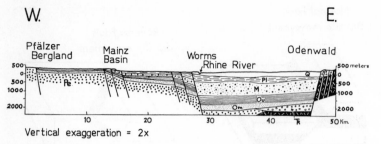

W.   E.

Pfälzer Bergland   Mainz Basin   Worms Rhine River   Odenwald

Vertical exaggeration = 2x

Fig. 24-19. Cross sections across the Rhine Graben. The Rhine River flows down a down-dropped trough-like depression called a graben (German for grave). Normal faults form both sides of the graben. (From Billings, 1960; after Dorn.)

the fact that a miner standing in a mined-out fault zone finds one of the blocks hanging over his head. He stands on the other block, so it is called the foot-wall side.

A number of movements between these two blocks are possible. If the fault is inclined, then any movement within the fault can be described in terms of the following components (if the movement of two points originally adjacent on opposite sides of the fault is traced it will follow one or a combination of these paths):

1. Movement parallel to the strike of the fault. If there is no vertical component, the movement is called strike-slip movement.
2. Movement at right angles to the strike, up or down dip, is called dip-slip movement.
3. Oblique-slip movement occurs if the displacement is partially up or down dip

and partially along strike, or if oblique movement occurs.

4. Rotation of the blocks relative to one another is also possible. In this case the motion may be described as scissor-like.

Types of faults. Steeply inclined faults are called normal faults if the relative motion of the two blocks is such that the hanging wall has moved downward in relation to the foot wall. They are called reverse faults if the relative motion is such that the hanging wall has moved up in relation to the foot wall. If the fault is inclined at a very low angle, on the order of 10° to 15°, it is a thrust fault. Most thrust faults are simply low-angle reverse faults.

Study carefully the illustrations depicting some of the possible shifts in the position and outcrop pattern of rock units brought about by faulting and erosion. These surface outcrop patterns appear on geologic maps. Usually geolo-

Fig. 24-20. Cross section across the central sector of the Turner Valley. Two large thrust faults and a number of smaller thrusts are shown. (From F. G. Fox, Bull. A.A.P.G., v. 43, 1959.)

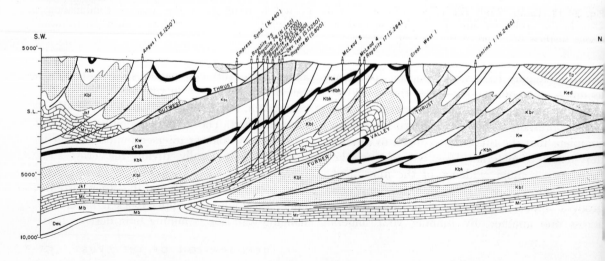

Fig. 24-21. Cross jointing in massive rocks exposed in western Australia. The simple pattern shown at the left is complicated by other fracture trends to the right in the photograph. (Photo by courtesy of the U.S. Air Force.)

gists must infer the presence of faults from the surface configuration of the outcrop patterns. The presence of a fault may have great significance economically, for faults are frequently the sites of localization of ores, oil, and gas, and they may be of great potential danger if they cross dam sites or other large structures.

Fault structures. Special names are applied to some structures formed as a result of faulting. All of these occur as large and small scale features. Some of the most important of these are:

1. *Graben.* The term is derived from the German word meaning "grave." The term is applied to elongate blocks bounded by normal faults on either side when the block has moved down in relation to the sides.
2. *Horst.* This term is applied to elongate blocks bounded by normal faults on either side when the block has moved up in relation to the sides.
3. *Klippe.* These are isolated blocks of rock separated from the underlying rocks by a fault. Usually the fault is

part of a low-angle thrust fault, and usually, though not always, the rocks in the Klippe are older than those underlying them.

4. *Nappe* or *Decke.* These terms are used to describe large masses of rock which have been moved a long distance from their point of origin. Most nappes are strongly folded until one limb of the fold is overturned, and the mass displaced more than a mile by thrusting and folding.

Fractures

Fractures are breaks in solid rock along which displacements have not occurred. They are present in most consolidated rocks of igneous, metamorphic, and sedimentary origin. Fractures may form as a result of either diastrophism or contraction. The two most common types are tension fractures and shear fractures.

Tension fractures occur when the rock is brought under tension. This occurs naturally in cooling lavas when the mass of molten rock begins to crystallize and its volume is reduced. This reduction in volume is taken up by a reduction in thickness and usually by a reduction in surface area. The latter is accomplished by the development of breaks along smooth planar or curved surfaces as the rock contracts. Cooling cracks form a number of different patterns. Some are radiating patterns, others are irregular intersecting curved surfaces, and hexagonal or polygonal patterns. Fractures formed in little-deformed sedimentary rocks may likewise originate through tension caused by compaction and shrinkage as sediments are consolidated into sedimentary rocks.

Tension fractures are also formed from diastrophism. If you flex a piece of wax you will see a fracture form about parallel to the axis of the flexure. This tension crack forms at right angles to the stress, tending to pull the top of the layer apart. If the sides of the wax sheet are restricted, then as the folding is continued tension cracks open up at right angles to the axis as elongation parallel to the fold axis occurs. Thus tension cracks form rectangular patterns on some upwarped structures. Another pattern that is typical of tension joints is found when strata are bent upward to form domes. Here two sets of tension fractures are

formed, one radiating out from the center of the dome and a second one with concentric fractures circling the dome.

Shear fractures are formed in rock under compression. Put a piece of soap or clay in a press or vise and compress it. The first fractures that open in the clay cut diagonally across the block. Two sets of shear fractures generally develop under compression. They intersect one another at angles of approximately 60°. The acute angle of intersection of the shear fractures usually faces the direction along which the compressive stresses acted.

Fractures and patterns produced by them provide tools with which we may study larger processes and gain an understanding of them. The particular fracture patterns found in any given place were caused by some specific stress fields. If the patterns and their mode of origin can be determined, then we have made a major step toward understanding the natures of the processes that bring about other deformations of the crust.

Rock cleavage is another form of fracturing. Cleavages are closely spaced fractures. The best examples of rock cleavage are found in folded shales and slates. The cleavage in these is oriented approximately parallel to the axial plane of the folds. Rock cleavage is a plane of weakness, but it should not be confused with mineral cleavage, which is determined by atomic arrangements and not by deformation.

Fig. 24-22. Fractures filled with calcite (white). (Photo by E. W. Spencer.)

Unconformities

Unconformities are surfaces of erosion or nondeposition that separate younger strata from older rocks. Unconformities may be formed in the process of either epeirogenic or orogenic deformations, but different types of unconformities result. If intense deformation precedes the development of the unconformity, an angular unconformity will be formed. The contact is called an angular unconformity if the beds beneath the erosion surface are folded or tilted so that there is an angular discordance between the young and old beds. But if there is no folding or faulting in connection with the unconformity the strata below and above may

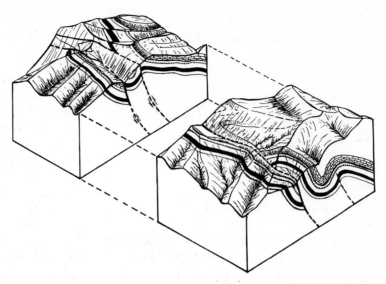

Fig. 24-23. Block diagram of the mountain front of the northern part of the Sangre De Cristo Mountains, Colorado. The margins here are both folded and faulted. (After L. R. Litsey, Bull. G.S.A., v. 69, 1958.)

have nearly identical attitudes. The unconformity is called a disconformity if the young units are laid down parallel to the older units below the erosion surface. Frequently in these cases it is possible to recognize the break if part of the old topography is buried by the young sediments. If no such features can be found then the disconformity may be recognized by the following means:

1. Presence of an old soil profile.
2. Recognition of the differences in ages of the strata on either side of the disconformity.
3. Identification of old stream channels or other features that might be expected on a nearly flat erosion surface.

OROGENY AND ITS CAUSES

To the person who has no knowledge of the earth or the processes taking place on and within it the presence of mountains is a fact to be accepted without question, but once we begin to pry into the nature of our universe and formulate questions about its origin, history, and how the features we see were formed, the question of the origin of mountains becomes intriguing. For many years geologists have studied mountain belts in hopes of finding or being able to formulate a hypothesis that could explain all we know about the mountains.

Many hypotheses have been advanced, but not a single one has been sufficient in itself to explain all we know about the structure and history of mountain ranges. The large-scale deformation necessary to form large folded mountain belts, and tight folds and low-angle thrust faults which characterize them is called orogeny.

Nature of orogenic belts

Before reviewing the more significant hypotheses that have been advanced to account for orogeny we should establish facts concerning mountain belts which must be explained. The following characteristics of mountain belts must be explained by any acceptable hypothesis.

1. The strata in every orogenic belt are folded and contain low-angle thrust faults. The movement is directed away from the central part of the mountain system toward the margins. Folds and thrusts are produced under compression. Thus there is at least local compression of the crust of the earth within orogenic belts during part of the orogenic cycle.

2. In mountain belts there is what appears to be a shortening of the crust, an apparent reduction in the circumference of the earth. The word "apparent" must be emphasized because the effects of crustal shortening might be caused by some other process.

3. Mountain belts are characterized by

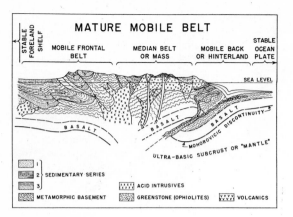

Fig. 24-24. Cross section of the complex central portion of a mountain belt (a schematic representation). (From L. G. Weeks.)

their eminent heights above their immediate surroundings. The amount of this uplift may reach 30,000 feet, the height of Mt. Everest. It is probable that mountain ranges of past geologic eras have been equally high.

4. Mountain belts are large features. Their lengths may be measured in thousands of miles, and their widths in hundreds. Stresses in the crust sufficient to lift masses of rock of this size must be available in any acceptable theory. Consider the weight of a single section across the Himalayas 1 mile wide, 200 miles long, and averaging 16,000 feet in elevation. The amount of rock in this section, which has been uplifted 16,000 feet above sea level, is approximately 600 cubic miles.

5. The sedimentary rocks found in folded mountains are of all types, but shallow-water marine sediments are the most common. That they were formed in shallow water is shown by the fossils present in the units.

6. One of the most common and outstanding sedimentary rocks found in the belts of mobility is graywacke. These are sandy sediments containing mixtures of feldspars and various minerals of volcanic origin. The stratigraphic sections of at least parts of all major mountain systems contain considerable quantities of volcanic debris and lava flows. Many of these flows are pillow-shaped masses of lava thought to form when lava is extruded under water.

7. In addition to the shallow-water sediments, some deep-sea sediments are also found.

These include such sediments as the radiolarian oozes, which are siliceous in composition.

8. Mountain ranges are the sites of most large-scale igneous activity outside the ocean basins. The large batholiths occur in folded mountain belts. More igneous rocks are found in the central and deeper portions of mountain ranges—that is, more igneous rocks are exposed in the deeply eroded mountains where the older rocks of the range are exposed.

9. The core of highly deformed mountains is a metamorphic complex usually intruded by magmas, partially assimilated and largely altered. Original structures may no longer be apparent. These zones are characterized by considerable alteration, flowage, and distortion.

10. One very interesting discovery made in recent years is that every orogenic belt contains ultrabasic intrusions. These may be peridotites, dunites, or serpentines. Extensive outcrops of these are not found, but the few isolated bodies known are aligned to form two parallel rows about 100 miles apart on either side of the axis of the mountain system. They occur so persistently in orogenic belts and not outside them that they must be related to orogeny.

11. The sedimentary units are thicker along the mountain belts than outside. It is apparent that most sediments now exposed in mountain chains were deposited in elongate trough-like depressions called geosynclines. The thickness of accumulation in a geosyncline before an orogeny reaches 50,000 or more feet as compared with the 2000 or 3000 feet of sediment which might have accumulated outside the geosyncline during the same period of time. The geosynclines obviously subsided during the time before the orogeny because the shallow water sediments usually occur all through the sequence. True geosynclinal accumulations presently lie off the eastern and Gulf coasts of America under the continental shelves and continental slopes.

12. Near the margins of most mountain belts the folding is less intense; the strata are only slightly folded or flexed. Toward the center of the belt the folding becomes increasingly intense, and the folds become more asymmetric toward the margins. In the central part of the

belt the folding is largely flow folding. The rocks have behaved like elastico-viscous materials and have flowed under the high temperatures and pressures. This flowage is almost certainly accelerated by the presence of magmas and emanations from magmas.

13. The pattern of entire mountain chains is complex. Refer to Fig. 10-5. They are usually relatively continuous structures, but their paths are by no means straight, and the structures in one part of a range may differ from those in another part of the same chain. The overall pattern of many such chains may be drawn as a connected series of arcs. Note the peculiar shape of the system starting in Alaska. These ranges first trend northeast, then curve southward and extend down through western Canada, the United States, and Mexico. Part of this system then bends back northeastward through Cuba and follows the island-arc system of the Caribbean, coming back to land in Venezuela, thence across northern Colombia along the west coast of South America in Peru and Chile. At Cape Horn the belt bends eastward again and runs through the south Sandwich Islands and then into the South Shetland Islands and the Palmer Peninsula of the Antarctic before disappearing under the ice cap. This sinuous belt extends over roughly half the circumference of the earth.

14. The position of many of the youngest mountain ranges along the continental borders may be a very significant fact, particularly since the island arcs occupy this position.

15. Certainly the island arcs are the sites of present-day orogeny. For that reason they are of special interest and importance in the theory of orogeny. Their characteristics have been described. They are sites of:

a. Igneous activity and volcanism.
b. Earthquakes and seismic instability.
c. A major fault or fault zone which dips under the continents.
d. Deep-sea trenches.

16. Study of the older mountain systems indicates that orogeny involves long periods of time, even millions of years. The activity may be dated by the presence of angular unconformities. There are usually many of these in any major mountain belt, and they are not all of the same age. Deformation does not take place simultaneously throughout the belt.

17. There appear to be several stages in the history of most folded mountains: First the formation of a geosyncline, subsidence, and accumulation of sediments. Secondly the orogenic episode in which the geosyncline is intruded, folded, faulted, and uplifted. This may be followed by a long interval of erosion and perhaps one or more renewals of uplift which are probably isostatic rises. Toward the end of the orogeny many high-angle normal faults cut the older structures, and these are displaced, forming large troughs of graben and horst structures such as those of the Basin and Range province of Nevada and the Southwest. The Connecticut valley, the lowlands of New Jersey, and the basin at Richmond, Virginia, are features of this sort.

Theories of orogeny

It is no wonder that no single theory has been devised to account for all the above observations. They are a varied and complex group. Their complexity, coupled with the lack of accurate information about the lower por-

Fig. 24-25. Cross section of a geosyncline showing great thickness of sediments in the trough-like depressions. (After Marshall Kay, 1951.)

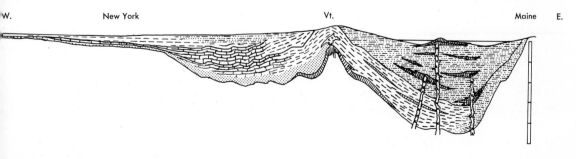

W.   New York   Vt.   Maine   E.

tions of the crust and subcrust, makes the explanation of orogeny most difficult. Of course it is possible that, instead of a single fundamental cause of orogeny, mountains may be formed under different circumstances in different parts of the crust. However, most geologists feel that there must be a fundamental cause of orogeny because of the remarkable similarities in orogenic belts throughout the world. The theories reviewed here have been offered to explain certain specific aspects of orogeny.

Theory of the contracting earth

One of the first attempts to explain mountain-building processes was based on the assumption that the earth is cooling, and as a

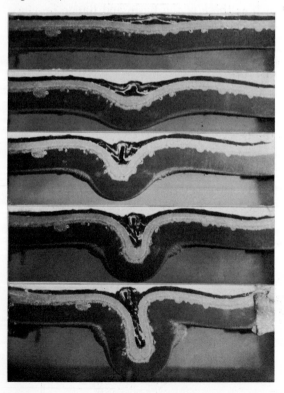

Fig. 24-26. Experiment in the formation of a tectogene. A floating plastic layer is shown as it is compressed. According to Vening Meinesz the downbuckle may be formed in the earth by the drag of convection currents on the crust. These photographs, representing five successive stages, were taken during an experiment by Ph. H. Kuenen. (From Vening Meinesz, Geol. Soc. Am., Special Paper 62.)

result contracting. This theory is tied in with another widely assumed hypothesis that the earth was pulled out of the sun as a molten mass and that it has been cooling ever since. Accordingly, the crust represents the already cooled portion of the earth, and the hot interior is part of the original molten mass. As the interior of the earth cools, the volume of the interior decreases, and the outer crust is forced to accommodate itself to a sphere of smaller radius. This is accomplished by wrinkling or folding of the crust. The process might be likened to that of a plum drying out to form a prune. The beauty of this theory is that it explains the compressional features found in the crust. In recent years the fundamental assumptions of the theory have been questioned. With the discovery of great quantities of radioactive minerals in the crust the question arises as to whether the interior is actually cooling and contracting, or heating and expanding. Radioactive decay is accompanied by the release of heat. In either case the rate is too slow for us to make any direct observations to determine expansion or contraction.

Another aspect of this problem has recently been brought to the attention of the scientific world. Experiments on the behavior of rocks and minerals under extreme confining pressures indicate the possibility that the earth might shrink through changes in mineral structure within the mantle.

Tectogene hypothesis

Vening Meinesz made extensive gravity surveys in the southwestern Pacific Ocean, particularly around Java and Sumatra, during and after World War II. These studies were carried out in submarines since the measurements had to be made below the surface zone of movement in the ocean. The results of these studies were most impressive. He demonstrated that large negative gravity anomalies are found over the deep-sea trenches and their surroundings. A negative anomaly means there is a deficiency of mass in the location as compared with an ideal homogeneous earth. The negative anomaly persists even after corrections are made for the differences in the density between rock and sea water in the trench. The interpretation of this anomaly has been that low-density rocks project down into the more dense subcrust under the island arc. Meinesz postulates that the lower-density rocks such as the sialic part of the crust have been pulled into a down-buckle. The force required for the formation of the downbuckle is provided by convection currents within the earth's mantle. The heat flow necessary for the convection hypothesis might come from heat generated by radioactive decay under the continental margins. The initial downward movement of the tectogene (large downfold of the granitic crust beneath an orogenic belt) would give rise to a geosyncline, and as the convection pulled the crust deeper and deeper a great accumulation of sediments would take place. As the sides of the tectogene are forced together the sediments are deformed. The bottom part of the tectogene is dragged so deeply that temperatures are raised enough to generate magma which is forced upward into the mountains that are formed and uplifted as the tectogene is compressed within the downbuckle. Thus the hypothesis successfully explains many observed features of mountains. But, like other hypotheses, it is questioned.

Among the criticisms of the tectogene hypothesis are the following. Seismic studies of the oceanic crust do not show a sialic or granitic

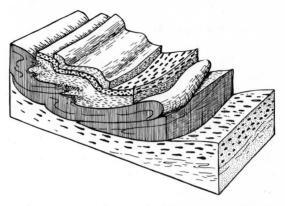

Fig. 24-27. Block diagram of folded structure suggesting flowage in Farm Blasskranz, Africa. (From Korn and Martin, Bull. Geol. Soc. Am., v. 70, 1959.)

layer thick enough to provide the low-density rock in the tectogene. Convection cells in a relatively homogeneous earth should be symmetrical. Mountain-belt patterns are not symmetrical. The convection cells would have to be very peculiar in form to account for the extended and irregular shapes of mountain systems. The hypothesis does not explain high positive gravity anomalies in the belts, or the orientation of the fault located under the deep-sea trenches. One of the most important criticisms is the discovery of an oceanic crust in island arcs by seismic methods which is incompatable with the tectogene in composition (density) and thickness.

Fig. 24-28. Profiles of the mountain face, Farm Blasskranz, Africa. Note the flowage-type structure which is characteristic of many orogenic belts. (From Korn and Martin, Bull. Geol. Soc. Am., v. 70, 1959.)

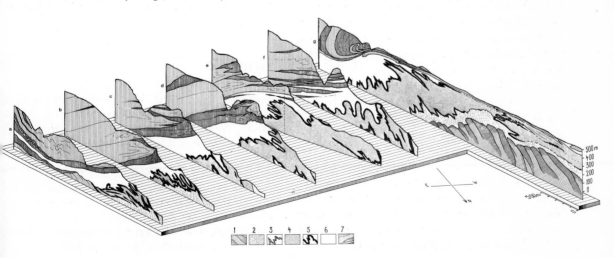

Gravity tectonics

Some puzzling aspects of orogeny have been clarified by the work of Dr. Walter Bucher. In particular he has pointed out the importance of the force of gravity in deformation of the crust. It is not unusual to find a statement such as follows: If the folds in the Appalachian Mountains were reconstructed it could be shown that they would stretch 200 miles; therefore, the crust of the earth was shortened by 200 miles during the Appalachian orogeny. Bucher points out that these folds, like those of the Jura Mountains in the Alps, may be "skin-deep" deformations. They do not involve the deeper parts of the crust. Such folding is caused by sliding of a comparatively thin sedimentary veneer under the pull of gravity. This movement is downward from the central uplifted core of the mountain belt. This reasoning removes one of the most serious problems in orogeny—accounting for great crustal shortening. Bucher has worked with scale-model experiments in attempts to reproduce tectonic structures. One of the most successful of these has been the reproduction of many of the flowage-type structures in the Alpine-like mountain systems. In the experiment layers of wax were laid down in a pattern to simulate a geosynclinal accumulation. The geosyncline was then compressed, and the waxes deformed first by an upward bulging, but being an elastico-viscous material the wax could not stand under its own weight and began to flow very slowly. The patterns of faults and folds produced resemble alpine structures even in many details.

One important question is just how much crustal shortening must occur to produce such features as the Alps. In so far as the mass of material which has been elevated above sea level is concerned, only a few miles of shortening of the crust is necessary to produce such mountains. Bucher considers the fault under the island arcs as a zone of movement between the continental masses and the oceanic crust. If the crust is under compression some of this could be taken up by movement along this fault. The fault provides the line of access for hot solutions and gases from below the crust which might metamorphose and partially melt the accumulation of sediments in the geosyncline at the edge of the continents in the island-arc system.

Serpentinization and uplift

In 1937 Dr. Harry Hess pointed out that there are many ultramafic bodies oriented along the axial zones of mountain systems. These ultramafic rocks (rocks rich in iron and magnesium) are often altered, by the addition of water, to form serpentine. They are tightly folded and are products of metamorphism. He also found these same characteristics within the deformed parts of the island-arc systems. This led to the concept that the island arcs are youthful orogenic zones. Hess (1960) points out that the work of a group research project in the Caribbean suggests that island-arcs and alpine mountains are not two stages in the history of a mountain system, but that they are expressions of the difference of the response of continental-type and oceanic-type coastal sections to the same type of deformation. One particularly important feature of these observations is that one possible cause of uplift within the oceanic crust could come from the alteration of an ultramafic subcrustal layer by rising waters from depth. With the alteration and serpentinization this layer might expand and swell, uplifting the strata above.

In summary we may say that the cause of orogeny is still an unsolved riddle and one of the greatest challenges to man's intelligence and imagination.

REFERENCES

ANDERSON, E. M., 1951, *The Dynamics of Faulting*, 2nd ed.: Edinburgh, Oliver and Boyd, 206 p.

BAILEY, E. B., 1935, *Tectonic Essays, Mainly Alpine*: Oxford, Clarendon Press, 200 p.

BILLINGS, M. P., 1959, *Structural Geology*, 2nd ed.: New York, Prentice-Hall, 514 p.

BUCHER, W. H., 1933, *The Deformation of the Earth's Crust*: Princeton, N. J., Princeton University Press, 518 p.

———, 1956, Role of Gravity in Orogenesis: Geol. Soc. America Bull., v. 67, p. 1295-1318

DALY, R. A., 1940, *Strength and Structure of the Earth:* New York, Prentice-Hall, 434 p.

DE SITTER, L. V., 1956, Gravitational Gliding Tectonics, Am. Jour. Sci., v. 252, p. 321.

———, 1956, *Structural Geology:* New York, McGraw-Hill Book Co., 552 p.

EARDLEY, A. J., May, 1955, The Riddle of Mountain Building, Utah Geol. and Min. Survey, Reprint 50, 31 p.

———, 1951, *Structural Geology of North America:* New York, Harper & Bros., 624 p.

GILLULY, JAMES, 1949, Distribution of Mountain Building in Time: Geol. Soc. America Bull., v. 60, p. 561-590

JACOBS, J. A., RUSSELL, R. D., and WILSON, J. T., 1959, *Physics and Geology:* New York, McGraw-Hill Book Co., 424 p.

JEFFREYS, HAROLD, 1952, *The Earth, Its Origin, History, and Physical Constitution,* 3rd ed.: Cambridge, Cambridge University Press, 382 p.

KAY, MARSHALL, 1951, North American Geosynclines: Geol. Soc. America Mem. 48, 143 p.

KING, P. B., 1959, *The Evolution of North America:* Princton, N.J., Princeton University Press, 189 p.

———, 1951, *The Tectonics of Middle North America:* Princeton, N.J., Princeton University Press, 203 p.

KUIPER, G. P., Editor, 1953–, The Solar System: 6 vols., Chicago, University of Chicago Press (v. 1, 1953, v. 2, 1954, v. 3-6 in press)

NEVIN, C. M., 1942, *Principles of Structural Geology,* 3rd ed.: New York, John Wiley & Sons, 320 p.

POLDERVAART, ARIE, Editor, 1955, *The Crust of the Earth:* Geol. Soc. America, Spec. Paper 62, 762 p.

SCHEIDEGGER, A. E., 1958, *Principles of Geodynamics:* Berlin, Springer-Verlag, 280 p.

UMBGROVE, J. H. F., 1947, *The Pulse of the Earth:* Hague, Martinus Nijhoff, 179 p.

WILSON, J. T., 1959, Geophysics and Continental Growth: Am. Scientist, v. 47, p. 1-24

INDEX

Index

Beryllium, 80
Bighorn River, erosion by, 265
Biotite
    orientation of, 411–412
    weatherng and, 237
Biotite mica
    in basaltic magma cooling, 124
    identification of, 96(ch.)–97(ch.)
    weathering of, 238
Birch, Francis, 204
Bird excrement, phosphatic deposits from, 158
Bismuth, 80
Black shales, as petroleum source, 26
Blind valleys, 354
Blocks
    defined, 137
    volcanic, described, 114
Blue Ridge mountain belt, 172
Bohr, Nils, 73
Boiling, defined, 68
Boltzmann, Ludwig, 69
Bombs, volcanic, 114, 137
Bonding, cleavage and, 83
Bones, phosphatic deposits from, 158
Bores, tidal, 362
Bornite, 90(ch.)–91(ch.)
Boron, 80
Bouguer effect, 207, 208
Boulder(s)
    defined, 149
    marine erosion and, 368
    traction transportation of, in streams, 258
Bowen, N. L., 123–125, 129, 237
Bowen's reaction series of magma crystallization, 123–125, 129, 237
Braided streams, 276
Brazilian Shield, 169, 196
Breakers, 365–366
Breccia
    described, 152
    in faults, 429
    volcanic, identification of, 138
Bridges, construction of, 32–33
Brunton compass, 48
Bucher, Walter, 438
Bulk modulus, defined, 197
Bury, Richard de, 3

C

Calcareous sedimentary rocks
    chemically deposited: caliche, 155; described, 154–155; dolomite, 155–156; travertine, 155
    deposition of, 154
    organically formed: chalk, 158; described, 158; fossiliferous limestones, 158; marl, 158
Calcite, 158
    contact metamorphism of, 410
    crystals of, 414
    deposition of, in caverns, 311, 315
    hardness of, 84
    identification of, 90(ch.)–91(ch.)
    in sedimentary rocks, 148
    weathering of, 238
    See also Calcareous sedimentary rocks
Calcium, 80, 81

Calcium carbonate, 157, 158
Calderas, of volcanoes, 102, 116
Caliche, described, 155
California, marine erosion and, 369
California current, 362
Cambrian Period, defined, 18
Canadian Shield, 169, 196, 212
    epeirogeny of, 422
    ice caps in, 295
    peridotites in, 186
Canyons, submarine, 389, 391, 395–397
Capacity, of streams, 258–259
Cape San Lucas Canyon, 395
Capillary fringe, 305
Carbon, 80
    deposition of, 158–159
Carbon dioxide, gas, 114
Carbon monoxide, 114
Carbonaceous sedimentary rocks, 158–159
Carbonate rocks, contact metamorphism of, 410
Carbonation, in weathering, 237
Caribbean, currents in, 361
Carmel Canyon, 395
Carnotite, 90(ch.)–91(ch.)
Carson, Rachel, quoted, 387
Cascades, land form evolution and, 342
Cassiterite, 90(ch.)–91(ch.)
Caucasus Mountains, 172
Cavendish, Henry, 206
Caverns, ground water and, 304, 311, 315, 352–354
Caves, 146, 324
Cenozoic, defined, 19
Central African Shield, 169
Chalcopyrite, 90(ch.)–91(ch.)
Chalk, described, 158
Chalk Cliffs, Dover, England, 369
Chamosite, described, 156
Channels, stream
    entrenched, land forms and, 344
    erosion and, 265
    ground water and, 302–303
    land form evolution and, 343
    load and, 259
    roughness of, 262, 263
    slope and, 270
    turbulence and velocity and, 260
    width of, 262, 263
Charge
    of electrons, 72
    of ions, electron loss and, 75
    of neutrons, 72
    of protons, 72
Chemical action, weathering by, 236–237
Chemical analyses, 36
Chemical deposition of sedimentary rocks, description of rocks from, 154–157
Chemical energy, 60, 62
Chemical properties
    of compounds, 77
    of magmas, 119
    of matter, 67
Chemical reactions, exothermic, in magma formation, 122
Chert
    in bedded siderites, 156
    described, 154

Decay *(cont.)*
  products of, 141–143, 148
Decke, of faults, 431
Decomposition, geomorphic agents and, 226
Deep sea
  currents, 398–399
  gradation in, 384–399
  trenches, 384
Deflation, in wind erosion, 322–323
Deformation
  of continental shields, 169, 172
  of earth's crust, 417–439; diastrophic features, 426–433; epeirogeny, 419–422; orogeny, 419–422, 433–438; strength of crust, 422–426
  gravity and, 438
  of island arcs, 179
  land forms and, 332, 346, 348–349
  of mountain belts, 172, 173, 174, 435
  of rocks: described, 423–426; Precambrian rocks, 169
  stress and, 424
  unconformities and, 19
Deglaciation, 378
Degradation, *See* Gradation
Deltaic coasts, 378
Deltas, 146, 274
Democritus, 69
Density
  distribution of: Airy theory, 209–210; in earth, 202–203; Heiskanen's theory, 211–212; Pratt's theory, 210–211
  of earth's crust, 421
  elevation and, 210
  of oceanic water, variations in, 360
  of rocks: path of seismic waves and, 199; velocity of seismic waves and, 198, 199
  separation by, in magma crystallization, 128
Density currents, *See* Turbidity currents
Deposition
  of alluvial fans, 270–271, 274
  of calcareous sedimentary rocks, 154
  of calcite, in caverns, 311, 315
  coasts and, 378
  of continental margins, 174
  of continental shelf, 175
  in earth's crust, 168
  by glaciers, 290–294; forms of, 291–294; materials in, 280–281, 290–291
  in Grand Canyon, 421
  of loess, 325–326
  marine, 371–383; atolls, 376–377; barrier reefs, 376–377; beaches, 371–372, 375–376; coast classification, 377–379; coastal evolution, 379–383; coasts and, 378, 379; offshore bars, 376
  of salts, 156–157
  of sedimentary rocks: chemical, description of rocks from, 154–157; mechanical, descriptions of rocks from, 151–154; organically formed, description of rocks from, 158–159
  of sediments: chemical reactions in, texture and, 148, 150–151; colloidal, 151; environments of, 145–146
  by springs, 316
  by streams, 265–266
  by turbidity currents, 395–397
  velocity and, 266

Deposition *(cont.)*
  by wind, 325–330
Depressions, wind erosion and, 324
Depth
  of Moho, 189
  pressure and, 405, 411
  of stream channels, 262, 263
  temperatures and, 411
Deserts, 146
  bajadas in, 337
  character of, 333–334, 336
  defined, 333–334
  drainage in, 334, 336
  land forms in, 336–339
  pediments in, 337–339
  playas in, 337
  rainfall in, 333–334
  temperature in, 334–336
  weathering in, 334
Diabase
  identification of, 136
  of Mid-Atlantic Ridge, 180
Diamonds
  hardness of, 84
  identification of, 92(ch.)–93(ch.)
  magmatic concentration of, 29
Diastrophism
  coasts and, 378
  elevation of earth and, 219
  faults and, 428–431
  folds and, 426, 428
  fractures and, 431–432
  land forms and, 332
  rocks and, 422–426
  unconformities and, 432–433
Diatoms, sedimentary rocks from, 158
Differentiation of magmas, 127–129
Dikes
  defined, 29
  metamorphism of, 404
  structure of, 131
Dilational waves (D waves) in earthquakes, 197, 198
Diorite
  of Appalachian mountain system, 188
  identification of, 135
Dip in geologic maps, 48
Dip-slip movement of faults, 430
Directed pressure stress, 405
Discharge of streams, 262, 269
Disconformity, 19, 433
Discontinuity
  of continental margins, 176, 177
  in earth's interior, 204; Moho, 167; origin of, 166–167
  seismic waves and, 199
Discordant intrusive igneous bodies, 131
Disintegration
  geomorphic agents and, 226
  rates of isotopes, 76
Dissolution, 264
Dolerite, 136
Dolines, 353–354
Dolomite
  contact metamorphism of, 410
  crystals of, 414
  described, 155

Gradients
    land form evolution and, 343
    law of equal slopes, 348
    stream erosion and, 265
    of streams, 262–263, 264; factors controlling, 268–
        270
Grand Canyon, 420
Granite(s)
    characteristics of granitic magma, 120–121
    classification of, 411–413
    in earth's crust, 167
    in folded mountain belts, 173
    graphic, 135
    identification of, 135
    occurrence of, 411, 412
    orbicular, 135
    origin of, 169
Granular pervious material, 306–307
Granular rocks, 405
Granulation, metamorphism and, 408
Granule, defined, 149
Graphic granite, 135
Graphite
    identification of, 94(ch.)–95(ch.)
    specific gravity of, 83
Gravel, 141
Gravimeters, principle of, 208
Gravity
    in Cortlandt complex, 189
    force of, 206
    glaciers and, 279
    gravitational attraction of matter, 67–68
    gravitational field of earth, 206–213; anomalies in,
        208; instruments in study of, 208; isostasy,
        209–213; variations in, 207–208, 212
    in island arcs, 177–178
    movement of ground water and, 305
    negative anomalies of, 212
    orogenies and, 436–438
    as potential energy, 64
    separation by, in magma crystallization, 128
    stream flow and, 255
    surface water movement and attraction of sun and
        moon, 360
Gravity tectonics, 438
Graywacke
    described, 152
    of mountain belts, 434
Great Barrier Reef (Australia), 377
Griggs, Robert, quoted, 106
Grooves, ice caps and, 287
Gros Ventre slide (Wyoming), 249
Ground moraines, 292
Ground water, 301–316
    artesian conditions of, 310–311
    in caverns, 304, 311, 315, 352–354
    Darcy's law and, 305–306
    geysers, 308, 310
    gradation of earth's crust and, 220, 221
    Karst geomorphic cycle and, 352–354
    movement of, 304–316
    rainfall and, 305
    sources of, 302
    springs, 315–316
    storage of, 302–304
    water table, 305, 306–308, 311

Guano, defined, 158
Gulf Coast, 419
Gulf of Mexico
    currents in, 361
    level of water of, 359
Gulf Stream, 361, 362, 366
Gunnison River, erosion by, 265
Gutenberg, Beno, 195
Guyots
    marine erosion and, 370
    in Pacific Ocean, 420
Gypsum, 156
    hardness of, 84
    identification of, 94(ch.)–95(ch.)
    from sea water, 157

H

Hales Bar Dam, 33
Half-life, defined, 77
Halite, 156
    identification of, 94(ch.)–95(ch.)
    ionic bonding of, 77
    from sea water, 157
Hangchow River, tides in, 362
Hanging valleys, 355
Hanging-wall side of faults, 429–430
Hardness of minerals, 84, 90(ch.), 92(ch.), 94(ch.),
        96(ch.), 98(ch.)
Haze, wind transportation of, 319–320
Heck, Nicholas H., 194
Heezen, Bruce, 385, 393
Heiskanen, W. A., 211
Heiskanen's theory of density distribution, 211–212
Helium, 75, 80
Hematite(s), 237
    identification of, 94(ch.)–95(ch.)
    oölitic, 156
    sedimentary, 156
    sedimentation and, 30
    specific gravity of, 83
Hess, H. H., 185, 438
Hexagonal symmetry of crystals, 83
Hillsides, 349
Himalayas, 172
Holmes, Chauncey, quoted, 350
Hornblende
    in basaltic magma cooling, 124
    in glacial deposits, 291
    oxidation of, in weathering, 237
Hornblendite, 136
Hornfels, 407, 416
Horns, glacial, 290, 356
Horst of faults, 431
Hudson River, canyon of, 395
Humid climates, 230
    Karst topography in, 352
    land forms in, 339–351
Hydration, defined, 237
Hydraulic processes
    land forms and, 343, 349–351
    in streams, 262–264
Hydrochloric acid, 114
Hydrofluoric acid, 114
Hydrogen, 74, 80
Hydrogen sulfide, 114

Hydrology, defined, 6
Hydrolysis, defined, 237
Hydrostatic pressure, 196, 405

I

Ice, glaciers and, 279, 281–282
Ice caps, See Continental ice caps
Idioblastic series, 413–414
Igneous activity
    on earth's crust, 168
    elevation of earth and, 219
    isostasy and, 422
    metamorphism and, 404
    on mountain belts, 173, 434
    volcanism and, 100, 114
    See also Igneous rocks
Igneous rocks, 118–138
    of Appalachian mountain system, 188
    classification of, 129–131
    composition of, 130–131
    crystals of, 130
    defined, 119
    identification of, 135–138
    magma of, 119–131
    on maps, 51
    metamorphic rocks and, 404, 411
    metamorphism of, 403
    of Mid-Atlantic Ridge, 180
    mode of origin of, 150–151
    of mountain belts, 173, 185, 434
    petroleum in, 25
    porphyry, 127
    structure of intrusive igneous bodies, 131, 134–135
    texture of, 130, 150
Ilha Nova Volcano, 111–112
Immiscibility in magma crystallization, 128–129
Impact
    in erosion by streams, 264
    in wind erosion, 322–323
Indian Ocean, currents in, 361
Inert gases, 75
Inertia of matter, 67
Influent streams, 307
Inlier, defined, 53
Intensity of earthquakes, Mercalli Scale for, 194–195
International Commission of Optics, 8
International Conference on Scientific Information, 8
International Geographic Congress, 8
International Geological Congress, 8
International Geophysical Year, 11, 55
International Oceanographic Congress, 8
International Paleontological Union, 8
International Petroleum Exposition, 8
International Symposium on Physical Chemistry of Extractive Metallurgy, 8
International Union of Crystallography, 8
International Union of Geodesy and Geophysics, 8
International World Petroleum Congress, 8
Interruptions, land forms and, 332–333
Intrusions
    aphanitic intrusive rocks, 136
    in earth's crust, 185–188
    granites in, 411
    in magma crystallization, 128
    in mountain belts, 173, 434

Intrusions (cont.)
    phaneritic intrusive rocks, 135–136
    structure of intrusive igneous bodies, 131, 134–135
Invertebrates
    ferruginous deposits from, 158
    limestones from, 158
    as petroleum source materials, 26
Ionic bonds in compounds, 77–78
Ions
    in earth's crust, 80–81
    electrons and, 75
    sediments and, 141, 148
    in solution, 78–79
Iron, 80
    concentration and ores of, 30
    contact metasomatism in ores of, 29
    in core of earth, 204–205
    in earth's crust, 81
    elements in, 80, 81
    oxidation of, in weathering, 237
    oxide, from sea water, 157
    sedimentation and ores of, 30
    sediments bearing, 156
    See also Ferruginous sedimentary rocks
Island arcs, 177–179
    features of, 177–179
    locations of, 177
    orogeny and, 434, 438
    stability of, 177
Islands, volcanic, in Pacific, 102, 107–112
Isometric symmetry of crystals, 83
Isostasy
    Airy theory, 209–210
    epeirogeny and, 421–422
    Heiskanen's theory, 211–212
    meaning of, 212–213
    Pratt theory, 210–211
Isotopes, 76

J

Jeffreys, Sir Harold, 202
Johnson, Douglas, 339
Jupiter, 13
Jura Mountains, folds in, 438
Jurassic Period, defined, 18
Juvenile water, 302

K

Kames, glacial deposition of, 293
Karst geomorphic cycle, 352–354
Katmai Volcano (Aleutians), 105–107, 119, 193
Kilauea Volcano (Hawaii), 107–111, 115
Kinetic energy, 60, 64
Kinetic theory of gases, 69
Klippe of faults, 431
Krakatoa Volcano, 101–103, 115
Krypton, 75
Kuenen, Ph. H., 392
Kunlun Mountains, 172
Kwanto earthquake (Japan), 192
Kyanite
    crystals of, 414
    identification of, 94(ch.)–95(ch.)

L

Labrador current, 362
Labradorite feldspar, 92(ch.)–93(ch.)
Laccoliths, defined, 134
Lagoons, 146
La Jolla canyon, 395
Lakes, 146; oxbow, 342
Laminae, defined, 144
Laminar flow of streams, 257, 260
Land forms, 36
    in arid and semiarid climates, 333–339, 349–351
    base level of, 222, 332
    deformation and, 332, 346, 348–349
    in deserts, 336–339
    evolution of, 226, 332–333, 341–349
    geomorphic agents and, 221, 225
    gradation of earth's crust and, 220
    in humid climates, 339–351
    interruptions and, 332–333
    Karst geomorphic cycle and, 352–354
    landscape evolution, 333–356
    mountain glaciation and sequence of, 354–356
    rejuvenation and, 343–344, 346
    rock structure and, 333
    terraces and, 344, 346
    time and, 333
    wind erosion and, 323–324
Landslide(s)
    earthquakes and, 217
    on mountains, 246–247, 249–252
    Turtle Mountain, 252
Lapilli, 114, 137–138
Lateral cutting by streams, 265
Lateral moraines, 292
Latitude, in geologic maps, 48
Laue, Max von, 82
Lava(s)
    andesite, 115
    basalts, 114, 116
    composition of, 189
    defined, 114
    flows, 434; calderas of, 116; coasts and, 378; collapse features of, 116; cones of, 115, 116; fumaroles of, 116; of mid-ocean ridges, 182; solfataras of, 116; without volcanic eruptions, 115
    of island arcs, 177
    plateau formation, 422
    rhyolites, 114
    of shield volcanoes, 115
    types of, 107
Law of V's, 51
Lead, 29, 80
Legend, in geologic maps, 48–49
Lehmann, I. G., 202
Lepidolite mica, 96(ch.)–97(ch.)
Levees, 342
Light year, defined, 13
Limbs, of folds, 428
Limestone(s)
    carried in solution in streams, 258
    in caverns, 311
    classification of, 154–155
    composition of, 148

Limestone(s) *(cont.)*
    contact metamorphism of, 410
    of continental shelf, 175
    in earth's crust, 167
    fossiliferous, 158
    Karst topography and, 352–354
    marine erosion and, 368
    in sedimentary rocks, 148
    weathering of, 238
Limonite, 94(ch.)–95(ch.), 237
Liquids, 67
    characteristics of, 68
    in magma crystallization, 128–129
Literature, search of, 38–39
Lithium, 80
Lituya Bay earthquake, 357
Load, stream, 262
    Arkansas River, 258–259
    changes in, 269
    deposition and, 266
    flood plains and, 274
    land form evalution and, 343
    slope and, 269
    sources of, 259
Loess, 291
    deposition of, 325–326
    described, 153
Longitude, in geologic maps, 48
Longitudinal dunes, 330
Longshore current, 364, 366–367, 379
Lopoliths, defined, 134–135
Love, A. E. H., 198
Lovering, T. S., quoted, 22–23
Love waves, 198
Lucretius, 69; quoted, 67
Luster, mineral, 85

M

Macelwane, J. B., quoted, 192
Mackin, J. H., quoted, 268
Madison Canyon (Montana)
    earthquake, 193
    landslide, 246–247
Magma(s)
    of Appalachian mountain system, 187, 188
    basaltic, 119
    composition of, 119, 120–121
    crystallization of; 123–131, 185; crystalline differentiation, 127–128; igneous rock classification and, 129–131; rate of, 125, 127; rock differentiation and, 127–129; texture and, 125, 127
    defined, 29, 100
    differentiation of, 127–129
    generation of, 114, 121–123
    metallic ore formation in, 29
    minerals in, 119
    temperature of, 119–120
    viscosity of, 120
Magmatic differentiate, defined, 186
Magmatic water, 302
Magnesium, 80
    compounds of, from sea water, 157
    in earth's crust, 81, 168
    elements in, 80, 81

Reverse faults, 430
Rhodesia, 186
Rhyolites, volcanic, 114, 189
Ria coasts, 378
Richter, C. F., quoted, 195–196
Ridges, 179–183, 348
Riecke's principle, 405
Rift, of Mid-Atlantic Ridge, 180, 182
Rills, land forms and, 341, 351
Rip currents, 366
Ripple(s)
    marks on sand dunes, 329
    on sea bottom, 397
Rise(s)
    continental, 179, 384–388
    oceanic, 179
River-deposition coasts, 378
River terraces, 344, 346
Rock(s)
    chemical analyses of, 36
    chemically active fluids and, 405
    classification of volcanic fragmental, 137–138
    composition of, metamorphism and, 406–407
    confining, 423
    contact metamorphism of, 410
    creep of, 246
    crystals of, 66–67
    deformation of, described, 423–426
    density distributions of, 209–213
    discontinuities and composition of, 166
    distribution by, age of, in geologic maps, 46
    in earth's crust, 167–168
    elastic properties of, 196–197
    fall of, 242–243
    flowage of, metamorphism and, 407–408
    formation of, 422–426
    glacial deposition of, 243, 245, 290–291
    in Grand Canyon, 421
    granulation of, metamorphism and, 408
    ice caps and, 287
    isostasy and, 422
    mapping distribution of, 36, 46
    marine erosion and, 368
    mass movement classification and, 253
    metamorphic, 403–416
    metamorphism of, 403–404, 408, 410, 411
    of Mid-Atlantic Ridge, 180
    minerals in, 79
    path of seismic waves and properties of, 199
    petroleum in, 25, 26–27
    phase changes in, 166–167
    porosity of: ground water and, 303–305; water
        table and, 306–307
    Precambrian, in continental shields, 169, 172
    pressure of, 196, 405, 423, 425
    recrystallization and recombination in metamor-
        phism of, 408, 410
    regional metamorphism of, 411
    stress and, 405, 423
    structure of, land forms and, 333
    texture of, crystallization rate and, 125
    theories on formation of, 118–119
    thermal expansion and contraction and, 233–234
    types of, 48, 173
    unloading of, 234
    velocity of shock waves and properties of, 198

Rock(s) (cont.)
    water in, metamorphism and, 406
    weathering of, 227–228, 233, 238, 259
    wind erosion and, 324
    wind transportation of, 319
    See also Rock units and under specific rocks, e.g.,
        Metamorphic rocks
Rock flour, 291
Rock pressure, 423, 425
    defined, 196
    metamorphism and, 405
"Rock seed" theory, 119
Rock units
    classic localities for, 18–19
    correlation of, 19
    distribution of, in geologic maps, 46
    geologic time scale and, 18–19
    land form evolution and, 341
    mapping distribution of, 36
    physical continuity of, 19
    Precambrian, 19
Rocky Mountain belt, 172, 351
Rotation, of earth, 64
Route location, 32
Rubidium, 80
Rudaceous rocks
    breccia, 152
    conglomerate, 151
    defined, 151
Running water, 255–277
    effectiveness of, 221
    erosion by, 264–265
    gradation of earth's crust and, 220
    land forms and, 349–351
    transportation by, 255–265
    See also Streams
Ruptures, formation of, 424
Rutile, 414

S

S waves (shear waves), 197, 198, 201, 202
St. Francis Dam (California), 31, 33
Salinas, 337
Saltation
    defined, 319
    of wind loads, 324
Salts
    carried in solution in streams, 258
    defined, 156
    deposition of, 156–157
San Andreas fault (California), 191–192
Sand(s)
    decay and, 141
    deep-sea transportation of, 367
    defined, 149
    in sedimentary rocks, 148
    shallow-sea transportation of, 367
    sources of, in sand dunes, 327
    surface of grains, 149, 323
    traction transportation of, in streams, 258
    transportation of, by waves, 364–365
    wind transportation of, 318–319
Sand blasting, 323

Seismology
  defined, 5–6, 189
  earth's interior and, 189–202
  history of, 189, 191
  instruments in, 199–200
  interpretation of seismographs, 200–202
Semiarid climates, 230; land forms in, 333–339, 349–351
Semihumid climates, 230
Sericite, 124
Serpentine(s)
  identification of, 96(ch.)–97(ch.)
  of Mid-Atlantic Ridge, 180
  of mountain belts, 434
Serpentinization, orogeny and, 438
Shale(s)
  composition of, 148, 406–407
  described, 153–154
  in earth's crust, 167
  metamorphism of, 406, 410
Shand, S. James, 189
Shear fractures, 432
Shear modulus, defined, 197
Shearing stress, defined, 196, 405
Sheet floods, 341
Sheeting, 234
Sheet runoff, 351
Sheets, wind deposition of, 325
Sheet wash, 264
Shepard, Francis, 378; quoted, 395
Shield volcanoes, 107, 115
Shores, See Coasts
Siderites, bedded, 156
Silent Valley Dam (Ireland), 33
Silica, 310, See also Siliceous sedimentary rocks
Silicates
  of earth's crust, 88–89
  iron-containing, 156
Silica tetrahedron, 120
Siliceous sedimentary rocks, 158
  chert, 154
  defined, 154
  organically formed: defined, 158; diatoms, 158; radiolarian oozes, 158
  sinter, 154
Silicon, 80
  in earth's crust, 81, 167, 168
  elements in, 80, 81
  in magmas, 120
Sillimanite, 96(ch.)–97(ch.)
Sills
  defined, 134
  metamorphism of, 404
Silt(s)
  defined, 149
  transportation of: deep sea, 367; shallow sea, 367; stream, 257; wave, 364–365; wind, 318–319
Siltstone, 152–153
Silty rocks, 152–153
Silver, 80
Sink holes, 352–354
Sinters, described, 154
Slickensides, 429
Sliding, 253
Slippage, stress and, 405

Slope(s)
  of continental rise, 175
  of continental shelf, 174–175
  elements in, 338–339
  land form evolution and, 341, 349
  law of equal, 348
  mountain glaciation and, 356
  of sea cliffs, 369
  streams and, 262–263, 268–277
  of surface of ocean, 359
Smith, William, 30–31
Smoke, wind transportation of, 319–320
Snell's Law, 199
Snow, glaciers and, 279, 281–282
Society of Economic Geologists, 10
Society of Economic Paleontologists and Mineralogists, 10
Society of Exploration Geophysicists, 10
Society of Vertebrate Paleontology, 10
Sodium, 80, 81
Sodium chloride, 156
  ionic bonding of, 77
  from sea water, 157
Soil(s)
  creep, 351
  earthflow, 249
  mudflows, 247, 249
  landslides, 246–247, 249–252
  mass movement classification and, 253
  Panama Canal construction and, 249–250, 252
  solifluction, 247
  types of, 238
  weathering of, 238–239
Solar system
  components of, 13
  earth in, 12–14
  mass of, 73
  orbits of, 73
Solfataras, volcanic, 116
Solids, 67
  characteristics of, 68
  clastic textures of sedimentary rocks from, 149
  sedimentation and, 148
Solubility, pressure and, 405
Solution(s)
  colloids in, 142
  in erosion by streams, 264
  ions in, 78–79
  marine erosion and, 368
  porosity and, 304
  in sedimentary rock formation, 151
  sedimentation and, 141, 148
  in water, 78–79
  weathering products carried in, by streams, 258
Sorting
  porosity and, 303
  wind and, 324–325
Spatter cones of volcanoes, 116
Specific gravity, 83
Spectrographology, 36
Sphalerite, 96(ch.)–97(ch.)
Spherulites, defined, 151
Spits, defined, 375
Springs, 315–316
Spurs, defined, 355

Stability
  of continental shields, 172
  of earth's crust, 417
  of elements, electron grouping and, 74–75
  of island arcs, 177
Stacks, marine erosion and, 370–371
Stalactites, 311
Stalagmites, 311
State Geological Survey, 10
States of matter, 67, 68
Staurolite, 98(ch.)
Steenland, N. C., 189
Stocks, 131
Strain(s)
  defined, 423
  in rocks, 196
Strata
  in deep-sea, 389
  defined, 144
  in mountain belts, 173, 174, 433, 434
  outcrop patterns and, 51
Stratification
  causes of, 144
  of sedimentary rocks, 143–144
Stratified drift, 291
Stratigraphy, defined, 5
Streak
  defined, 86
  of minerals, 86, 91(ch.), 93(ch.), 95(ch.), 97(ch.), 98(ch.)
Streams, 146
  affluent, 307
  alluvial fans of, 270–274
  barrier of, slope and, 270
  braided, 276
  capacity of, 258–259
  channels: entrenched, land forms and, 344; erosion and, 265; ground water and, 302–303; land form evaluation and, 343; load and, 259; roughness of, 262, 263; slope and, 270; turbulence and velocity and, 260; width of, 262, 263
  competence of, 258–259
  deltas of, 274
  deposition by, 265–266
  discharge of, 262
  drainage patterns of, 276–277
  erosion by, 264–265; deformation and, 346, 348–349; land forms and, 341–343, 349–351
  flood plains of, 274, 275
  flow of: gravity and, 255; nature of, 255–257
  graded, 266–270, 341, 343
  gradient of, 262–263, 264
  hydraulic factors in, 262–264
  influent, 307
  Karst topography and, 352–354
  load of, 262; deposition and, 266; sediment in, 262–263; sources of, 259; traction and, 258
  meandering, 274–276
  mountain glaciation and, 355–356
  piracy of, 348–349
  profile of, 269–270
  in rejuvenated landscapes, 343–344, 346
  river terraces, 344, 346
  slopes, 268–277; law of equal slopes, 348; patterns on low and moderate, 270–277

Streams (cont.)
  solution by, 258
  streaming of, 260
  transportation by, 257
  turbulence of, 256–257, 259–260, 262, 265–266, 317–318
  velocity of, 262–263, 264; decreases in, 266; distribution of, 259–260, 262
Stress
  defined, 423
  deformation and, 424
  metamorphism and, 405
  pressure and, 425
  rocks and, 196, 423–426
Striations, ice caps and, 287
Strike, defined, 48
Strike-slip movement of faults, 430
Strontium, 80
Structural geology, defined, 5
Structure
  of atoms, 70, 73–75
  of continental margins, 175–177
  defined, 51
  of faults, 431
  on geologic maps, 51–53
  of intrusive igneous bodies, 131, 134–135
  of Mid-Atlantic Ridge, 180–181, 182
  of mountain belts, 174
  of silicates, 88–89
Subhedral crystals
  defined, 81
  in magmas, 123
Submarine canyons, 389, 391, 395–397
Submerged coasts, evolution of, 381–383
Subsidence
  mass-movement classification and, 253
  in mountain belts, 173
Sulfates, 157
Sulfur, 80, 98(ch.)
Sulfuric acid, 114
Sun
  attraction of: earth's gravitational field and, 207; surface water movements and, 360
  described, 12–13
  radiant energy from, 63
  solar radiation: climate and, 229–230; glaciation and, 297–299
  thermal energy of, 63–64
Surface area, metamorphism and, 406
Surface creep, land form evolution and, 341
Surface water, oceanic, 358–363
  Coriolis force in, 360
  currents and, 361–362
  density variations of, 360
  factors in, 358–361
  ocean floor configuration and, 360–361
  ocean slope and, 359
  tides and, 362–363
  waves and, 363–366
  wind in contact with, 359–360
Surveying, 43
Suspension
  colloids in, 142
  of wind loads, 324
Swallow holes, 354
Swamps, 146

Turbulence of streams, 256–257
  distribution of, 259–260, 262
  stream channel and, 265–266
Turner, F. J., quoted, 189
Turtle Mountain slide (Alberta), 252
Twinning, in minerals, 87

U

Ultrabasic instructions, 434
Ultramafic rocks, 438
Unconformity, 432–433
  angular, defined, 19
  defined, 19
  disconformity and, 19
  factors in production of, 53
  in geologic maps, 53
  geomorphic agents and, 226
  land forms and, 341, 346, 348–349
  in mountain belts, 435
Underground rivers, ground water and, 352–354
Undertow of oceans, 366
Uniformitarianism, defined, 226
Unloading, as weathering force, 234
Unpaired terraces, 344, 346
Uplands, 342
Uplift
  epeirogenic, rates of, 422
  land form evolution and, 341, 343
  magma formation and, 122–123
  of mid-ocean ridges, 182–183
  of mountain belts, 433–434
  orogeny and, 438
  of rocks, described, 403–404
Ural Mountains, 173
Uranium, 80
Uranus, 13
Uvala, defined, 354

V

Valley(s)
  blind, 354
  hanging, 355
  land-form evolution and, 342
  law of equal slopes and, 348
  of Mid-Atlantic Ridge, 180, 182
  mountain glaciation and, 355–356
  stream piracy and, 348–349
Valley glaciers, 279
  erosion by, 285–290
  erosional features of, 288–290
  movement of, 283
  occurrence of, 283
  transportation methods of, 287
Vanadium, 80
Velocity
  of P waves, 200–201, 202
  of S waves, 201, 202
  of streams, 262–263, 264; decreases in, 266; deposition and, 266; distribution of, 259–260, 262; flow and, 257; traction load and, 258
  of wind, 317; load and, 324
Vening Meinesz, F. A., 436–437
Ventifacts, defined, 323
Venus, 13

Verhoogen, J., quoted, 189
Volcanic ash, 114, 138
  in folded mountain belts, 173
  wind transportation of, 321
Volcanic debris
  of mid-ocean ridges, 182
  of mountain belts, 434
Volcanic rocks
  fragmental, classification of, 137–138
  of Mid-Atlantic Ridge, 180
Volcanism, 99–117
  causes of, 114
  coasts and, 378
  of continental shields, 172
  elevation of earth and, 219
  glaciation and, 299
  of island arcs, 178
  volcanic islands in Pacific, 102
  See also Volcanoes
Volcanoes
  acids of, 107–111, 115
  activity of, 100, 115
  barrier reefs and, 376, 377
  calderas of, 116
  Chile (1960), 194
  collapse features of, 116
  cones of, 115, 116
  earthquakes and, 189, 192
  eruption forms of, 115–116
  explosions of, 101
  extrusions of, in earth's interior study, 189
  fissure eruptions, 115–116
  formation of, 100, 422
  fumaroles of, 107, 116
  gases from, 114
  igneous activity of, 100
  Ilha Nova, 111–112
  Katmai, 105–107
  Kilauea, 107–111, 115
  Krakatoa, 101–103, 115
  lavas from, 114, 115
  Mauna Loa, 107–111, 115
  mineral dispersion about, 107
  Mt. Pelée, 103
  Paricutín, 99
  pyroclastic materials of, 114
  shield, 107, 115
  solfataras of, 116
  spatter cones of, 116
  Tamboro, 100–101, 115
  Vesuvius, 103, 105
  warps of, 109
  See also Volcanism

W

Wadies, 336
Warps, of volcanoes, 109
Washes, 336, 341
Water
  circulation of oceanic, 359–360, 363–364, 397–399
  covalent bonding of, 78
  deep-sea circulation of, 397–399
  density of oceanic, 360
  freezing of, in weathering, 235

STUDY SET OF TOPOGRAPHIC
AND GEOLOGIC MAPS

STUDY SET OF TOPOGRAPHIC AND GEOLOGIC MAPS

This set of maps includes portions of the following maps, listed in the order of their appearance:

Shaded relief topographic map of the Ennis Quadrangle, Montana

Glacial map of the United States east of the Rocky Mountains

Geologic map of Rockingham County, Virginia

Geologic map of California, Santa Cruz sheet

Shaded relief topographic map of the Orbisonia Quadrangle, Pennsylvania

These maps are included as a supplement to the text material in general and more specifically to the chapters dealing with methods used in geologic research. The maps included have been selected to include a wide range of topographic features, geologic structures, and rock types. Note that several of the geologic maps are printed as overlays on topographic maps. This is particularly useful in studies of the relationship between topography and the underlying rock type and structure. The maps provide a useful basis for study of maps outside of laboratories. Refer to the map symbols on the back inside cover.

Eight pages of additional geologic maps will be found in *Basic Concepts of Historical Geology.*

Shaded Relief Topographic Map of the Ennis Quadrangle, Montana

Available through the U. S. Geological Survey, Washington 25, D.C.

scale 1 / 62,500

contour interval 40 feet

north is at the top of the page

among the features shown are:

braided stream pattern in the Madison River

Madison River Canyon where the river cuts through an elevated mass of crystalline igneous and metamorphic rocks

river terraces

Ennis lake, a reservoir

consequent drainage

glaciated valleys as well as unglaciated valleys

Glacial Map of the United States East of the Rocky Mountains

Geological Society of America

by Committee of National Research Council, R. F. Flint, Chairman

symbols:

Dots with lines through them indicate the direction of ice movement as shown by striations and grooves

(yellow)   Pleistocene stream deposits

(blue)   lake deposits including varved clays

(dark green) moraines formed during the Wisconsin glaciation

(light green) drift deposits formed during the Wisconsin glaciation

(pink and orange) Pre-Wisconsin glacial deposits

Geologic Map of Rockingham County, Virginia

Geology by Allen, Brent, Harnsberger, King, Thornton, and Young

Courtesy of Virginia Division of Mineral Resources

James L. Calver, Commissioner

scale 1 / 62,500

contour interval 20 feet

abbreviations:

Mp	Mississippian	Pocono sandstone
Dhs	Mississippian	Hampshire sandstone
Dch	Devonian	Chemung sandstone and shale
Db	Devonian	Brallier shale
Dma	Devonian	Millboro shale
Dri	Devonian	Oriskany sandstone
Dhl	Devonian	Helderberg limestone
Scy	Silurian	Cayuga group (limestone)
Scl	Silurian	Clinton sandstone
Sm	Silurian	Massanutten sandstone

Sc	Silurian	Clinch sandstone	Pc	Pliocene	nonmarine deposits
Oos-Oj	Ordovician	Oswego sandstone and Juniata formation	Pml	Pliocene	marine deposits
Omb	Ordovician	Martinsburg shale	Mu	Miocene	marine deposits
Oe	Ordovician	Edinburg formation	Mc	Miocene	nonmarine deposits
Oln	Ordovician	New Market limestone	Mm	Miocene	marine deposits
Ob	Ordovician	Beekmantown dolomite	Ø	Oligocene	marine deposits
Och	Ordovician	Chepultepec limestone	E	Eocene	marine deposits
€co	Cambrian	Conococheague limestone	Ku	Cretaceous	marine deposits
			m	Pre-Cretaceous	metamorphic rocks
			Mv	Miocene	volcanic rocks
			Ti	Tertiary	intrusive rocks
			Kjf	age uncertain	Franciscan group (metamorphics)
			gr	Mesozoic	granitic rocks undivided

Geologic Map of California, Santa Cruz Sheet
Courtesy of the California Division of Mines
Ian Campbell, Chief
  scale 1 / 250,000
  contour interval 200 feet (supplementary contours at 100 foot intervals)
  abbreviations:

Qs	Quaternary	sand dunes
Qal	Quaternary	alluvium
Qt	Pleistocene	river terrace deposits
Qm	Pleistocene	marine and marine terrace deposits
Qc	Pleistocene	nonmarine deposits
QP	Plio-Pleistocene	nonmarine deposits

Shaded Relief Topographic Map of the Orbisonia Quadrangle, Pennsylvania
Available through the U.S. Geological Survey, Washington 25, D.C.
  scale 1/62,500
  contour interval 20 feet
  north is at the top of the page
  among the features shown are:
    water gaps
    consequent and subsequent drainage
    topographic expression of folded strata of different resistance to erosion
    wind gaps
    hog backs
    stream flood plains

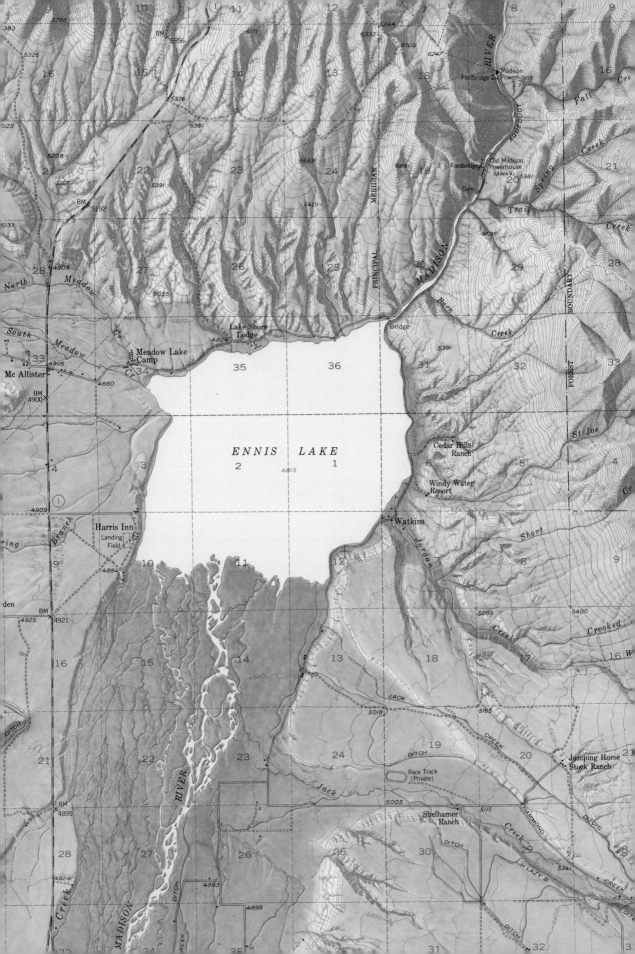

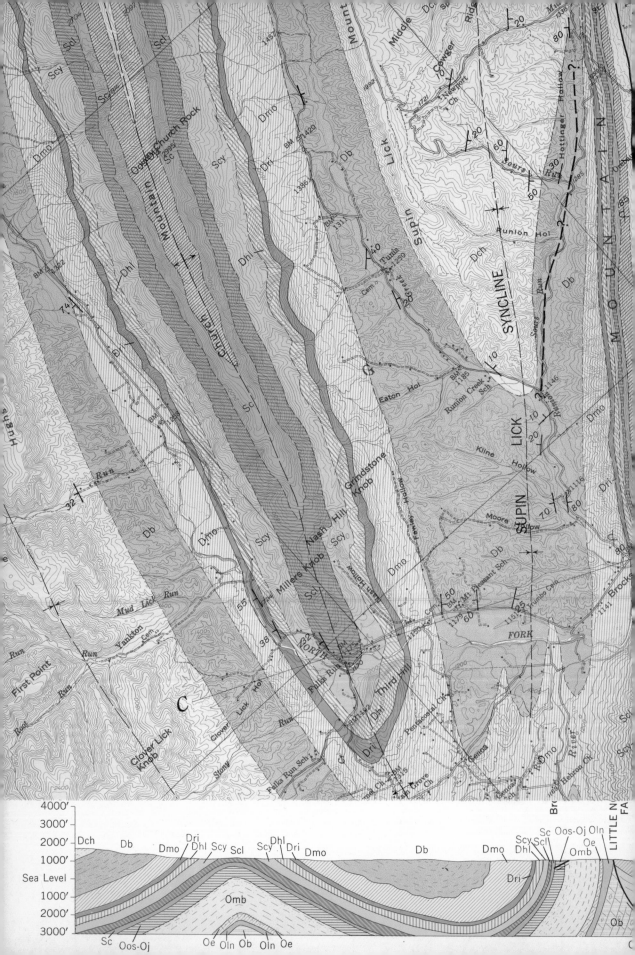

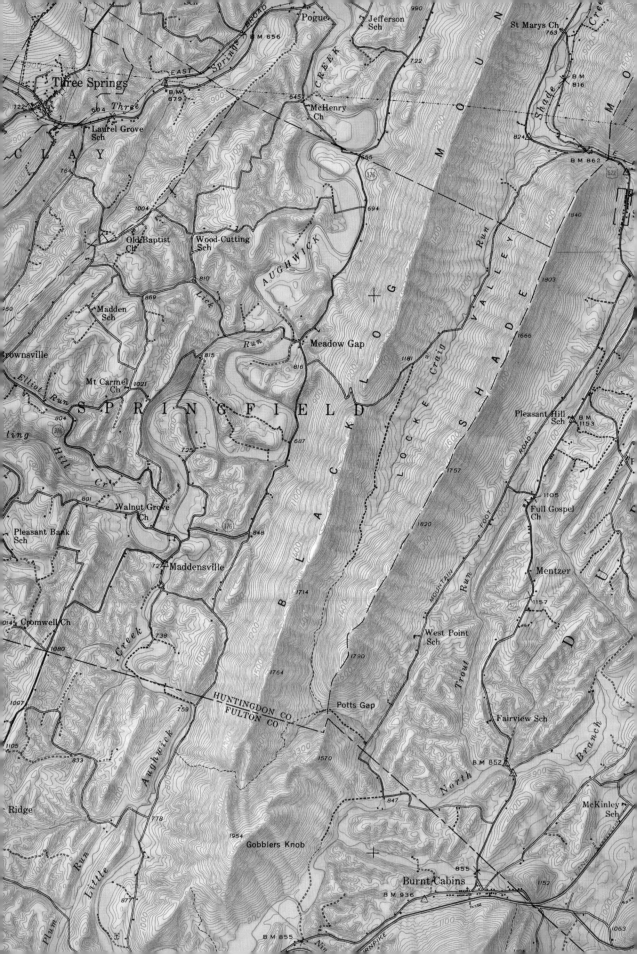